NATURAL LANGUAGE AND THE COMPUTER

UNIVERSITY OF CALIFORNIA
ENGINEERING AND SCIENCES EXTENSION SERIES

Balakrishnan Space Communications
Beckenbach Modern Mathematics for the Engineer, First Series
Beckenbach Modern Mathematics for the Engineer, Second Series
Brown and Weiser Ground Support Systems for Missiles and Space Vehicles
Dorn Mechanical Behavior of Materials at Elevated Temperatures
Garvin Natural Language and the Computer
Huberty and Flock Natural Resources
Langmuir and Hershberger Foundations of Future Electronics
Leondes Computer Control Systems Technology
Leondes Guidance and Control of Aerospace Vehicles
Parker Materials for Missiles and Spacecraft
Puckett and Ramo Guided Missile Engineering
Ridenour Modern Physics for the Engineer, First Series
Ridenour and Nierenberg Modern Physics for the Engineer, Second Series
Robertson Modern Chemistry for the Engineer and Scientist
Sines and Waisman Metal Fatigue
Zarem and Erway Introduction to the Utilization of Solar Energy

Natural language and the computer

Edited by

PAUL L. GARVIN
Member, Senior Staff
The Bunker-Ramo Corporation

McGRAW-HILL BOOK COMPANY, INC.
New York San Francisco
Toronto London

NATURAL LANGUAGE AND THE COMPUTER

Library of Congress Catalog Card Number 63-19307.

II

22915

THE AUTHORS

Paul L. Garvin Member, Senior Staff, **The Bunker-Ramo Corporation,*** Canoga Park, California

Robert P. Stockwell Professor of English, University of California, Los Angeles, California

Thomas A. Sebeok Chairman, Indiana University Research Center in Anthropology, Folklore, and Linguistics, Bloomington, Indiana

W. Karush Principal Scientist, System Development Corporation, Santa Monica, California

Michel A. Melkanoff Associate Professor of Engineering, University of California, Los Angeles, California

L. C. Ray Chairman, Special Interest Group on Information Retrieval of the Association for Computing Machinery, Santa Monica, California

M. E. Maron Member, Senior Research Staff, The RAND Corporation, Santa Monica, California

H. P. Edmundson Member, Senior Staff, **The Bunker-Ramo Corporation,*** Canoga Park, California

David G. Hays Project Leader, Linguistic Research Projects, The RAND Corporation, Santa Monica, California

Kenneth E. Harper Consultant, The RAND Corporation, Santa Monica, California, and Associate Professor of Slavic Languages and Literatures, University of California, Los Angeles, California

Jules Mersel Member, Senior Staff, **The Bunker-Ramo Corporation,*** Canoga Park, California

Don R. Swanson Dean, Graduate Library School, University of Chicago, Chicago, Illinois

Robert M. Hayes Division Manager, Advanced Information Systems Division, Hughes Dynamics, Inc., Los Angeles, California

Larry E. Travis Member, Artificial Intelligence Research Staff, System Development Corporation, Santa Monica, California

*The Bunker-Ramo Corporation is a jointly owned company of Thompson Ramo Wooldridge Inc. and Martin-Marietta Corp. and includes the former TRW Computer Division.

ACKNOWLEDGMENTS

Robert P. Stockwell I am indebted to Noam Chomsky and Robert Lees for criticism of "The Transformational Model of Generative or Predictive Grammar."

Thomas A. Sebeok An early draft of "The Informational Model of Language: Analog and Digital Coding in Animal and Human Communication" was discussed in the symposium *Comparative Aspects of Human Communication,* held under the auspices of the Wenner-Gren Foundation for Anthropological Research at Burg Wartenstein, Austria, September 4–10, 1960. The present material was completed during the author's residence as a Fellow at the Center for Advanced Study in the Behavioral Sciences. The opportunities afforded by the Foundation and the Center are gratefully acknowledged.

Michel A. Melkanoff The preparation of "Computer Languages" was sponsored by the Office of Naval Research. Reproduction in whole or in part is permitted for any purpose of the United States Government.

Paul L. Garvin "A Linguist's View of Language-data Processing" is in part based on research done under contract AF 30 (602) -2223, Study for Automatic Abstracting, with the Intelligence Laboratory of the Rome Air Development Center of the U.S. Air Force. "Syntax in Machine Translation" is based on research initiated at Georgetown University under the sponsorship of the National Science Foundation and was developed at Thompson Ramo Wooldridge Inc., RW Division (now TRW Computer Division), under Contract AF 30 (602) -2036, Machine Translation Studies of Semantic Techniques, with the Intelligence Laboratory of the Rome Air Development Center of the U.S. Air Force and as part of the company's General Research Program. The views expressed in this paper were in part previously stated in the author's "Syntactic Retrieval" in H. P. Edmundson (ed.), *Proceedings of the National Symposium on Machine Translation,* pp. 286–292, Prentice-Hall, Inc., Englewood Cliffs, N.J., 1962 (1). Passages are reprinted by permission.

Jules Mersel "Programming Aspects of Machine Translation" is based on work done under Contracts AF 30 (602) -2036 and AF 30 (602) -2643 with the Intelligence Laboratory of the Rome Air Development Center of the U.S. Air Force, and under Contact NSF C-233 with the National Science Foundation.

Don R. Swanson Most of "The Formulation of the Retrieval Problem" is based on or inspired by work performed at Thompson Ramo Wooldridge Inc., TRW

Computer Division, under the sponsorship of the Council on Library Resources, Washington, D.C.

Robert M. Hayes The work described in "Mathematical Models in Information Retrieval" was supported in part by the National Science Foundation under Contract No. C-162. It has appeared with some other material concerned with models for file reorganization as a chapter in *Introduction to Information Storage and Rertieval: Tools, Elements, Theories,* John Wiley, New York, 1963.

Larry E. Travis Most of the work on "Analytic Information Retrieval" was done while the author was associated with Planning Research Corporation, Los Angeles, California, under a subcontract with Ramo-Wooldridge, now the Computer Division of Thompson Ramo Wooldridge Inc., the prime contract being AF 30 (602) - 1814 with the Rome Air Development Center of the U.S. Air Force. The ideas on fact retrieval presented in this discussion were developed over a period of eighteen months in 1959 and 1960, and for help in their development I am indebted to my many coworkers at Planning Research Corporation and at the TRW Computer Division during that period. For help with the particular ideas manifested in this paper, I am especially indebted to coworkers D. Black, C. Miller, H. Bohnert, C. Kellogg, and M. Savas. I have benefited much from comments on an early draft of this paper, especially the comments of Professor Bar-Hillel; of J. Olney and R. Wyllys of SDC; and of J. Kuhns of the TRW Computer Division.

Paul L. Garvin and W. Karush Garvin's work on "Overview" was done under the sponsorship of the AF Office of Scientific Research of the Office of Aerospace Research, under Contract No. AF 49 (638) -1128. Karush's work was carried out as part of the independent research program of the System Development Corporation. The authors have benefited from extensive discussions with Jack Fromkin of Colortran Industries, Inc., and Madeleine Mathiot.

PREFACE

This book has grown out of a lecture series in the Engineering and Physical Sciences Extension Division of the University of California, Los Angeles, held in the fall semester of 1960–1961. Its purpose is to survey the emerging field of language-data processing, in which by "language" is meant a natural language such as English or Russian, and not an artificial language such as the languages devised by mathematicians or logicians.

The discussions in Part 2 are designed to give introductory information to the nonspecialist. The remaining articles present a cross section of opinions and approaches, with the aim of being representative of major trends in the field rather than of reflecting the editor's own viewpoint.

The division of the book into six parts is intended to represent the logical structure of the field. In order to deal with natural language efficiently for any purpose, we should know something about its properties. The first part deals with some approaches that professional linguists have devised in order to conceptualize and analyze natural languages. The second part deals with mathematics and computation. Part 3 is an attempt to relate the properties of natural languages to the general problem of processing data on a computer, from a linguistic, a logical, and a mathematical standpoint. Parts 4 and 5 deal with the two areas of language-data processing which so far have shown the most tangible results: machine translation and information retrieval. The final discussion, which constitutes Part 6, gives an evaluative overview of the field.

Paul L. Garvin

CONTENTS

NATURAL LANGUAGE AND THE COMPUTER

Three linguistic models of language

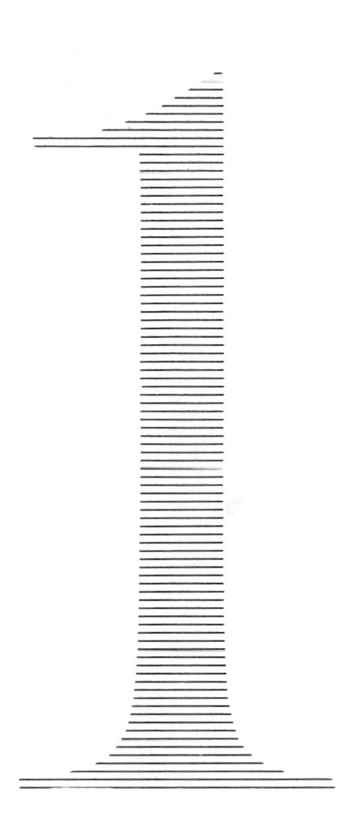

PAUL L. GARVIN

The definitional model of language

The briefest and most usual way of defining the field of linguistics is to call it the "science of language," where "language" is intended to mean a natural language. This is not a sufficient definition, since there are other sciences of language such as the psychology of language, the sociology of language, and similar disciplines. How does linguistics differ from these other fields?

Linguistics can most readily be differentiated from other sciences of language by expanding its original definition to read: Linguistics is the science of language with language as its primary objective of cognition. Other sciences may also deal with language, but their interest in language is as a tool for studying the particular scientific field. In the psychology of language, for example, the major focus of interest is speech behavior as part of human behavior in general; language is considered to the extent to which it affects this primary concern. In the sociology of language, where such problems as class differences in speech or the effect of speech patterns on group identification are studied, interest is centered on social relations, to which language is used as an ancillary. In linguistics, on the other hand, language is studied for its own sake, and social and psychological or other factors are brought into the picture only in so far as they illuminate our insight into the workings of language.

In the older approaches to linguistics, much of which was commonly referred to as philology, the study of problems of language history and of the relationship among languages was of primary interest. The study of the history of individual words and expressions, well known under the name of etymology, was a part of this traditionally historical orientation.

Many linguists still pursue this historical interest; however, a second direction in linguistics has become increasingly significant: the study of language as a phenomenon without regard to its history. Perhaps the most appropriate label that can be applied to this branch of linguistics is "synchronic linguistics." The center of interest is structure—what language, or a particular language, is like, rather than how it came to be that way. The question of what language is like can be answered by a reasonable theoretical discussion of the nature of natural human language; or, in the case of a particular language, it can be answered by an orderly description of that particular language. In a sense then, the two pursuits germane to synchronic linguists are linguistic theory and linguistic description. The two are interrelated in that the concepts of linguistic theory can be used as points of departure for the methodological devices of linguistic description.

It is obvious that for purposes of language-data processing historical linguistics is of little interest, since the goal is to deal with languages as they are. In this connection "models of language" are those in synchronic linguistics and not in historical linguistics.

The use of the term "model" in linguistics is fairly recent. For more than a generation descriptive linguists have been interested in a generalization of their procedures and results as applied to a variety of languages but have not always used the model terminology to refer to these generalizations. It used to be more common to talk of "theoretical frameworks" or "descriptive frameworks," but "model" can be applied with some justification to those earlier frameworks, since they often were thought out along lines similar to present approaches.

The attempt to use models in the social sciences may be brushed off by some as just another desire to attain the prestige of the physical sciences by copying some of their devices. While this is undoubtedly a common motivation on the American academic scene, it is not quite fair to leave it at that. On the contrary, it is eminently worthwhile to consider whether models in the strict mathematical sense or perhaps models in a looser metaphorical sense are not reasonable tools in the description and interpretation of social and human phenomena.

Some of the models currently vying for popularity in linguistics are intended to have definite mathematical properties; indeed, in modern American linguistics there has been a distinct shift away from an orientation toward behavioral psychology in the direction of a stronger orientation toward mathematics and symbolic logic. Much of this new orientation is characterized by extensive symbolization and mathematical and/or logical terminology. Thus, instead of using conventional terms such as *verb, noun,* and *adjective,* the tendency is to use symbols such as x, y, z or abbreviation-derived symbols such as V, N, A. Instead of writing

A subject followed by a predicate and an object constitutes a sentence.

this statement would be symbolized by something like

$$S + P + O = sent$$

Instead of saying

This noun constitutes a subject.

the symbolization may be

$X \in S$

Similarly, linguistic writings are replete with such terms as *correlation, transformation,* or *product,* used in the most varied senses. Frequently such symbols and technical terminology result in a certain brevity and an appearance of logicality, although on closer scrutiny, the actual content of a discussion is often not greatly different from previous linguistic discussions in which terminology more of a social-science or humanistic type was employed.

It is suggested here that the use of models, terms, and symbols is to an extent something of a fad in linguistics, just as it has become something of a fad in other social sciences. Once recognized, this matter can be viewed with detachment; we can consider the proper place of a model within the field of linguistics, and more important, we can also consider what kind of model, if any, is best suited for the purposes of descriptive linguistics.

According to colleagues in engineering and the physical sciences, one of the essential characteristics of a real mathematical model is that it allow for genuine and interesting predictive computations, often based on the application of real mathematical theorems. This is equally true of symbols and formulae in engineering and the physical sciences: some real mathematics is applicable to them. Unfortunately, none of the symbolizations or models in linguistics is mathematical in this rigorous sense. Thus, if the term "model" is to be used in linguistics, it will have to be in the looser nonmathematical sense.

THE USEFULNESS OF MODELS IN LINGUISTICS

Even though at present we are far from being able to formulate and prove interesting theorems about natural language, there still remain the two objectives of synchronic linguistics: the theoretical interpretation of the nature of language and the description of a particular language. The usefulness of a model can then be measured by the extent to which it contributes to these two objectives.

The Purpose of Theoretical Models For the theoretical interpretation of language, a model should be capable of accounting for the two apparently contradictory conclusions that have emerged as basic insights from the experience of the profession. One is that all the languages of the world are similar to each other, in that they all are languages. The other is that all the languages of the world are dissimilar to each other, in that they all are different languages. Any theoretical framework or model must account for both the similarity and the dissimilarity in such a way that they become logically compatible. A theoretically useful model, therefore, must be specific enough to stipulate all the necessary properties of natural human language; it also must be general enough to accommodate the variety of different individual features of particular languages that have been uncovered by the efforts of linguistic analysis over the past few generations.

The Definitional Model The general properties stipulated by the model should be defined in such a way that they can serve as suitable points of departure for the study of any language. Each of the concepts used in the model, in other words, should reflect one of these general properties of natural languages and should allow the development from it of analytic procedures specifically suitable for the investigation of the detailed conditions prevalent in a particular language. A theoretical framework which in such a commonsensical way stipulates the properties of the object of cognition as derived from observational experience is thus more of a definition or set of definitions in the classical sense than a model in the modern logical mathematical sense. This is why it is called here a "definitional model."

This definitional model of language should include a genus and a differentia specifica. The genus portion of the model must set forth those properties which natural language shares with other comparable objects and on the basis of which it can be included in a larger class of phenomena. The differentia specifica portion of the model must then set forth those properties which make natural language a particular species of this larger genus of phenomena and differentiate it from other related objects within the same class.

The latter aspects of the definitional model are particularly important in the present context, since the term "language" is so frequently used nowadays to designate objects other than natural languages. This use of the term has undoubtedly been a contributing factor, though perhaps not the major factor, in the common tendency to investigate simple systems that are not natural languages, in order to generalize the results of these investigations to apply to natural language as well. The presumed advantage of such an approach is that a particular linguistic problem can be simplified by dealing with it under a set of conditions which are arbitrarily simplified by the investigation. Such a simplification very often allows the derivation of logically neat and sometimes even mathematically manipulable solutions. The only question is: What problem has been solved by such solutions? Was it a real problem of natural-language-data processing, or was it a problem rendered ficticious by the simplification?

The above is not intended as a rejection of the technique of simplification for purposes of problem solving. It is intended as a necessary caution that results should be not only neat—that is, simple and rigorous—but also relevant to the real problem. Thus, any simplification of a genuine natural-language problem should be based on a recognition of the essential structural properties of a natural language. The simplification should be such that none of these properties is lost in the process. The simplified problem should adequately represent the real situation, in order for its solution to remain applicable to the original more complex problem or at least allow an extension of its applicability to it.

It is for this reason that a statement of the presumable properties of a natural language has great operational significance, even before one becomes involved in the actual development of linguistic analytic procedures from such a statement.

The point of the above discussion is that in a definitional model *all* the necessary properties of the object of cognition should be stipulated in order to ensure its applicability. In addition, it is equally important that *only* the necessary properties be stated and no additional ones, in order not to distort the reality of the phenomenon by forcing it to conform to a model which is too specific.

The classic example of such a model, which by its specificity destroys the reality of the phenomenon, is the traditional Latin model of grammar. Until the advent of the descriptive interest in linguistics early in the century, most grammars of the well-known languages followed the medieval tradition of being patterned after Latin, and new grammars of previously undescribed languages, prepared mostly by such dedicated amateurs as missionaries and travelers, likewise followed the Latin model. That is, all languages were described as if they had some of the characteristic features of classical Latin (such as six cases, six tenses, three moods, etc.), or they were described in terms of those features of Latin that were present and those that were absent. Traditional grammars for such languages as Russian, which indeed has a case system, or for Italian, which after all is historically very closely related to Latin, turned out to be fairly adequate for most practical purposes. But for a language such as English, which very definitely has a structure rather different from classical Latin, the traditional grammar patterned on Latin is patently unusable for most scientific and practical purposes.

Some of the models proposed by modern investigators differ from the traditional Latin model merely by proposing another set of extremely specific characteristics to be shared by all languages; that is, instead of forcing any given language into the old Latin mold, they now force the variety of human languages into a different equally detailed, and therefore equally distorting, bed of Procrustes. In their attempts at a modern analysis, some linguists have recently succeeded in making English, for instance, look not like Latin, but like Turkish, or in making Russian look like an American Indian language. In summary then, it is necessary to proceed with caution in proposing a model to be sure that it will be at the same time general enough not to prejudge the results, and yet specific enough not to be trivial.

In order to arrive at such a reasonable model, the most appropriate approach seems to be to draw on both the commonsensical and analytic insights of the profession and of gifted amateur investigators. There is a fairly consistent body of experience to draw on, from which there have emerged some observations on the basic attributes of natural languages. From these observations a number of general conclusions can be drawn which, when appropriately formalized in terms of a commonsensical rather than a formal logic, may be presented in the form of a general theory or model of language.

Because such a model is essentially rooted in common sense and experience rather than an extraneous logical system, it lends itself to the formulation of analytic suggestions which are not contraditory to analytic practice. Whether the procedures that can be developed to implement these suggestions are "real" procedures in a very strict logical sense is not as important as whether they allow a verified and controlled acquisition of knowledge about a particular language. Fundamentally, linguistic procedures can do no more, but definitely should do no less, than formalize at each stage of the analysis the intuitive insights of the trained investigator about the nature of his data. Highly significant is the step-by-step formalization of individual small intuitions which by their very smallness and separateness become tractable, where a more extensive body of intuition might lend itself to empirical verification with much more difficulty.

THE GENUS AND DIFFERENTIA SPECIFICA OF THE DEFINITIONAL MODEL

The Genus As stated above, the definitional model, like all classical definitions, consists of a genus and a differentia specifica. The genus portion of the definitional model reads: Language is a system of signs.

This is a statement upon which investigators of language have agreed since classical antiquity. Note that this definition of language—after the Swiss linguist Ferdinand de Saussure, who is considered by many the founder of modern synchronic linguistics—is less detailed than some of those found in recent textbooks of linguistics. A number of these definitions speak of language not merely as a system of signs but as a system of vocal symbols. The qualification *vocal* is purposely omitted, since the material manifestation of the system through the medium of sound is not one of its essential structural properties; one of the fundamental insights of data processing has been that systems can easily be transposed from one medium to another by means of machines, provided their structural properties are known. In regard to natural language, it seems reasonable to require that its definition should not be limited to spoken language alone, but should include all its isomorphic or not so isomorphic representations in other media such as writing or, for that matter, computer code. A further qualification often found in textbook definitions of language is that it is a system "by means of which the members of a human community interact." This qualification seems redundant, since the term *sign,* or *symbol,* seems to imply to most observers the presence of human interactors. Similarly, the qualification *arbitrary,* which is often added before *sign* or *symbol,* is redundant, since signs or symbols, unless they are iconic in Charles Peirce's terms, are arrived at by convention and hence are arbitrary in the sense that their physical shape is not necessarily related to their meaning.

Language is a *system* of signs in the sense that it consists of a set of discrete entities which are in some meaningful way related to each other. These relations are in the experience of linguistic analysts mostly nonstatistical in nature, since the pattern of occurrence of the discrete entities making up a natural language is largely nonrandom. The concept of discreteness in the linguistic consideration of language is discussed later in "Syntax in Machine Translation." It is necessary here to stress the property of relatedness in terms of which language is considered a system. This implies that a language must be described by the relations of the elements that comprise the system rather than by a mere listing of those elements.

The elements which make up the system of a language are thus signs of a particular kind. To make this definition meaningful we must say something about the nature of signs. The classical definition of the sign is that it is "something that stands for something else." It is possible to rephrase this definition in terms of modern psychology to read: A sign is a potential stimulus object the response to which is governed, not by its physical properties, but by a convention pertaining thereto.

The term *potential* is used here in the redefinition of *sign* because many linguists consider language an abstract system that allows for concrete manifestations in the process of speech or writing. Hence the elements of language are *potential* objects, in that they are capable of concrete manifestation in a particular process. Signs are termed potential *stimulus* objects because an element of the abstract system in each of its concrete manifestations has as its function to serve as stimulus for a response by a qualified hearer, reader, or other receiver. The response, if any, to such a stimulus is, as stated above, not directly related to the physical properties of the stimulus object; this is the significant criterion which makes it noniconic in Peirce's sense. Consider the following illustration of the difference between a stimulus object that does not constitute a sign and one that does.

Assume that you are driving down a highway somewhere and that you suddenly notice a fallen tree sprawling across the road. Presumably your response to this visual stimulus will be to stop your car and to do whatever else you may consider proper under the circumstances. It is reasonable to assume that your response was in some way directly related to the physical properties of the stimulus object; such a stimulus object is thus not the manifestation of a sign.

Imagine now the same situation again, but instead of noticing a tree sprawling across the road you just see a small red flare placed in the middle of your lane. Chances are you would again bring your car to a stop; it is reasonable to assume, however, that your response here was not governed by the physical properties of this latter stimulus object, but by your awareness of the convention embodied in the traffic code. This, of course, was an instance of the manifestation of a sign.

In addition to the defining property discussed above, signs which form part of a system have an additional property first stated by the Austrian psychologist Karl Bühler in his book on the theory of language.[1] This property is called by him "the principle of abstractive relevance." It can be stated as follows: Not all of the physical characteristics of a sign are relevant to its communicative function, but only certain abstracted ones. Thus, in the above example it is only the red color of the flare which is relevant to signal danger, not its size or its design. Nor is the shade of red a necessary detail of the signal, so long as it is clearly recognizable as red.

An elaboration of abstractive relevance, which we may call the "principle of contrastive differentiation," reads: The abstractively relevant characteristics of each sign in a system are differentiated by contrast with the other signs of the system. In the well-known system of traffic lights, for example, the redness of the red light is recognized as red by contrast with the amber and green. The principle of contrastive differentiation leads to the further corollary that the permissible range of variation of an abstractively relevant characteristic of a sign depends on the number of signs with which it is in contrast. The redness of a red light which is opposed to both amber and green has a smaller range of variation than the redness of a red light which is opposed to green only.

Some further significant attributes of signs, as discussed by Karl Bühler, are worth pointing out here. The characteristics considered above are those that signs have by virtue of forming part of a system; they can therefore be called system-derived. Each manifestation of a sign, however, takes place in a particular environment. The environment may consist in part of other signs of the same system, in which case it can be called a *context*. It may further consist of the set of circumstances in which the sign is used, in which case it can be called the *situation*. It can be observed that in each instance of use, a sign with its system-derived characteristics is placed into its environment—that is, its possible context and situation—and is modified by that environment. The additional charac-

[1]Karl Bühler, *Sprachtheorie*, Jena, 1934.

teristics thus derived can be called environmentally derived and further specified as contextually derived or situationally derived. The latter distinction is of some significance in language-data processing, and is discussed further in "A Linguist's View of Language-data Processing."

Consider again the example of the traffic lights to illustrate the relation between system-derived and situationally derived characteristics; to illustrate contextually derived characteristics, a more complex system would have to be cited. The system-derived meaning of the lights, as everyone knows, is "stop," "caution," "go." In the normal situational environment of an intersection, this meaning is translated into appropriate responses by drivers. In the situation of a driver's vision test, where a replica of the traffic lights may be used, the system-derived meanings of "stop," "caution," and "go" are retained, but situationally derived elements of meaning modify the response in terms appropriate to the different conditions.

The general characteristics of signs disclosed above can be summarized as follows: Signs have both form and meaning (that is, they constitute stimuli–form–to which conventional responses are expected–meaning) ; when they form systems, their abstractively relevant characteristics are differentiated by opposition; when signs are used, their system-derived characteristics are modified by environmentally derived characteristics. Since natural language is here considered a system of signs, all these properties of signs must also apply to the elements of natural language.

From the association of form and meaning follow the linguistic equivalence principle and relevance criterion.

The linguistic equivalence principle differentiates between what is same and what is not same in liguistics as follows: Same is what is structurally equivalent, and not necessarily what is substantively identical. Variant spellings of the same word–to choose a simple example from written language–have different forms but the same meaning; they are substantively not identical, but structurally equivalent. Conversely, homonyms are substantively identical, but structurally not equivalent. Thus, sameness and difference can be established only if form and meaning are considered together. A consequence of the linguistic equivalence principle is the linguistic relevance criterion: That which affects structural equivalence is relevant; that which does not affect structural equivalence, although it may affect substantive identity, is not relevant.

In linguistic analysis, the intent of the description is to determine the elements of a natural language and their relations to each other. Let us consider how, from the general properties of signs as stated above, some of the basic techniques of the linguistic analysis of hitherto undescribed languages can be derived.

The source of information about an unknown or little-known language is a native speaker of the same, called an informant by linguists. The techniques employed in obtaining information from an informant are summarized under the heading of informant work or, if such work is conducted in the territory of the language to be investigated, field work.

One of the corollaries of the relation between the form and the meaning of the sign is that there exists a certain degree of covariance between these two properties. This covariance can be utilized in informant work to elicit linguistic responses in a systematic way, in a manner comparable to a psychological experiment in which controlled stimuli are presented and responses are observed for their systematicity. Most psychologists refer to such controlled stimuli as the independent variable and to the observed responses as the dependent variable. In informant work, the covariance of form and meaning is exploited by utilizing one of the two variables as the independent variable and observing the other as the dependent variable. In most instances, bilingual informants are used for this purpose. One mode of exploiting the covariance of form and meaning is to control the meaning of the informant's responses and observe their form. This is done, in effect, by presenting the informant with short examples in English, for example, and asking him for the equivalent in his native language. By making sure that the English examples are in some way systematically similar to each other, the investigator may observe whether comparable systematic similarities emerge in the informant's answers. This allows the investigator to obtain an initial inventory of elements in the language under investigation, since it may be assumed that the systematic differences in the informant's answers which vary with the systematic differences in the English questions are related as forms and meanings of signs.

It is evident that the principle of contrastive differentiation similarly enters into the initial procedure of linguistic analysis: Forms are elicited not singly but in sets, and elements are separated from each other by a constant comparison of the forms within a set in order to observe the similarities and differences by means of which these elements may turn out to be in opposition to each other within the system. It can also be seen that this elementary technique of linguistics consists in observing the manifestations of the signs in a language in order to infer from them the abstract system which is the ultimate objective of study.

The relation between system-derived and environmentally derived characteristics is taken into account in informant work by attempting to eliminate so far as possible situationally derived characteristics through the creation of the artificial environment of the "informant session," which is the linguistic analog of laboratory conditions. Contextually derived characteristics are minimized in the beginning of informant work by using short stretches of speech.

The Differentia Specifica This second portion of the definition of language reads: Language is a system of signs, structured in terms of three sets of levels.

Most descriptive linguists call the various structural aspects of language "levels"; in their theoretical presentations they like to say that in a language there are *x* levels of analysis, or that linguistic analysis should be conducted on *x* levels; linguists also often debate whether or not in the analysis or in the description it is legitimate to "mix" levels, and so on.

A level can best be defined as a set of structural relations pertaining to a particular qualitative aspect or property of language. Since a natural language can be assumed to have more than one pertinent structural property, it is not unreasonable to talk of several levels, each level dealing with one of these.

The reason three *sets* of levels are postulated here rather than simply a specified *number* of levels is that language can be considered as having not merely a number of properties in this respect, but three sets of properties, each in terms of a particular defining criterion. One of these dimensions is concerned with the types of linguistic units that can be posited, the second with their varying degree of complexity, and the third with the nature of the relations between the units.

The first set of levels, which we can call *levels of structuring,* is defined in terms of the nature of the elements of natural language that can be singled out by linguistic analysis: units which themselves constitute signs—that is, have both form and meaning—as opposed to units that merely serve to differentiate signs without themselves being signs—that is, sign components.

Consider a simple example from written English. The form *misleader* as used in a recent political speech, can be said to consist of three formal constituents, each with its own meaning: *mis-*, *-lead-*, and the final *-er*. These three constituents each have a form and a meaning—the meaning of the final constituent *-er* can be rendered by some such paraphrase as "one who performs the action indicated by the preceding constituent." They are thus by our previous definition manifestations of signs. Linguists call such elementary linguistic signs *morphemes*. Note in this connection that morphemes are not the same as words, since in our example the written English word *misleader* was analyzed into the manifestation of three consecutive morphemes. Note also that morphemes are not the same as syllables, since division into syllables is based on considerations of pronunciation and spelling without necessary regard to features of meaning. One possible division into syllables of *misleader* would thus be *mis-lea-der,* which is not like the above division into *mis-*, *-lead-*, and *-er*.

The form *-lead-* in the above example can be said to consist of three differentiative components: the letter *l,* which serves to differentiate it from forms such as *read;* the letter combination *ea,* which differentiates it from forms such as *lad* and *loud;* and the letter *d,* which differentiates it from forms such as *leak*. Note that the letter combination *ea* in *-lead-* is deliberately retained as a single component, instead of the form *-lead-*

being broken up into four letters. This is done because the sequence *ea* indeed functions here as a single differentiative element in the English spelling system, as opposed to the same sequence of letters in a form such as *reactivate,* where each of the two letters has its own separate differentiative function. The above letters and letter combinations into which the example is divided are thus, by our definition, manifestations of linguistic sign components. Linguists call the elementary sign components of written language *graphemes.* Note that a particular grapheme may be manifested by a single letter, or by a letter combination, or indeed by no letters at all—as in a nonalphabetic writing system such as the Chinese, where the individual symbols are not usually considered letters.

Until recently, linguists have been primarily interested in the description of spoken rather than written language. While they have applied the term *morpheme* to include the signs of both spoken and written languages—and differentiated between spoken and written morphemes when necessary—they have consistently used the term *phoneme* to refer to the sign components of spoken language, and reserved the term *grapheme* for the discussion of written language only. The distinction between phonemes and graphemes is justified, not only by the different substantive manifestations of each, but also—and primarily—by the observation that the phonemic structure of spoken language and the graphemic structure of written language are not necessarily in a one-to-one correspondence. English is a well-known example: English speakers are well aware of the fact that theirs is not what is popularly called "a phonetic language"—that is, a language such as Spanish or Finnish, for which the written graphemes are more or less reasonable equivalents of the spoken phonemes of the preferred pronunciation.

Phonemes are related to the speech sounds of phonetics in a similar way as graphemes are related to letters: Phonemes are manifested by a wide range of sounds sharing the same differentiative function, just as graphemes may be represented by single letters or by letter combinations. The phonetic range of a phoneme may be illustrated by the standard English example used by linguists: The two English forms *pit* and *spit* are both said to contain the phoneme /*p*/.[2] The phonetic shapes of the pertinent sound types contained in the two forms differ: in *pit,* the /*p*/ is pronounced with a relatively forceful release of the air as the lips are opened, accompanied by an extra puff of air called aspiration; in *spit* the release is less abrupt and the aspiration is absent. In spite of these differences, the aspirated sound [p^h] of *pit* and the unaspirated sound [*p*] of *spit* are both included in the range of the same phoneme, because the

[2]In line with linguistic usage, letters representing phonemes are enclosed in slants, letters representing sound types are enclosed in square brackets.

presence or absence of aspiration depends on the surrounding phonetic substance: no aspiration when an [*s*] precedes, aspiration when no [*s*] precedes and a strongly stressed vowel follows. Hence this difference has no differentiating function, and only the common attributes of the two sound types (that is, absence of vocal-cord noise, lip closure followed by instantaneous release) are carriers of the function of the phoneme /*p*/ to which they both belong. By virtue of these attributes the phoneme /*p*/ is contrasted with other phonemes in the language, such as /*b*/, which is marked by the presence of vocal-cord noise, or /*f*/, which is marked by friction between lower lip and upper teeth.

Finally, consider a classic example of the difference between spoken and written morphemes. The third-person-singular ending of English verbs, although it takes more than one phonetic or written shape, is considered by linguists a single morpheme with several variant forms. In written English, there are two possible spellings of this morpheme: *-s,* as in *he gives, -es* as in *he wishes.* In spoken English, on the other hand, there are three possible pronunciations which differ in their phonemic composition: /*-z*/ as in *he gives,* /*-s*/ as in *he cuts,* and /*-ɨz*/ as in *he wishes.* The same morpheme has two variant forms, called allomorphs, in written English, but three allomorphs in spoken English. There is no necessary one-to-one correspondence between spoken and written morphemes, any more than there is between phonemes and graphemes. Written language thus has to be described in terms of graphemes and morphemes, spoken language in terms of phonemes and morphemes. Since graphemes are the written analogs of phonemes, we can for our present purposes subsume graphemic under phonemic and simply speak of *two levels of structuring*—the phonemic and the morphemic. Anything said about phonemes will then apply analogously to graphemes as well.

The important difference between phonemics—the description of the phonemic level—and morphemics—the description of the morphemic level—thus lies in the different nature of the units that are dealt with. This difference can be restated in terms of the covariance of form and meaning discussed above.

Since phonemes and phonemic units in general are not themselves signs but merely serve to differentiate signs, their participation in the form-meaning covariance is of a different nature from that of morphemes and morphemic units in general. (The question of units in general is discussed further below.)

In case of morphemes, there is a specific covariance of form and meaning, in the sense that the form of a particular morpheme varies with the meaning of that morpheme (with some disturbances brought about by homonymy or homography). This means that wherever morpheme *A* is replaced by morpheme *B,* form *A* is replaced by form *B* and meaning *A* is replaced by meaning *B.* Note that in each instance of the use of form *B* in replacement of form *A* we also have a use of meaning *B* in replacement of meaning *A*.

For phonemes, the nature of the covariance is not specific, if indeed one can speak of covariance at all. When in a sample of speech—that is, an utterance—one phoneme is replaced by another, there is a concomitant change of meaning, but the change of meaning is not directly related to the particular phonemes being exchanged for each other. In one sample, the replacement of phoneme *A* by phoneme *B* will bring about the replacement of meaning *X* by meaning *Y*, but in another sample, the replacement of the same phoneme *A* by the same phoneme *B* will bring about the replacement of meaning *Z* by meaning *W*.

Thus, whenever in English the morphemic form *I* is replaced by the morphemic form *you*, there is a corresponding change of meaning—always the same change of meaning: the meaning *first person* or *speaker* is replaced by the meaning *second person* or *person or persons spoken to* in all instances in which the replacement of forms has taken place. On the other hand, whenever the phonemic form /*p*/ is replaced by the phonemic form /*b*/, there is a replacement of meaning, but the particular meanings which are replaced by each other vary from case to case: when the /*p*/ in *pall* is replaced by /*b*/, the resultant form is *ball*, when the /*p*/ in /*pit*/ is replaced by /*b*/, the resultant form is *bit*. Although the phonemic forms that have been replaced by each other are the same, the meanings that have been replaced by each other are not the same.

This difference in the covariance relation has an extremely significant consequence for the procedures of linguistic analysis, The technique stated above, in which meaning is used as the independent variable in order to observe form as the dependent variable, is applicable to morphemic analysis only—that is, to the analysis which has as its aim the description of morphemes. We can elicit related sets of examples in the language under investigation by asking appropriate English questions, and can expect to be successful in using these sets to arrive at an initial inventory of morphemic forms. In translation of the English examples *I am going there, you are going there, he is going there,* we can obtain the forms *ikoola, kekoola, ekoola* in the Micronesian language of the island of Ponape. Comparing these forms, we can make the assumption that *i-*, *ke-*, *e-*, and *-koola* each represent a separate morpheme, with the respective meanings *I, you, he,* and *go there*. The three forms *i-*, *ke-*, and *e-* can be suspected to belong to one morphemic set, and the form *-koola* to another, in terms of the known similarities in the English forms of which they are translations.

In phonemic analysis, it is not possible to obtain phonemically related sets of forms by simple elicitation. No set of English examples can be found, the translations of which can be expected to exhibit systematic phonemic similarities. The Russian translations of *pit* and *bit*, which in

English are phonemically similar, are not particularly similar to each other: they are *yama* and *kusok,* respectively. The only thing that the phonemic investigator can control in the beginning of the analysis is the length of his examples; by asking for the translation of short English examples, he may expect to elicit forms that are short enough so that he can follow them and record them. He then has to make up his own sets of phonemically related forms by classifying his data according to the suspected phonemes which they seem to have in common and those by which they seem to differ.

The second set of levels has to do with the relative order of complexity of a linguistic unit. This set of levels is based on the assumption that the elements of language, both phonemes and morphemes, do not merely form sequential chains, but are integrated into units of a higher order of complexity which function as wholes and are characterized by certain over-all qualities that transcend the characteristics of the mere sum of their components. Units of this higher order may be called *fused units.* This, as can be seen, is an extension to linguistics of the well-known Gestalt principle of perception psychology.

Consider the following English examples to illustrate the concept of the fused unit. Linguists agree that a form such as *houses* represents two morphemes—a stem morpheme *house-* and a suffix morpheme *-s.* They would further agree that this example illustrates what may be called a *diagnostic context* for the analysis of the occurrence pattern, or *distribution,* of English morphemes. Stretches which are found to precede this suffix morpheme *-s* and to follow some equally clearly specified boundary—that is, which occur in the diagnostic context ________*-s*—can be said to constitute a distributional class in English morphemics, namely, the class of *noun stems.* On further examination of English data, it becomes apparent that the above diagnostic context can be occupied not only by single morphemes, but by small chains of morphemes, as in the forms *environ-ment-s, real-iz-ation-s,* and the like. Thus chains of morphemes occupying the diagnostic context ________*-s* are permissible replacements of single morphemes, such as *house-* in the initially cited example. Although these chains consist of more than one morpheme each, they nonetheless have a common replacement characteristic which belongs to the entire chain rather than to its individual components. They are thus fused units in the sense in which the term is used above.

These examples represent a relatively low order of fused unit, which can be called morpheme cluster. In a language such as English (and for that matter, in languages very unlike English as well) there are many more orders of fused units of increasing complexity. The examples were chosen from the morphemic level of structuring; fused units of different orders of complexity can also be ascertained on the phonemic level of structuring, the best-known instance of which is the syllable, which in many languages has over-all characteristics that are not simply a result of the sum of the properties of the phonemes composing it.

It is not unreasonable to posit a separate "level" for each order of fused units encountered in a language, be it on the phonemic or the morphemic level of structuring. It is furthermore reasonable to assume that in any given language there will be more than one of these levels, but not reasonable to assume any particular given number of these levels. These may be called *levels of integration.*

The assumption about the over-all properties characterizing the fused unit as a whole allows for a significant corollary with important consequences for linguistic analysis—namely, there is no necessary relation between the internal structure and the external functioning of a given linguistic unit. This allows us to formalize the common observation by linguists that units of the most varied internal structure in a given language often may have the same modes of external functioning, and conversely, units of the same internal structure may have different modes of external functioning. In the first instance, such units can be called functionally equivalent; in the second instance, such units can be called identically constituted.

A classic example of functionally equivalent units in English with the most varied internal structure is the use of entire clauses as modifiers such as in the expressions *a come-hither look* or *with a don't-come-near-me expression on her face.* It seems apparent that the external functioning of these modifying constructions cannot be meaningfully related to their internal structure, but must be explicated through the assumption that internal structure and external functioning are separately statable and partially independent properties.

Conversely, English nominal constructions of the type *John Henry* or *Jackie Anderson* are found not only in such examples as

John Henry is a good friend of mine.

where they can be said to function as subjects, but also in utterances such as

Don't you Jackie Anderson me.

where they can be said to function as predicates. These constructions illustrate how units that are identically constituted may differ in their external functioning.

In linguistic analysis the assumption of fused units implies that, in addition to ascertaining elements such as phonemes and morphemes in a given language, their integration into units of a higher order of complexity has to be described. This assumption also allows the application of a single unifying operation to an entire chain of elements, since it then will be based on the presumable over-all characteristics of this chain which is assumed to constitute a fused unit. The corollaries regarding the separateness of internal structure and external functioning, leading to the properties of functional equivalence and identical constitution, permit the analyst to ignore internal structure while investigating external functioning, and vice versa. This is particularly significant in that it allows the analyst to ignore certain conditions of detail without violating the consistency of the analysis; it is perfectly possible to describe a set of units in a given language as to their external functioning and ignore the question of their internal structure, without thereby invalidating the statements pertaining to their functions. In many cases, the details of internal structure of infrequently recurring units are obscure, and no conspicuous analytic advantage would be gained by delaying the procedure in order to ascertain them; the description of the structure of the language as a whole can well proceed without the inclusion of these details. This is particularly true of the many instances in which grammatical elements, such as the stem portions of nouns or verbs, seem to consist of more than one morpheme, but where for a number of reasons the detailed description of this morphemic composition is not readily accomplished. It is then more efficient to describe these potential units as to their external functioning only, and to ignore their internal structure in order not to impede the progress of the analysis. The classical example of such units are the many English forms of Latin origin, such as *receive, detect,* and the like (which recur quite infrequently by comparison with such elements as the suffix *-s*), in which the original Latin morphemes seem to persist in English, but the rigorous application of linguistic procedures does not yield clear-cut morpheme boundaries.

The third set of levels deals with the manner in which the units of a natural language—both elementary units and fused units—are organized.

Any sign system by definition contains more than one sign; hence, in each instance in which the system is used, a selection has to be made from among the signs available within the system. This principle of selection applies to natural language as well; in each instance of the use of language, one or several of the many available linguistic units have to be selected. In many sign systems, selection is the only organizing principle present; most ordinary road signs are a good example of this. The function of each individual road sign is usually independent of the presence of any possible preceding or following signs along the same road; only the selection of the particular given sign matters in each instance of use.

In the case of language, however, the function of each of a sequence of linguistics units may be closely related to, or even governed by, the presence of other units within the sequence. That is, in addition to the selection of the units in each instance of use, the sequential arrangement of units is relevant. The classical examples are the two English sequences *dog bites man* and *man bites dog*, in which the same units have been selected but the arrangements are different, and these two sequences constitute different messages because of these differences in arrangement.

In natural language, therefore, both the selection and the arrangement of the units are relevant organizing principles. We may refer to selection and arrangement as the two *levels of organization* of natural language, by which natural language differs from systems with a single level of organization (selection only) such as the system of road signs.

Some linguists refer to the level of selection and arrangement as the *paradigmatic* and *syntagmatic* levels respectively. Going back to the discussion of diagnostic contexts above, the distributional class allowed in a particular diagnostic context can be called a paradigmatic class, since in each particular instance of speech (or writing) one member of the class is selected to occupy the given context. The relation between the paradigmatic class and its diagnostic context can be called a syntagmatic relation, since the sequential position of the components of the context with regard to the blank into which the class fits, is one of the diagnostic criteria. That is, the diagnostic context *You* ______ *Mary* is different in diagnostic value from the context *Mary* ______ *you,* since the former allows occupancy by forms such as *love, see,* whereas the latter allows occupancy by forms such as *loves, sees.*

Consequently, the description of a language can not be limited to a listing of the paradigmatic classes and their members, to the extent permitted by the size of the class. It must also contain a statement of the syntagmatic relations in terms of which these classes are defined, and by virtue of which individual members can be assigned to these classes.

The Czech linguist V. Mathesius in the late thirties considered the two levels of organization of language significant enough to propose a basic division of linguistics into onomatology and syntax, representing the two levels of selection and arrangement respectively. While this distinction has not gained currency in the profession, it represents an interesting attempt to render more specific the very useful traditional distinction between dictionary and grammar which, for most practical purposes, corresponds closely enough to the two levels of selection and arrangement.

The most productive techniques of linguistic analysis are related to this distinction between the levels of selection and arrangement, as well as to the differentiation of external functioning and internal structure as discussed earlier. Two of these techniques are cited briefly below.

One is the very well-known technique of substitution, which, if properly specified, is extremely useful in linguistic analysis. It consists of investigating what units are interchangeable in the same diagnostic context. This investigation can be conducted either through informant work, by presenting the informant with an appropriate series of questions, or through an extensive analysis of a large body of text in which minimally different stretches are compared to each other. The substitution technique results in the definition of a paradigmatic class, as discussed above. Examples of such paradigmatic classes would be the class of noun stems or the class of verb stems in a language such as English.

Another technique based on these two sets of levels is that of dropping. It consists of testing whether the omission of one portion of a given sequence leaves a viable residue—that is, one which is acceptable as an utterance in the language under investigation. The dropping technique is used to ascertain a syntagmatic relation of dependence: *A* is dependent on *B*, whenever *B* is the necessary condition for the occurrence of *A*. In the dropping test, the omission of *A* will leave a viable residue; the omission of *B* will not. In the English sequence

The houses were built last year.

the omission of the article *the* leaves a viable residue

Houses were built last year.

On the other hand, the omission of *houses* does not: *The were built last year* is not an acceptable English utterance. The results of the dropping test yield a clue (but, of course, only one clue) to the syntagmatic relation between *the* and *houses*: it will be more reasonable to assume that *the* depends on *houses* for its occurrence, than to assume the converse. Needless to say, additional tests will be necessary to validate this assumption.

Let us now summarize the discussion so far and restate the definition of language in its complete form: Language is a system of signs, the structure of which is specified in terms of three sets of levels—namely, two levels of structuring, two levels of organization, and more than one level of integration.

The above definition can now be applied to any given system of signs in order to ascertain whether or not it is a language in the sense of being the linguist's proper object of cognition—that is, a natural language. If the system under consideration—whether it is called a language or not—exhibits all the properties specified above, it can be considered a natural language (or a complete isomorph of one, which for data-processing purposes ought to be the same); if the system lacks any of these properties, it is not a natural language.

Thus, when logicians talk about a simplified language as defined, for instance, by the vocabulary *a, b, c,* and the syntax +, −, =, it is not a language in our sense, since, although it does have the two levels of organization, it lacks both the required two levels of structuring and the levels of integration. Similarly, the language of the bees as described by von Frisch is not a linguist's language, since it, too, is limited to the two levels of organization and lacks the other two sets of levels (*cf.* Sebeok's discussion in "The Informational Model of Language"). On the other hand, written English, for instance—although it is far from being a complete isomorph of spoken English—is as much of a natural language as any of the spoken dialects, since it exhibits all the structural properties set forth in the definitional model of language, although, of course, their substantive manifestation is graphic rather than phonetic. By defining natural language in terms of its structural and relational rather than any substantive characteristics, the definition becomes applicable to written as well as spoken language. This means that although descriptive linguists have heretofore concentrated the bulk of their efforts on the analysis of spoken languages, the techniques of descriptive linguistics are equally applicable to written languages.

In conclusion, consider the point of view which this definitional model suggests for linguistics and language-data processing.

Since language is viewed as consisting of a system of units of different defining characteristics and orders of complexity which are linked to each other—and defined—by the relations into which they enter, the basic objective of descriptive linguistics becomes one of defining these units and of stating these relations. In terms of concrete analytic practice, defining the units means being able to ascertain their boundaries: The definition of a linguistic unit should be such that given a particular analytic input (either a sample of speech or a set of units of a lower order obtained by a previous procedure) and this definition only, the application of this definition should yield unequivocally the boundaries of the units so defined.

The definitional model of language discussed here thus requires that in analytic practice, units and relations beyond a certain minimal order of complexity be appropriately defined rather than accepted as primary assumptions. This means, in effect, a requirement that the primitive terms of linguistic analysis be pushed back as far as possible, so that only terms of maximum generality are permitted as primitives. Specifically, this means that only such general terms as *phoneme, morpheme, fused unit, dependence relation,* or *substitutability relation* are allowed as axiomatic; more particular terms such as *stem, verb, noun,* or *phrase* should not be allowed as primitive terms, but should be defined in terms of the relation of the real primitive terms to each other and to the analytic input. In so doing, this definitional model allows a somewhat greater control over the investigator's intuition than would a less demanding point of view. Although many of these more special terms of the analysis may appear to be intuitively obvious, by being forced to give their proper definition, the analyst is compelled to verify his intuition at each step. This allows him to ascertain whether, in terms of the data before him, his intuition was or was not in error on some point. When confronted with the strict requirements of data processing on a computer, he will then be able to rely more securely on his results.

ROBERT P. STOCKWELL

The transformational model of generative or predictive grammar

Some of the better-known activities that have gone on under the name *grammar* have been termed prescriptive grammar, formalistic grammar, notional grammar, and generative grammar. It will be useful to discriminate between them.

A set of assertions about the respects in which any individual's control of a natural language must be modified to conform with any given norm is a *prescriptive grammar.* The term *prescriptive* is not pejorative; it is intended only to characterize a purpose of grammatical description, doubtless the most familiar one. Obviously any type of description, from the viewpoint of any model, may be the basis for prescriptive use. All descriptions, *qua* descriptions, are neutral with respect to the aim of prescription.

A taxonomy of linguistic forms based exclusively on certain surface properties (fixed sequential order, permitted affixes, shape of stress pattern, position or shape of intonation and juncture) is a *formalistic grammar,* also known as *signals grammar* when the surface properties are viewed as signals used by the hearer to differentiate one structure from another. In discussing this kind of analysis, which he views as superficial, Lees[1] cites the following examples in which all formalistic properties are identical:

talking machine	machine which talks
eating apple	apple for eating
washing machine	machine for washing things
boiling point	point of boiling
laughing gas	gas which causes laughing

From these examples he concludes that it is impossible to find "universally and automatically applicable analytic procedures for assigning grammatical structure to arbitrarily chosen expressions. . . ." There are many varieties of formalistic grammars; we shall make no distinc-

[1]Robert B. Lees, "The Grammar of English Nominalizations," *International Journal of American Linguistics,* Part II, vol. 26, 1960.

tion among them, since they do not characterize sentences in the explicit fashion which is of interest in the present context (i.e., they do not provide generative, enumerative, predictive rules of sentence formation).

Chomsky has attempted to infer the shape of the rules that their statements imply,[2] but there has not been time for those whom he is second-guessing to affirm the accuracy of his representation. In discussing the shape of what he calls *taxonomic* grammars, Chomsky infers that the rules are at best only an unordered set of the context-restricted phrase-structure variety: $X \rightarrow Y$ in environment $W{-}Z$. This kind of rule is discussed below.

A taxonomy of linguistic forms based on semantic criteria and logic (e.g., the meaning of the compounds above) is a *notional grammar.* Grammatical *subject-verb-object* may be classified notionally as *actor-action-goal.* Most first-rate classical grammars are notional at least in part, and it is still true that no other grammar of English approaches in fullness of exemplification that of Poutsma,[3] in which notional categories consistently override formal or formalistic ones. There is a sense in which modern grammars – whether definitional, finite-state, formalistic, constituent-structure, transformational, or any combination of these—remain embryonic and programmatic until they have produced a work which in fact enumerates the characteristics of English sentences as fully as the best of the traditional notional grammars. There is another sense, however, in which such grammars may be said to characterize only those sentences which they cite as examples, simply by virtue of citing them as examples. That is, they fail to provide explicit rules which predict the structure of sentences beyond the cited examples, which are of themselves merely an organized collection of data with a more or less revealing commentary. The reason such grammars are useful is that the intelligent reader has the ability to extract from the examples the generalized rules of sentence formation, which, in turn, are what a fully explicit grammar endeavors to formalize. Notional grammars have been rejected by formalistic grammarians on methodological grounds, claiming, for example, that their definitions of parts of speech are not in terms of observable concrete properties. But a stronger reason for rejecting them, along with formalistic grammars, is simply that they do not adequately explain the generalizations that human beings somehow arrive at as the basis for constructing, apparently without effort, new sentences never uttered before which conform to the constraints inherent in the sentences to which they have been exposed.

[2]"The Logical Basis of Linguistic Theory," *Ninth International Congress of Linguists,* to be published.

[3]H. Poutsma, *A Grammar of Late Modern English,* Groningen, 1928.

A finite set of rules which enumerate an indefinitely large number of grammatical sentences in a language is a *generative grammar.* Unlike the types of grammar listed above, these grammars do not leave to the reader the construction of new sentences on the "analogy" of those that are cited and analyzed. They explicitly characterize the permitted analogies, the regularities shared by new sentences with old ones; they do not leave the extensional task to the intelligence and intuition of the reader.

Empirical science aims to encompass an unlimited corpus of events within a finite set of generalizations which have the power to enumerate those events that have been observed and to predict events which have not been observed. One aim of linguistic science is to construct general rules capable of enumerating indefinitely many of the sentences of a language, and to predict that sentences never previously uttered will be characterized by the same set of generalizations. (We wish ultimately to go beyond the enumeration and prediction of sentences in a single language, or any given set of specific languages, and seek out the systematic properties of human language in their most general terms.)

The task of the grammarian is, therefore, to construct a model which will generate sentences in such a way as to characterize certain linguistic abilities and limitations of the speaker of a given natural language. A few of these are (1) the ability to construct (and understand) sentences never heard or uttered before in the life history of the individual; (2) the ability to accept as grammatical or reject as ungrammatical any utterance, quite apart from whether it is a "sensible" utterance or not (for example, a nonsensical utterance, still grammatical, such as *Purple cows usually smoke blue and white bananas.*); and (3) the ability to "parse" certain sentences in more than one way in the presence of grammatical ambiguity (as in Lees's example, *They ordered the police to stop drinking after midnight*).

There have been, in recent years, three models of language structure that were generative, predictive, and explanatory in the sense outlined above. They are the following:

1 A set of rules of the form $S_i \rightarrow a\ S_j$ (where S_i and S_j are the names of states in an arbitrary finite automaton and a is the transition symbol produced as the device moves from S_i to S_j) is a *finite-state grammar.* If we assign probabilities to the interstate transitions, the device is a probabilistic finite-state grammar. Though Chomsky[4] has demonstrated that, either with or without probabilities, the model is inadequate to generate all the sentences of a natural language insightfully, it is still being urged by Hockett[5] to explain the procedures through which the

[4]Noam Chomsky, *Syntactic Structures,* 's-Gravenhage, 1957.

[5]"Grammar for the Hearer," *Proceedings of Symposia in Applied Mathematics,* vol. 12, pp. 220–236, 1961.

hearer (receiver) passes in decoding a message. Hockett's insistence on this point is all the more difficult to understand in view of the apparent fact that the rules of which one can infer the shape from Hockett's discussion are a weak form of phrase-structure rules, not finite-state at all.[6]

2 A model which more nearly approaches adequacy is the IC (immediate-constituent) model. The IC model has been fashionable for a couple of decades; its pretransformational application to English was worked out most fully by Nida.[7]

3 An ordered set of IC rules, subjected to certain tight constraints and formalized as a phrase-structure grammar, is capable of generating sentences with many of the characteristics of natural language, including nested concordances of indefinite extent (a capacity not shared by the finite-state model). It is evident, however, that there are important sentence types that the IC model will generate only with serious loss of insight and naturalness in explaining relationships within and between sentences. These limitations are discussed below also. In order to generate the sentence types that exceed the capacities of IC grammar, the notion "transformation," devised by Harris[8] in working with discourse analysis—where it was desirable to reduce all sentences to their simplest possible structures, in order to specify equivalence classes (e.g., active = passive) —

[6]See Paul Postal, *Constituent Structure: A Study of Contemporary Models of Syntactic Description,* Baltimore, 1964.

[7]*A Synopsis of English Syntax,* doctoral dissertation, University of Michigan, 1943, Glendale, Calif., 1960.

[8]"Discourse Analysis," *Language,* vol. 28, pp. 1–30, 1952; and Discourse Analysis: A Sample Text," *Language,* vol. 28, pp. 474–494, 1952.

[9]*Cf.* Noam Chomsky, "Systems of Syntactic Analysis," *Journal of Symbolic Logic,* vol. 18, pp. 242–256, 1953; "Semantic Considerations in Grammar," *Georgetown University Monograph Series in Languages and Linguistics,* no. 8, pp. 141–153, 1955; "Transformational Analysis," doctoral dissertation, University of Pennsylvania, 1955; "Three Models for the Description of Language," *Proceedings of the Symposium on Information Theory, IRE Transactions on Information Theory,* vol. IT-2, 1956; "A Transformational Approach to Syntax," *Third Texas Conference on Problems of Linguistic Analysis in English,* 1958, pp. 124–158; "The Transformational Basis of Syntax," *Fourth Texas Conference on Problems of Linguistic Analysis in English,* 1959; "On Certain Formal Properties of Grammars," *Information and Control,* vol. 2, pp. 137–167, 1959; "Explanatory Models in Linguistics," in Suppes et al. (ed.), *Logic, Methodology and Philosophy of Science,* Stanford, 1962; "On the Notion 'Rule of Grammar'," *Proceedings of Symposia in Applied Mathematics,* vol. 12, pp. 6–24, 1961; "Some Methodological Remarks on Generative Grammar," *Word,* vol. 17, pp. 219–239, 1961; *The Logical Structure of Linguistic Theory* (mimeographed, available from MIT in microfilm); "The Logical Basis of Linguistic Theory," *Ninth International Congress of Linguists,* to be published. See also Robert B. Lees, review of Chomsky's *Syntactic Structures* in *Language,* vol. 33, pp. 375–407, 1957.

was taken by Chomsky and formalized as a set of rules to go beyond the limitations of IC grammar.[9]

Without doubt, there are infinitely many ways of constructing generative grammars besides finite state, phrase-structure rules, and phrase-structure rules plus transformations. For instance, the group of linguists led by Kenneth L. Pike (at the Summer Institute of Linguistics) claim that their "tagmemic" formulas are generative in capacity, though it is not clear just what the explicity generative rules of their grammars might look like, since they have not, up to now, sought to formulate them in terms of this specific objective. It appears, in fact, that their rules, if made explicit, would be context-restricted phrase-structure rules identical in form with those which make up the first part of a transformational grammar. This discussion is concerned only with the phrase-structure and transformational types, but it must be emphasized that gross coverage of the facts (i.e., success in generating actual sentences) is not a sufficient goal for linguistic description, even though it may be adequate, for example, for a computer program. In addition to covering the facts, linguistic description must seek to reveal the high level of regularity, uniformity, and patterning that characterizes natural languages, and reveal it in a way that conforms with the intuition of speakers of the language.

PHRASE-STRUCTURE GRAMMAR

A transformation is, broadly and typically, a rule which embeds one sentence in another, or which converts one sentence type into another. Thus a nominalizing transformation may introduce one sentence into another:

He said it
He is going → *He said that he was going.*

A passive transformation converts an active into a passive:

John killed Mary. → *Mary was killed by John.*

For such rules to be possible, there must be a source for the sentences that undergo the transformation — that is, at least one sentence type must be derivable from some nontransformational source, if only to trigger the transformational mechanism.

An ordered set of context-restricted phrase-structure rules is used by Chomsky to generate the source sentences (or, more accurately, the string of symbols that lie behind the source sentences) to which he gives the label *kernel* sentences: the simple, active, declarative sentences containing no expanded elements within them. Following are the important kernel-sentence types in English; they are not exhaustively listed or specified in complete detail:[10]

$NP + aux + V_i\ (adv)$ (1)

John ran home.
The ice fell on the floor.

$NP + aux + V_t + NP\ (adv)$ (2)

John killed Mary.
The heat melted the ice easily.

$NP + aux + \mathbf{be} + NP\ (adv)$ (3)

The story was a hoax.
John is a bore.

$NP + aux + \mathbf{be} + adj\ (adv)$ (4)

The problem was difficult.
The table was red.

$NP + aux + V_{io} + NP + NP\ (adv)$ (5)

She gave him the air.
They built John an office.

$NP + aux + V_{tc} + prt + NP\ (adv)$ $[\ldots NP + prt\ (adv)]$ (6)

They took over the country.
They took their fingers out.

$NP + aux + V_s + adj\ (adv)$ (7)

He felt good.
It tasted awful.

An eighth kernel type is arguable. Chomsky[11] establishes an empty element complement (*comp*), which occurs in the process of derivation but which can be expanded to meaningful words only by transformations:

$NP + aux + V_c + comp + NP\ (adv)$ (8)

[10]The following abbreviations are used in the subsequent formulae and discussion: *adj*, adjective; *adv*, adverb; *aux*, auxiliary; *comp*, complement; *D*, determiner (the article of traditional grammar); *M*, modal; *MV*, main verb; *N*, noun; *NP*, noun phrase; *prt*, particle; *S*, sentence; *SC*, structural change; *SD*, structural description; T_{comp}, complement transformation; T_{intrg}, interrogative transformation; T_{pass}, passive information; *Te*, tense; *V*, verb; V_i, intransitive verb; V_{io}, transitive verb taking indirect object; V_s, verb of sensation (e.g., feel, smell, taste); V_t, transitive verb; V_{tc}, transitive verb taking complement; *VP*, verb phrase.

[11]*Op. cit.*, fn. 4

They put ***comp*** *it + the car was in the garage*
They put the car in the garage.

They wanted ***comp*** *it + they went*
They wanted to go.

However, the eighth type can also be derived without use of an empty element *comp* by a transformation which replaces the direct object with a shortened form of a separate kernel sentence:

They wanted it
They went → *They wanted to go.*

There are problems in either way of generating such sentences.

IC analysis of the conventional variety long used in linguistic analysis consists in assigning layers of bracketing to the elements in sequence, assigning a label to each such cluster or group, and ultimately tying all the clusters together into a single symbol, *S* (sentence). This kind of analysis is really, therefore, only a kind of diagramming, somewhat more sophisticated than what conventionally goes under that name. Given the sentence

The heat melted the ice easily.

suppose the string of elements of which it is composed are these:

The + heat + ***past*** *+ melt + the + ice + easily*

Conventional IC analysis has been stated procedurally:[12] We seek to determine which two-element sequences can be replaced by a single element without changing our sense of the grammatical structure. These we can bracket and assign a label:

The heat ***past*** *melt the ice easily*

NP *NP* (1)
(John) *(ice)*

Continuing the same process, we obtain

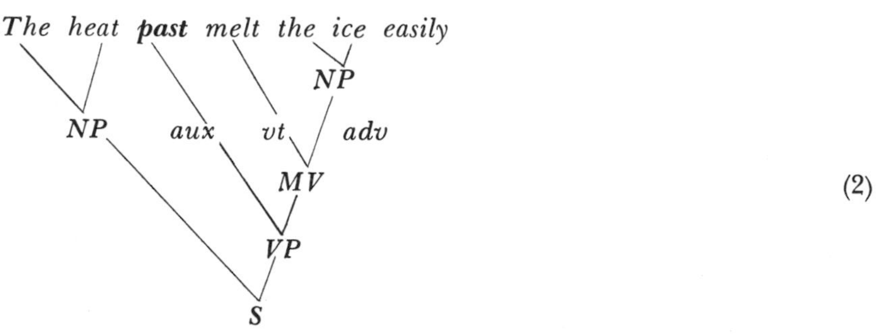

12H. A. Gleason, *Introduction to Description Linguistics,* 2d ed, New York, 1961.

There is no discovery procedure for producing the most useful set of braces automatically. We might, for example, have started out this way:

The heat **past** *melt the ice easily* (3)

We would then continue

The heat **past** *melt the ice easily.* (4)

This bracketing closely resembles a familiar diagram (not in its physical shape, but in the relational values assigned the elements):

The heat | *melted* | *the ice* (5)
easily

There are strong reasons for arguing that (2) is a more useful analysis than (4): *tense* (present, past) is a fixed element in all verb phrases (a function of the *aux*), whereas the portion of the sentence assigned to *MV-adv* in (2) is enormously variable (it may include an object or not, it may include two objects, it may include one or more complements, etc.). The entire *MV* can be nominalized, but only by the replacement of *aux* [*his melting the ice easily, (he wanted) to melt the ice easily,* etc.]. However, there is nothing in IC analysis itself which provides a clear advantage of (2) over (4); it is only the utility of (2) in describing large structures (in fact, its ultility in transformations) that causes it to be preferred.

The set of braces drawn under the completed sentence above can be inverted and a rule written to produce the split from each node of the braces, or *tree*. In this way, starting from *S* and applying the rules in order, the sentence can be *generated,* and by increasing the lexicon and adding certain choices within the rules, all kernel sentences can be *enumerated*. Thus, to produce the topmost branch, our rule might be this:

Rule a: $S \rightarrow NP + VP$

Following the rule, we have this tree:

S
NP *VP* (6)

To split *NP,* we have

Rule b: $NP \rightarrow D + N$

(7)

A lexical rule specifying which words belong to the class represented by each general symbol will then rewrite D as *the* and N as *heat:*

Rule c: $D \rightarrow$ *the*

Rule d: $N \rightarrow$ *heat, ice*

(8)

On the right-hand branch of the tree, the following rules operate in the same way:

Rule e: $VP \rightarrow aux + MV \ (+ \ adv)$

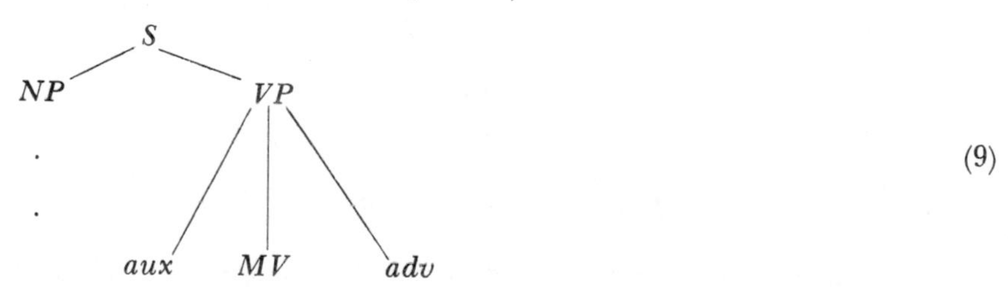

(9)

Rule f: $aux \rightarrow$ *past* / *present*

Rule g: $MV \rightarrow V_t + NP$

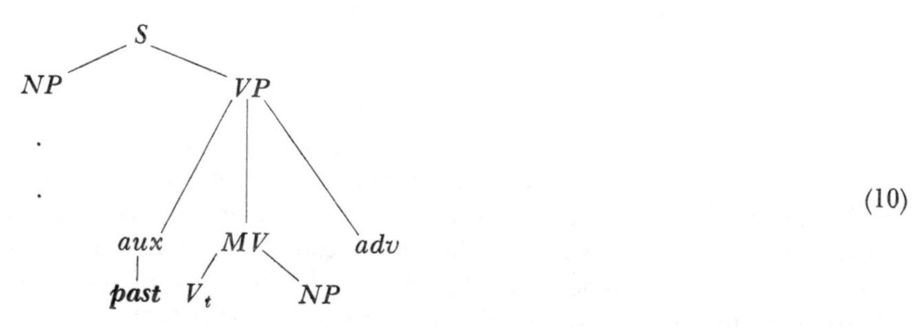

(10)

We already have rules *b, c,* and *d* to expand *NP,* so the tree is nearly complete:

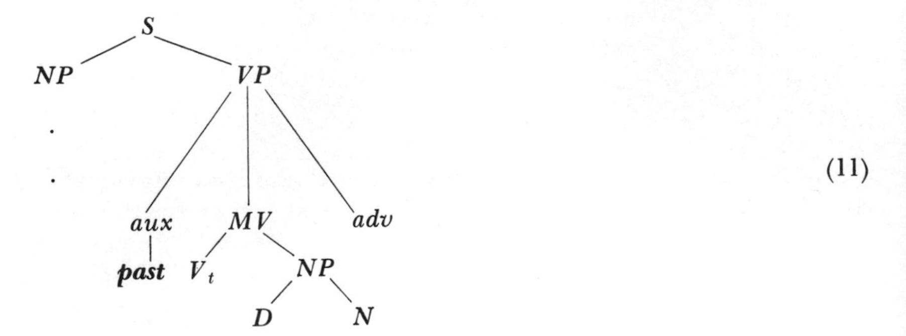

We need lexical rules to specify V_t and *adv:*

Rule h: $V_t \rightarrow$ *melt, . . .*

Rule i: adv $\rightarrow$ *easily, . . .*

We can now complete the tree:

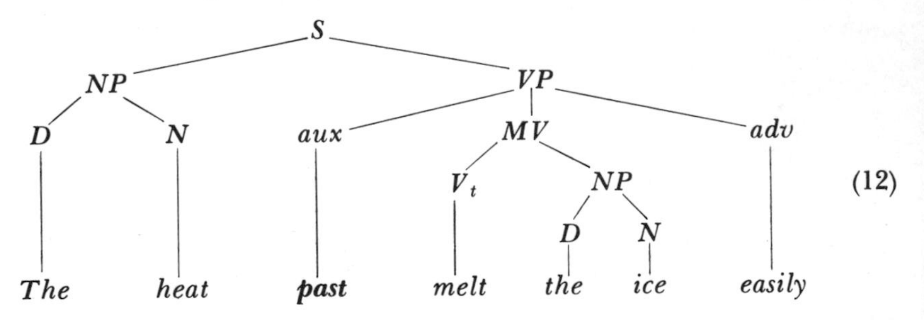

Rules *a* through *i* are obviously extremely fragmentary and of no real interest since they are simply *ad hoc* to this particular tree (12) and to this particular sentence. It is, however, relatively simple to elaborate them to generate all the kernel sentence types listed above. In this fuller form they will enumerate a long list of sentences which fit the eight patterns, but a finite list, since the lexicon is finite and since, for reasons that are discussed below, we wish to place certain limits on the form of the rules.

Let us, for the moment, assume the existence and adequacy of such a set of phrase-structure rules for generating kernel sentence types in English, rules which we will call the *parsing component* of a transformational grammar. Many years of work still remain before the parsing component will incorporate all the enormously complex restrictions on the structure of kernel sentences in English. The formulation of these rules will require the solution of certain theoretical problems that are known to exist in all current versions of the rules and that are perhaps inherent in the constraints now placed upon the shape of such rules. Since we have illustrated them so fragmentarily, it may be well to consider their structure briefly in more general terms.[13]

Phrase-structure rules cannot be permitted to be simply unconstrained rewriting rules, where any string of elements *X* may be rewritten as any string of elements *Y*. One of the necessary properties of these rules for the grammarian is that they be capable of assigning structure (the labeled bracketing, or tree) in a uniform manner. If it were permitted that a string *PQ* be rewritten as a string *XYZ*, there would be no way to assign the structure of *XYZ* to its source *PQ*:

Clearly, therefore, only one symbol can be rewritten at a time, and no deletions can be permitted. The first two of the above diagrams can be achieved in two steps each; the last two must be disallowed within phrase-structure rules:

$P \rightarrow XY$ *in env* $-Q$ $\qquad$ $P \rightarrow X$ *in env* $-Q$
$Q \rightarrow Z$ *in env* $P-$ $\qquad$ $Q \rightarrow YZ$ *in env* $P-$

It is hard to overstate the importance of this property of phrase-structure rules: they provide, in a mechanical fashion, a uniform labeled bracketing of every string that they generate. It is this property which makes it possible to specify the structural description of the strings on which transformational rules, in turn, operate.

There are certain other useful restrictions for such rules. One is that a symbol to the left of the arrow may not be repeated at the right of the arrow—that is, no rule of the form $Y \rightarrow XY$. The reason for this, even though it removes all recursive power from the phrase structure and hence amounts to a hypothesis that some type of rule beyond phrase structure is minimally necessary for grammar, is that the resulting tree appears to be counterintuitive in all instances where it has been used to generate repeated elements in natural languages:

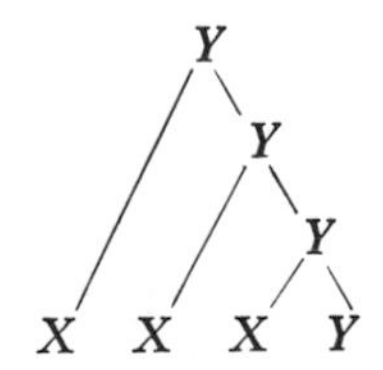

Such a string might be, say, *very, very, very nice,* where one feels that each *very* is merely another increment of niceness; however, the tree suggests

[13]For detailed treatment of this question, see Postal, *op. cit.*, fn. 6.

that *nice* is modified only once by *very*, then *very nice* is modified in turn by *very*, and *very, very nice* again is modified by *very*.

If the above restriction is accepted, then it is unnecessary to add a restriction that disallows metathesis of elements:

$XY \rightarrow YY$

$YY \rightarrow YX$

so that XY has become, in two steps, YX. Otherwise, such a restriction against metathesis must certainly be included, or one would have curious trees like this:

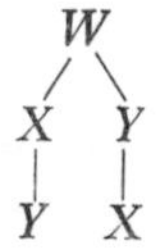

```
  W
 / \
X   Y
|   |
Y   X
```

which says that X is a Y, and Y is an X, where it was only intended to say that XY may be metathesized to YX.

Finally, a distinction should be noted between context-free phrase-structure rules and context-restricted ones. In the former, a rule applies wherever the *left* symbol turns up in a string; in the latter, it applies only when the *left* symbol turns up in a permitted context. It is obvious that the latter type are what grammarians must use in the description of natural languages (where phrase-structure rules are used at all), since, among many other reasons, there is no other known way of discriminating between homonyms.

When the parsing component is perfected, it will still enumerate only a fraction of English sentences. We turn now to the question of how this inventory of sentences can be extended to include all possible types. We first will naturally ask why rules of this type are not satisfactory for doing the whole job; that is: Why do we not merely increase the number and complexity of the parsing rules to generate all English sentences?

The answer lies in several inherent weaknesses of phrase-structure rules, and partly in the restrictions we have placed on them in order to have them assign structure uniformly and correctly in clear instances: (1) They cannot derive discontinuous constituents if restricted as above, and if they are not so restricted, the resulting tree violates the relation of class membership that must obtain between a higher node and the elements beneath it on the tree. (2) They require enormous complexity and duplication in a set of rules that might be designed to generate any but the simplest strings (i.e., they cannot form a sentence from a pair of partially formed sentences, they require that parallel grammatical constraints be specified at several points in the rules, etc.). (3) They cannot generate coordinate structures of indefinite length except by the introduction of excessive (and counterintuitive) bracketing. (4) They fail to show relatedness between sentences of differing phrase structure where the native speaker knows it exists.

The inconvenience of deriving discontinuous constituents may be illustrated by comparing declarative with interrogative sentence types in English. Suppose we have the sentence

The boy can go now.

with this tree derivation:

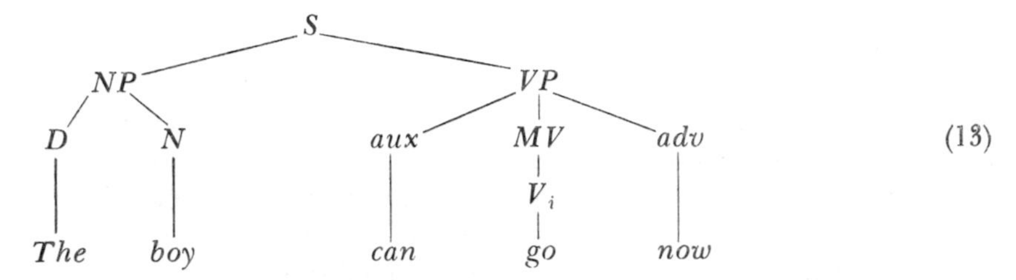

To make this sentence interrogative, we would need rules to give us

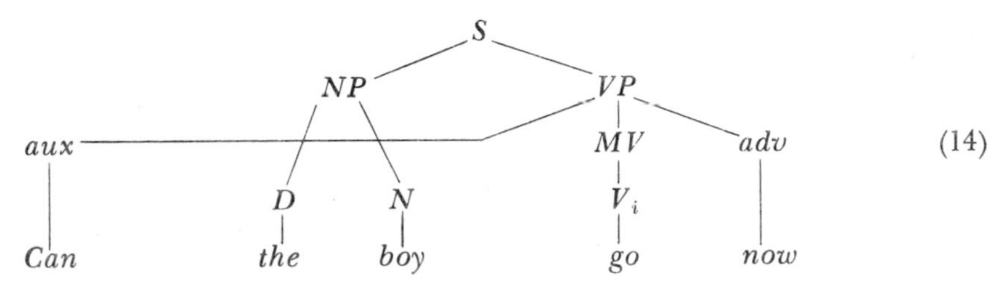

In order to get this tree with crossing branches, the rule about *VP* would presumably be:

$VP \rightarrow aux + \cdot \cdot \cdot + MV\ (adv)$

instead of rule *e*. The three dots would symbolize the possibility of inserting something between *aux* and *MV*. However, the rule does not specify *how much* to insert: by this rule, we could have generated (15) instead of (14):

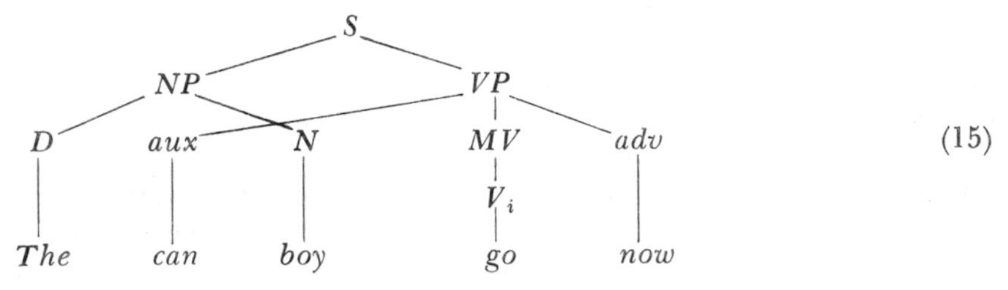

For this particular instance an *ad hoc* adjustment in the rules can easily be imagined. But a general provision for the exact discontinuity needed in all instances requires that the rule be formulated in a way that goes well beyond the power of phrase-structure rules. What is required is that the rule identify the structure of the string in which the elements of the discontinuity occur; that is, it must be possible, within the terms of the rule for the interrogative above, to discriminate between a preceding noun and a preceding noun phrase, which requires that the tree as a whole be available within the rule itself. This, in fact, is precisely what is made available in a transformational rule; but a rewriting rule of the phrase-structure type applies only if the appropriate symbol occurs in the specified environment: given *NP*, and a rule $NP \rightarrow D + N$, the rewrite must be carried out regardless of the structure of the rest of the sentence.

The second weakness of parsing rules, when they are considered as the sole generating device for sentences, should suffice to make the grammarian seek stronger kinds of rules: the fact that as soon as we go beyond the simplest sentence we are involved in multiple statements of the co-occurrence restrictions between classes of elements. The only way of expanding the sentence is by assigning ever more complex membership to each node of the tree. Suppose we wish to generate

Orbiting astronauts are popular.

We can do it by the following modifications in the phrase-structure rules cited earlier as *b, c,* and *d*:

Rule b_1: $NP \rightarrow (D) + (adj) + N$

Rule c_1: $D \rightarrow$ *the, . . .*

Rule c_2: $adj \rightarrow \begin{matrix} adj_1 \\ V + ing \end{matrix}$

Rule d_1: $N \rightarrow$ *heat, ice, astronauts (s), . . .*

That is, we can allow *adj* in the *NP,* and then allow *V* plus *-ing (orbiting)* as a member of the class *adj*. We are now in serious difficulty; we will presumably wish to have a rule later that will add *very, rather, quite,* etc., in front of adjectives *(very nice astronauts, rather brave astronauts, quite intelligent astronauts)*. But if $adj = V + ing$, we must also allow *very orbiting astronauts,* etc. It is possible to escape this difficulty by allowing *very, rather, quite* only with certain subclasses of *adj* (say, adj_1 in rule c_2). We still are not out of trouble, however, because some classes of $V + ing$ allow *very (very interesting, very annoying)*. Even if this difficulty can be avoided by ever-more-detailed subclassification, we are faced with a really critical failure of our grammar when we note that *astronauts* is the subject of *orbiting* in *orbiting astronauts are . . .* but the object in *orbiting astronauts is popular.* That is, a basic syntactic fact about verbs (that they have subjects and, in some classes, objects) is not lost simply because the verb happens to occur in a noun phrase. But all our machinery for explaining such facts about verbs is outside the *NP* from which, by rule c_2, we wish to derive *orbiting*. We must, therefore, either duplicate the *VP* inside the *NP* or conclude that there must be some better way than IC rules to generate such sentences.

If we restrict the abstract structure of our rules such that $Y \rightarrow XY$ is not permitted, then coordinate structures are at once placed beyond the capacity of the rules. If we had phrase-structure rules as the only device for sentence enumeration, we would have to reject this restriction in order to allow rules such as $N \rightarrow N$ *and* N, which would give us trees like this:

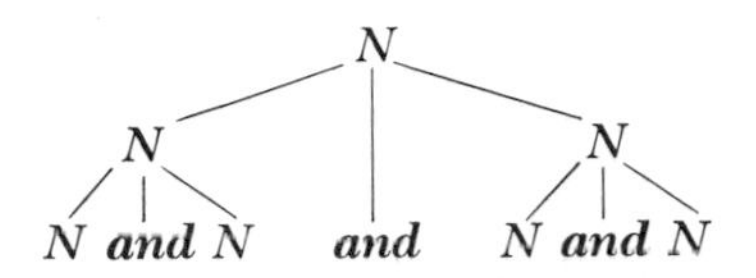

Such a tree is a possible one—*John and Mary* (as one group), and *Bill and Jane* (as the other group)—but it is not the only one we wish to be able to construct, since these items may be related as beads on a string.[14] We wish to have that possibility in our grammar, though it is beyond the limits of phrase-structure rules if we assume that such strings may be of indefinite length. So the restriction that a left-side symbol cannot appear also as a right-side symbol in a rewrite rule disables the rules for discontinuities and coordination and requires that there be some more powerful kind of rule; this is already required by the duplication and complexity of such rules in any case.

The fourth weakness of phrase-structure rules is that they fail to show relatedness between sentences which the native informant knows to be related, and in some instances even suggest wrong relationships by the accident of identical phrase structure. This is illustrated partially by the compounds cited from Lees above (*talking machine, eating apple,* etc.), and more fully by Chomsky,[15] using the following examples:

John ate an apple.	declarative	
Did John eat an apple?	*yes/no* question	interrogative
What did John eat? / *Who ate an apple?*	information questions	interrogative

To classify these sentences by phrase-structure (parsing or immediate-constituent) characteristics alone, the first and last go together by word-order criteria against the second and third; by intonational criteria, the

[14]See R. E. Longacre, "String Constituent Analysis," *Language*, vol. 36, pp. 63–88, 1960.

[15]*Op. cit.*, fn. 4, pp. 90–91.

others go together against the second. Phrase-structure rules are incapable of providing formal motivation for what is surely the correct classification, shown with the examples.

TRANSFORMATIONS

In attempting to formulate more powerful rules than phrase-structure parsing rules to generate complex sentences, we have found that most complex sentences contain, in some sense, several simpler sentences. For example:

> *I imagined myself persuading a friend to look into the question of taking one course under Professor X while trying to persuade himself that he should really return to school for full-time study.*

We can break it down, intuitively, as follows:

I imagined it *I persuaded a friend*	→	*I imagined myself persuading a friend . . .*
A friend looks into the question	→	*to look into the question . . .*
He takes one course under Professor X	→	*of taking one course under Professor X . . .*
He tries to persuade himself	→	*while trying to persuade himself . . .*
He should really return to school	→	*that he should really return to school . . .*
He should study full time	→	*for full-time study*

We will have noted, for example, that the phrase *of taking one course under Professor X* has all the syntactic properties of *he takes a course under Professor X,* except that the subject has been eliminated and the verb form has an affix *-ing* which *nominalizes* the phrase. Similarly we will have noted the equivalences between the other sentences and the partials that appear embedded in the complex sentence of the column on the right.

Our parsing rules will, ideally, already generate all the left-column sentences above. We would therefore quite reasonably seek to formulate rules which would combine these in the shape of the right-column complex sentence. This, in essence, is the transformational principle.

To characterize transformational rules fully, we might simply quote Chomsky's "On the Notion 'Rule of Grammar',"[16] where a full formal

[16] *Op. cit.,* fn. 9.

characterization is given. Only an informal exemplification of typical transform types is provided here. One particular reservation must be stated about the manner of exemplification: a fully specified transformational rule maps a bracketed string into a derived string, also bracketed. That is, the rule does not operate on a final string, even given class labels for the terminal symbols of which the string is composed. It operates on the string as bracketed by logically prior (not chronologically precedent) phrase-structure rules and transformational rules. If this were not the case, then the interrogative transform of the sentence

John was the boy who was going at nine.

could be any of the following (depending on the analysis taken for the initial *NP*) :[17]

Was John the boy who was going at nine?
**John was the boy was who going at nine?*
**Was John the boy who going at nine?*
**John was was the boy who going at nine?*

Only a bracketing which shows that *the boy who was going at nine* does not contain the *VP* of which *John* is subject keeps this absurd result from following quite naturally from a simple linear-transform rule (i.e., in effect simply an unrestricted rewrite rule). With this strong reservation, then, we may exemplify several types[18] of transformational rules:

1 Rules which add elements to sentences generated by prior rules or delete elements from them:

$AB \rightarrow AXB$
$AB \rightarrow A$

[17]In line with linguistic usage, asterisks (*) are used to indicate nonexistent or fictitious forms.

[18]P. Postal, in his (unpublished) dissertation, "Some Syntactic Rules in Mohawk" (Yale, 1962), classifies transformations in four groups: deletions, adjunctions, permutations, and substitutions. Deletions and adjunctions correspond with (1) in the list above—essentially the processes are subtractive and additive respectively. Permutations correspond with (2), and have been called metathesis earlier in the present discussion. Substitutions correspond with (4): they consist of subtraction of an element from the first string and the addition of one or more from the second string (i.e., replacement). All transformations may be viewed as the application of subtractive or additive processes, since even permutations consist of subtraction at one point in a string and addition at another point. But beyond these two simple processes they include, in a full formulation, the bracketing of the source string(s), and a new bracketing assigned by the transformation to the resultant string.

For example,

They ***past*** *leave*	→	*They* ***do past*** *leave*
They left.		*They did leave.*

Here an emphatic element has been inserted.

They ***past*** *smoke cigarettes all day*	→	*They* ***past*** *smoke all day.*
They smoked cigarettes all day.		*They smoked all day.*

2 Rules which shift the relative sequence of elements in sentences generated by prior rules:

$AB \rightarrow BA$

For example,

He will leave → *Will he leave?*

3 Rules which combine (1) and (2):

$AB \rightarrow BXA$
$AB \rightarrow BX$

For example,

John killed Mary. → *Mary was killed by John.*

4 Rules which operate like (1), (2), and (3), but which start from two sentences rather than one:

I said it
I was leaving → *I said that I was leaving.*

There are several ways of presenting such rules. The following typical transformations are only illustrative. *SD* (structural description) is the abstract constituent structure of any sentence to which the rule can be applied. *SC* (structural change) is the transforming rule itself. The symbols for grammatical classes are conventional; these examples of transformational rules are from Chomsky,[19] except that the complement example is modified for simplicity.

T_{intrg}: To generate simple *yes/no* interrogatives as transforms of declarative assertions (intonation is ignored for simplicity) [20]

[19]"A Transformational Approach to Syntax," *op. cit.,* fn. 9.

[20]See Robert P. Stockwell, "The Role of Intonation in a Generative Grammar of English," *Language,* vol. 36, pp. 360–367, 1960.

SD: *NP*	*Te*	VP_1
	Te + ***have***	*X*
	Te + *M*	*X*
	Te + ***be***	*X*

SC: 1 2 3 → 2 1 3

Examples:

He ***past*** *watch the plane* → ***Past*** *he watch the plane*
He watched the plane. *Did he watch the plane?*

There is an obligatory rule which supplies *do* as the empty carrier of the displaced tense form *past*.

He ***past*** + *have en* + *be* + *ing* + *work* →
Past + *have he en* + *be* + *ing* + *work*
Had he been working?

He ***past*** + *can be* + *ing* + *work* → ***Past*** + *can he be* + *ing* + *work*
Could he be working?

He ***past*** + *be ing* + *work* → ***Past*** + *be he ing* + *work*
Was he working?

T_{pass}: To generate passive sentences from active transitive sentences

SD: *NP aux* V_t *NP X*
SC: 1 2 3 4 5 → 4 2 + *be* + *en* 3 (*by* + 1) 5

Example:

John ***past*** *kill Mary yesterday* →
Mary ***past*** + *be* + *en kill* (*by* + *John*) *yesterday*
Mary was killed by John yesterday.

T_{comp}: To generate verbal objects (i.e., nominalized verbals as replacements of simple *NP* objects)

SD: *NP aux* + V_c ***it*** *NP aux VP*
SC: 1 2 3 4 5 6 → 1 2 ***to*** + 6
Condition: 1 = 4

Example:

John ***past*** + *expect it John* ***past*** *go home* →
John ***past*** + *expect to* + *go home*
John expected to go home.

The above examples are extremely simple. The third one, the complement transformation, has in fact about a dozen subtypes, allowing for such complements as these:

John wanted to go.
John wanted Mary to go.
John saw Mary going.
John avoided going.
John elected him president.
John thought her beautiful.

There are still serious problems not entirely solved in the formulation of transformational grammars, though one of them, the question of intersecting classes, lies in fact within the phrase-structure component of the grammar.[21] One question of some interest is the specification of the bracketing of strings derived by transformations. Postal has given this question some attention and formulated general rules which describe how the assignment would be made in particular types of transformations. In the case of deletions, additions, and replacements the derived bracketing seems clear: the appropriate nodes are deleted, or new material is tied to them, or they are replaced by material from a second string which carries its own bracketing. The derived structure in permutations remains unclear, and Lees and Postal have suggested somewhat different solutions, neither of which is entirely satisfactory. A different kind of problem arises from the fact that transformational rules are in a sense more powerful than we need: we seek ways to limit their power, to avoid the formalization of relationships that are not really structural ones, but are, say, semantic or situational. Finally, a problem of very considerable complexity for any particular transformational grammar is that of the traffic rules, the sequence in which different rules may be successively applied.

PHONETIC RULES

The phrase-structure rules constitute the parsing component of the total grammar, where essentially all the differentiation of the lexicon into syntactic classes takes place. The output of these rules is a representation

[21]See Paul Schachter's review of Lees' *Grammar of English Nominalizations,* in the *International Journal of American Linguistics,* vol. 28, no. 2, pp. 134–146, 1962. Schachter and this author have developed an elaborate device within phrase-structure rules—a matrix of simultaneous categories—which seems to provide at least a partial solution to this problem. The first explicit proposal known to me along these lines appeared in a seminar paper by Tommy R. Anderson in 1958, subsequently incorporated in his dissertation (UCLA, 1964). Chomsky, in a forthcoming article, "A Fragment of English Grammar," is said to have developed a similar matrix device and Emmon Bach, at the Ninth International Congress of Linguists, presented a paper entitled "Subcategories in Transformational Grammars," which contained similar devices.

of sentences (or sentence partials) in the form of labeled, bracketed strings of formative elements. This representation may be said to be a *linguistic level.*

The transformational rules constitute another linguistic level, in which the representation takes the form of a series of operations performed on the output of the parsing component in accordance with explicit instructions for the formation of new labeled, bracketed strings of formative elements.

These strings must be converted into phonetic symbols (of some variety) as the final level—the most direct one/one correspondence with the sounds of speech or symbols of writing. The rules at this level, called *morphophonemic* rules, are undergoing intensive investigation[22] at this time. These rules appear to need the least constraint in form among the rules of the three levels: they include essentially unrestricted rewrite rules (*go* + **past** → /*wɛnt*/) and also a transformational cycle which performs certain regular operations repeatedly (such as vowel reduction in unstressed syllables). From the viewpoint of traditional American structuralism, an interesting aspect of their shape is that they evidently do not require an independent "phonemic" level intermediate between the morphophonemic and phonetic levels.

GRAMMATICALNESS AND CHOICE

Two further fundamental concepts are the concept of grammaticalness and the concept of choice.

Presumably the notion "grammatical sentence" is characterized by the grammar itself, since in principle we formulate our rules in such a way as to generate only and always such sentences. It is a question of some interest whether there is a possibility of characterizing this notion independently of the grammar. It seems extremely unlikely that there is, and we will be forced to operate empirically with the machinery of the grammar, treating each sentence that it generates as a hypothesis to be tested for grammaticalness against the reaction of native speakers. For each sentence rejected, we either revise the grammar to exclude the sentence (if we believe the rejection is on proper grounds—that is, not motivated by school grammar or the like), or we revise the grammar to generate the sentence in some special status (i.e., as only partially well formed). Each sentence accepted is, of course, a confirmation of the validity of the rules up to that point. Informant reaction is difficult to handle, because such reactions involve much more than merely the question of grammaticalness. It is obvious, for example, that nonsense can be perfectly

[22]See Noam Chomsky and Morris Halle, *The Sound Pattern of English,* forthcoming from Harper-Row, 1963.

grammatical, and yet, even with nonsense, there seems to be a scale of grammaticalness:

He bottles beer.
He bottles sincerity.
He bottles of.

The first sentence is grammatical and sensible; the second is grammatical but nonsensical; the third is presumably simply ungrammatical. On the other hand,

He avoided to go.
He expected going.

are perfectly sensible, but ungrammatical. Finally, to show how complex the issue of grammaticalness can be, compare a sequence such as

All the queer little old square black Chinese paper boxes are here.

with the same words in a slightly different sequence:

All the old queer square little Chinese black paper boxes are here.

It is not clear that this last sequence is ungrammatical, but certainly the order is strange. With such a long list of adjectives in sequence, the first sequence is surely more grammatical.

One might consider the utilization of grammar by a speaker as follows. The essence of meaning is choice; every time an element is chosen in proceeding through the rules, that choice is either obligatory (in which case it was not really a choice at all, since there were no alternatives), or it is optional (in which case the choice represented simultaneously both the positive decision and the rejection of all alternatives—the meaning of the choice inheres in the constrastive value of the chosen element as compared with all the possible choices that were rejected). Thus these are the choices involved in a simple sentence such as

Did the boy leave.

$NP + VP$	Obligatory
$D + N$	Obligatory
$D =$ *the*	Optional
$N =$ *boy*	Optional
$aux + VP_1$	Obligatory
$aux =$ ***past***	Optional
$VP_1 = V_i$	Optional
$V_i =$ *leave*	Optional
T_{intrg}	Optional
Inversion of Te	Obligatory
Empty carrier for ***past***	Obligatory
Rising intonation	Obligatory

Of the twelve choices, half are obligatory—either initiating the derivation, or following out obligatory consequences of optional choices. The additional rules of the phonetic component are nearly all obligatory. To include these would increase the obligatory choices to about twice the number of optional choices. In fact, it is quite probable that in real discourse even the element *the* is obligatory (that is, the choice of *the* versus *a* seems quite predictable in a larger context). This would leave us with only five meaning-carrying (optional) choices. Everything else that goes into making up the sentence is in a valid sense perfectly mechanical, perfectly automatic. It can be argued that a grammar must maximize the obligatory elements and cut the optional choices to the barest minimum in order to get any reasonable understanding of how the human brain is capable of following complex discourse at all. That is, the hearer's attention is focused on matching, with his own generating machinery, the sequence of optional choices; since he has identical obligatory machinery, the rest takes care of itself. In this way, the same grammatical model accounts for both encoding and decoding. We do not need separate and distinct analogs for both sending and receiving messages.

Encoding or decoding does not imply that a speaker or hearer proceeds step by step in any literal sense through the choices characterized by the grammar in order to produce or understand sentences. The capacities characterized by the grammar are but one contributing factor of undetermined extent in the total performance of the user of language. The grammar enumerates only well-formed sentences and deviant sentences, which, recognized as ranging from slightly to extremely deviant by the language user, are interpreted somehow by comparison with well-formed ones. The grammar enumerates sentences at random; it does not select, as the user does, just that sentence appropriate to a context. The grammar clacks relentlessly through the possible choices; the user starts, restarts, jumps the grammatical traces, trails off. A generative grammar is not a speaker-writer analog. It is a logical analog of the regularities to which the language user conforms or from which he knowingly deviates.

Although the title of this book suggests the machine processing of natural-language data, it should not be assumed that the transformational model of the structure of language is in any way geared to machines of any kind, either historically or in current development. On the contrary, it is a natural extension of traditional scholarly grammar, an effort to make explicit the regularities to which speakers of a language conform, which has been the focus of grammatical studies for over 2,500 years. The effort to formulate discovery procedures for the systematic inference of grammatical structure is quite recent; few if any transformationists believe such a goal has any possibility of success—at least, not until much more is known about the kinds of regularities which grammarians seek to discover and to formulate in explicit terms.

The transformational model consists of three components, each component being an ordered set of rules of specific types: (1) a parsing component, containing context-restricted nonrecursive expansion rules, the output of which is bracketed strings of formative elements (like words) which correspond to well-formed sentences of the simplest type in a given language; (2) a transformational component, containing recursive rules of two types—those which operate on a single string and those which operate on two strings, the output of which is new bracketed strings which correspond to well-formed sentences of all types beyond the simplest; and (3) a phonetic component, containing, for the most part, obligatory rules, the output of which is the phonetic specification of formative elements in terms of some universal grid of phonetic features. It is at least imaginable that other components are still needed: for example, a set of rules of deviation to make explicit the manner in which we interpret parasitic[23] or fragmentary sentences, or a set of rules of idiom formation (suggested by Householder[24]). In all three components there are difficult unresolved problems: (1) the manner and extent of sub-sub-sub-classification in the parsing rules; (2) the traffic rules of transformations, so that the output of some or all may serve as input of others; (3) the manner of achieving derived bracketing in the output of transformations; (4) the ordering of phonetic rules, and the extent and manner in which syntactic bracketing operates within the phonetic component. All these and others are currently under intensive investigation.

[23]C. E. Bazell's word for phrases like *a grief ago* in *Word,* vol. 18, p. 140, 1962.

[24]Review of C. F. Hockett's *A Course in Modern Linguistics* in *Language,* vol. 35, pp. 503–526, 1959.

THOMAS A. SEBEOK

The informational model of language: analog and digital coding in animal and human communication

Speech communication may be studied as an information system and natural language as the code used in the system.[1] From this point of view it seems useful, on the one hand, to investigate the analog and digital characteristics of human communication and, on the other, to compare human and animal communication systems as to the manner in which they code information.

Communication engineers often distinguish between two kinds of control machines: those for counting and those for measuring. The former, which are "all-or-none" devices, are sometimes called *digital;* they are of a "yes/no" type. The latter, which operate on the basis of connections between measured quantities and the quantities they represent, are, by contrast, known as *analog;* they are of a "more-or-less" type. The prototype of a digital system is the abacus, that of the analog, the slide rule. The chief limitation of analog systems relates to their accuracy; those physical systems, on the other hand, which are able to make yes/no decisions can achieve any desired precision, given sufficient capacity and time.

A further observation—developed by N. Wiener, among others—is that the functioning of the nervous system is *prima facie* digital:[2] If a combination of incoming messages will not cause an outgoing fiber to fire, it is said to be *below threshold;* otherwise, it is said to be *above threshold.* Nervous pulses can thus be viewed as two-valued markers: the presence of a pulse (release of acetylcholine?) above threshold represents one value, say, the binary digit 1, and the absence of a pulse (release of cholinest-

[1]See C. F. von Weizsäcker, "Sprache als Information," *Sprache,* Darmstadt, 1959, pp. 33–53; and R. Jakobson, "Linguistics and Communications Theory," *Proceedings of Symposia in Applied Mathematics,* vol. 12, pp. 245–252, 1961. See also the section on information-theoretic models in W. Plath's survey of "Mathematical Linguistics," in C. Mohrmann, A. Sommerfelt, and J. Whatmough (eds.), *Trends in European and American Linguistics, 1930–1960,* Utrecht, Antwerp, 1961, pp. 21–57.

[2]N. Wiener, *The Human Use of Human Beings,* Boston, 1950, p. 74.

erase?) another value, say, the binary digit 0. That the brain is not, however, merely a glorified digital machine, but that it is a mechanism built upon a more primitive analog basis, and that the processes which pass through the nervous system may repeatedly change their character from digital to analog and back to digital was set forth in a posthumous book by J. von Neumann:[3]

> Nerve pulses, i.e., the digital part of the mechanism, may control a particular stage of such a process, e.g., the contraction of a specific muscle or the secretion of a specific chemical. The phenomenon is one belonging to the analog class, but it may be the origin of a train of nerve impulses which are due to its being sensed by suitable inner-receptors. When such nerve pulses are being generated, we are back in the digital line of progression again. . . . Such changes from a digital process to an analog one, and back again to a digital one, may alternate several times. Thus the nerve-pulse part of the system, which is digital, and the one involving chemical changes or mechanical dislocations due to muscular contractions, which is of the analog type, may, by alternating with each other, give any particular process a mixed character.

The decisive property of a digital organ or mechanism, then, is that it is almost always found in one or another of its two extreme discrete states, i.e., that the dynamic probability of its standing in the intermediate state which forms the connecting continuum is very small. It thus appears that the phenomena called digital are, in reality, also continuous although largely indifferent to subliminal variations of the input stimuli. One treats such by ignoring the transition states—that is, by assuming that information is being conveyed in a binary code.[4] (By coding is meant an operation, governed by strict and logical rules, to gain increased efficiency by having elementary signals organized into patterns of alternative

[3]*The Computer and the Brain,* New Haven, 1958, pp. 68–69. *Cf* W. Sluckin, *Minds and Machines,* Baltimore, 1960, pp. 127–128: "It may be pointed out that on fuller investigation the nervous impulse turns out to be not fully digital in its behaviour. But then, even the digital elements of an 'electronic brain,' the relay and the valve, are ultimately made up of continuous-operator elements put together in such a way as to exhibit digital functioning. The electromagnetic relay, the thermionic valve and the nerve cell are, in fact, complex mechanisms which under certain specific operating conditions function as digital units." See also the terminological strictures of P. Elias in "A Note on the Misuse of 'Digital' in Neurophysiology," in W. A. Rosenblith (ed.), *Sensory Communication,* New York, London, 1961, pp. 794–795.

[4]M. Weinberg, "Mechanism in Neurosis," *American Scientist,* vol. 39, pp. 74–98, 1951. Weinberg's proposition "that the living organism resorts to the method affording ultimate efficiency and economy, which is, in the case of elements for coding information, ternary rather than binary . . . ," presents another but needlessly complicated model where the signal may take the forms +, *stimulate;* —, *inhibit;* and 0, *no effect.*

actions; by code is meant everything that the source and the receiver know a priori about the message.)

Whatever the exact situation may be in the central nervous system—a problem which R. W. Gerard, among others, has impressively elucidated[5]—the model sketched above has certainly proved of heuristic value, even though some may feel that the digital procedure is a human artifact invented for the sake of description, and that the underlying reality is truly analog. Gerard pictures the nervous system as "made up of relatively uniform units, which can be combined in various ways, rather than of highly particularized units, each one of which stands for something specific." Proof of this is the existence of synapses, which are, in effect, foci of decision. This model can then be extended to encompass speech; as E. L. DuBrul recently put it:[6] Speech is the spark that spans the synapse between two nervous systems.

This discussion will focus on the hypothesis that whereas subhuman species communicate by signs that appear to be most often coded in analog terms, in human speech (contrary to the opinion of certain linguists) some information is coded in analog terms and other information is coded in digital terms. The digital mechanism of speech may, therefore, be regarded as a late development in the phylogenetic series and perhaps a uniquely human faculty. It is not, of course, our contention that the differential use of these two types of mechanisms is the *only* mark that sets off speech from communicative behavior via other modalities and in other species. C. F. Hockett, for example, identified seven[7]—later thirteen[8]—"universal" properties of language, with a surprisingly broad area of overlap, and even this list is doubtless not exhaustive. Thus one might add a property of *multiple-coding potential*—that is, the possibility that language is the only communicative system permitting the transmutation of one set of verbal signs (e.g., speech) into another set (e.g., script). A view is also maintained that no single linguistic attribute is unique to man but that human language is, on the contrary, distinguished unequiv-

[5]See, for example, *Transactions of the Seventh Conference on Cybernetics,* New York, 1951; see also a summary essay on "Brains and Behavior," in J. N. Spuhler (ed.), *The Evolution of Man's Capacity for Culture,* Detroit, 1959.

[6]*Evolution of the Speech Apparatus,* Springfield, Ill., 1958, p. 90. The notion of a theoretical continuity between the nervous system and the linguistic system is elaborated in H. C. Shands, *Thinking and Psychotherapy: An Inquiry into the Processes of Communication,* Cambridge, Mass., 1960.

[7]"Animal 'Language' and Human Language," in *The Evolution of Man's Capacity for Culture, op cit.,* fn. 5.

[8]"The Origin of Speech," *Scientific American,* vol. 203, pp. 89–96, 1960, and "Logical Considerations in the Study of Animal Communication," in W. E. Lanyon and W. N. Tavolga (eds.), *Animal Sounds and Communication,* Washington, D.C., 1960, pp. 392–430.

ocally from communicative systems in other species merely by virtue of the particular combination of characteristics—a complex form of encoding which has evolved to meet the needs of human communication.[9]

To elaborate somewhat crudely in the neurological domain: In speech, emotions may be codified in analog terms, in which case neocortical as well as limbic or neurohumoral areas are simultaneously involved; other, i.e., "rational," aspects of existence are codified in digital terms, presumably involving centrencephalic integration only.[10] In his reexamination of Von Frisch's classic studies of bee "language,"[11] A. L. Kroeber similarly distinguished between signs and symbols as to their respective functions (emotive versus cognitive). His study leaves the door open to the possibility that certain subhuman species, notably the social insects, may partially communicate by systems of symbols, but the evidence for this is far from persuasive.[12]

Speech is the principal, but by no means the only, mechanism whereby communities are knit into social organizations via a systematic flow of messages exchanged over interpersonal communication channels. These channels are made up of a number of different bands over which messages can move synchronously. There is a vocal-auditory band which couples movements of vocal muscles with stimulation of auditory receptors. There is also a gestural-visual band which couples movements of facial and body

[9]See O. Koehler, "Thinking without Words," *Proceedings of the Fourteenth International Congress of Zoologists* (Copenhagen, 1953), vol. 75, 1956.

[10]J. Ruesch, "Nonverbal Language and Therapy," *Psychiatry*, vol. 18, pp. 323–330, 1955. The parts of dominant cortex and thalamus that are devoted to the learning of speech and its uses are delineated in W. Penfield and L. Roberts, *Speech and Brain-Mechanisms*, Princeton, 1959. On "rational" and "emotional" speech in pathology, and a survey of the philosophical idea that "outcries of emotion represent the basis of all language," see K. Goldstein, *Language and Language Disturbances*, New York, 1948, chap. 4.

[11]K. von Frisch, *Bees: Their Vision, Chemical Senses and Language*, New York, 1950. The latest research results on this subject are brought together in M. Lindauer's *Communication Among Social Bees*, Cambridge, Mass., 1961.

[12]A. L. Kroeber, "Sign and Symbol in Bee Communication," *Proceedings of the National Academy of Sciences*, vol. 38, pp. 753–757, 1952. (In a discussion shortly before his death, Kroeber observed to the author that he no longer held the view expressed in the cited paper.) For another relevant discussion of "the difference between sign behavior, which is pre-linguistic intelligent behavior, and linguistic behavior, which is behavior mediated by the symbol system we call language," see J. H. Greenberg, "Language and Evolution," in *Evolution and Anthropology: A Centennial Appraisal*, Washington, D.C., 1959, pp. 61–75. Several linguists have analyzed human speech in contrast to bee communication: Gy. Laziczius, *General Linguistics* (in Hungarian), Budapest, 1942, p. 31; J. Lotz, "Speech and Language," *The Journal of the Acoustical Society of America*, vol. 22, pp. 712–717, 1950, and in *Word*, vol. 7, pp. 66–67, 1951; and E. Benveniste, "Animal Communication and Human Language," *Diogenes*, vol. 1, pp. 1–7, 1952.

muscles with stimulation of visual receptors. Interpersonal messages in everyday communication travel simultaneously over these auditory and visual avenues, typically reinforcing one another but occasionally conflicting in certain situations.[13] Other sensory modalities (such as touch,[14] smell, taste, and temperature) may participate in communication; they certainly do in the case of other species,[15] and the remarkable feats of Helen Keller show that they can be highly discriminating even in the human. However, they usually contribute in limited and unintentional ways, since they are seldom under voluntary control. Finally, there is what might be called the manipulational-situational band which, by the mediation of "things" manipulated and observed, couples source and destination.[16]

The variety of communication channels deserves further illustration and emphasis. Thus, N. Tinbergen has convincingly shown that gulls communicate with one another by means of not only calls but also postures and movements; and L. T. Evans, speaking of Crocodilia, reported:[17] "When the mature male American alligator roars, his middle section lies about 2 inches beneath the surface of the water. The terrific reverberation of the bellow . . . is such as to send up a fountain of water above his body. The combined effect of the roar, the musky odor emitted

[13]A striking illustration of within-band contradictions was pictured in *Life,* vol. 48, no. 9, pp. 106–122, 1960. A patient was told under hypnosis she must raise her right index finger to indicate an affirmative answer, left for negative. Brought out of trance, she was questioned by her doctor. Unable to face her emotional problem, she shook her head viogorously in manifest negation, but her right finger shot up, showing that the correct answer was *yes.* For a general clinical assessment of normal and pathological communicative behavior, see J. Ruesch, *Disturbed Communication,* New York, 1957.

[14]L. K. Frank, "Tactile Communication," *Genetic Psychology Monographs,* vol. 56, pp. 209–255, 1957.

[15]*Cf.* J. B. S. Haldane, "Animal Communication and the Origin of Human Language," *Science Progress,* vol. 43, pp. 385–401, 1955; P. Marler, "Developments in the Study of Animal Communication," in P. R. Bell (ed.), *Darwin's Biological Work: Some Aspects Reconsidered,* Cambridge, 1959, chap. 4.

[16]C. E. Osgood and T. A. Sebeok, *Psycholinguistics: A Survey of Theory and Research Problems,* Baltimore, 1954; J. Ruesch and W. Kees, *Nonverbal Communication,* Berkeley, Los Angeles, 1956; E. T. Hall, *The Silent Language,* New York, 1959; E. Goffman, *The Presentation of Self in Everyday Life,* Garden City, N.Y., 1959. F. C. Hayes has published a comprehensive working bibliography of gestures in *Southern Folklore Quarterly,* vol. 21, pp. 218–317, 1957.

[17]*Transactions of the First Conference on Group Processes,* New York, 1955, p. 274. Speaking earlier at the same conference, M. Mead identified as the gifted individual that person "who has had the luck to have had all . . . possible modalities stimulated. If you analyze communication, the person who gets over the greatest communication to the group is the person who uses several sensory modalities." *Ibid.,* p. 241.

from the glands at the corners of his jaw, as well as the fountain, serve to attract the female and perhaps to repel a rival male."

The most general model of a communication network postulates that one system—a source—influences another system—a destination—by dispatching alternative signals that are carried in the channel connecting them. The information source is conceived as producing one or more messages which must be transformed, or encoded, by a transmitter into signals which the channel has the capacity to carry; these signals must finally be transformed, or decoded, by a receiver back into messages which can be accepted by the destination.[18] This model of the communication process, developed in connection with engineering problems, was not intended as a blueprint of human communication. For one thing, it implies normal separation of source and destination, of transmitter and receiver, whereas the individual human functions more or less simultaneously as both; indeed, he regularly decodes through various homeostatic mechanisms the messages he himself has encoded.

In so far as the messages which are being interchanged belong to speech, they constitute the traditional preoccupation of linguists. Other partially or wholly verbal messages may include myths, the various aspects of ritual, marriage rules and kinship systems, customary law, certain modalities of economic exchange, and the like. These form the subject matter of social anthropology in general, as well as of such special disciplines as law or economics or folklore in particular.[19]

In a widely influential model, especially as developed by K. Bühler, the act of speech was confined to three aspects: those features of sound which are characteristic of the source (1), *Kundgabe,* the first person of the addresser; those which constitute an appeal to the destination (2), *Appell,* the second person of the addressee; and those which refer to the designation (3), *Darstellung,* the so-called third person—someone or something spoken of.[20] It would seem useful now to expand this triadic model into a hexagonal one, which involves the following dimensions: an addresser or actor (1) who selects—i.e., encodes according to specific statistical constraints—a message (5) out of a code (6) which to permit decoding must be fully or at least partially shared by an addressee (2), or reactor; the message also requires a referent (3), or context; and a channel (4) allowing the participants to establish and maintain contact. That portion of a communication which intrudes into the message en route from source to receiver is noise; it is mixed intimately, although

[18]C. E. Shannon and W. Weaver, *The Mathematical Theory of Communication,* Urbana, Ill., 1949; R. M. Fano, *Transmission of Information,* New York, London, 1961.

[19]C. Lévi-Strauss, "Leçon inaugurale," Chair d'Anthropologie Sociale, Collège de France, Paris, 1960.

[20]K. Bühler, *Sprachtheorie,* Jena, 1934.

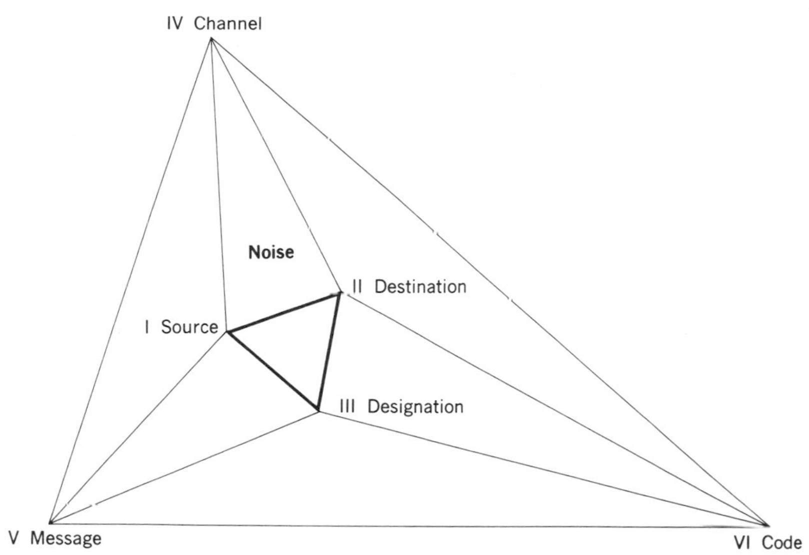

Morley's theorem illustrates the relation between Bühler's model (the small equilateral triangle) and a more comprehensive information theoretical model of a communication network. The encoder and decoder are often the same individual.

in varying proportions, with the signal—that portion of a communication which originates with the addresser.

The relation between Bühler's model and an information theoretical model of a communication network may be illustrated by a Morley triangle,[21] as shown in the figure.

These six factors determine the hierarchial order of linguistic functions, and the verbal structure of any particular message depends on the function which predominates. Although orientation toward the referent—the so-called denotative, cognitive, or referential function—is the principal burden of many messages, the other five accessory functions are ever present and must also be accounted for.

Kroeber comments as follows on his distinction between signs, which in our terminology focus on the source (1), and symbols, which focus on the context (3):[22]

[21]Morley's theorem asserts that when a triangle of any shape is drawn, and its three angles are trisected, the trisecting lines always meet at the vertices of an equilateral triangle. See H. S. M. Coxeter, *Introduction to Geometry,* New York, London, 1961.

[22]A. L. Kroeber, *op. cit.* fn. 12. See also L. A. White, "The Symbol: The Origin and Basis of Human Behavior," *Philosophy of Science,* vol. 7, pp. 451–463, 1940; E. Cassirer, *An Essay on Man,* New Haven, 1944, pp. 31–32; and C. Morris, "Signs in Animals and Men," in *Signs, Language and Behavior,* New York, 1946, pp. 52–55. The notion of context has recently been elaborated by T. Slama-Cazacu, in her *Langage et Contexte,* 's-Gravenhage, 1961.

In function, signs that serve to communicate are action responses to sensory or visceral stimuli and are probably always accompanied by emotional affects. Directly, they convey information to recipient individuals only as to the condition of the sign-producing individual. They alert one organism as to the condition of another, which is often useful. True symbols, however, can convey information on other matters than the condition of the communicating organism. Such external information may fairly be called objective, as compared with the essentially subjective nature of what is communicated by non-symbolic signs.

This dyadic model of sign/symbol certainly represents an oversimplified picture of what happens in speech, and probably in some forms of animal communication as well: it fails to accommodate at least four functions other than the emotive and cognitive. One of these was observed and described by B. Malinowski, who named it "phatic communion . . . a type of speech in which ties of union are created by a mere exchange. . . ."[23] Messages which serve primarily to establish, prolong, or discontinue communication, to check whether the channel (4) works in good order, occur not only in human discourse (e.g., this legend on a greeting card: "This Card Serves No Useful Purpose—except to make money for the manufacturer and to assist me in communicating with you and sustaining our relationship"), but also among frogs and certain birds, such as the sparrows and the psittacines (bird to bird as well as bird to human).[24] In speech, orientation toward the destination (2) may result in sentences which have no truth value (viz., vocatives and imperatives); whether such messages, with a chiefly conative (appeal) function, occur in subhuman species as well seems controversial.[25] Perhaps the deictic "chink" call of the common English chaffinch *(Fringilla coelebs)* serves such a function: If a bird of prey, such as an owl, is perched prominently in a tree, "the small birds will often make them-

[23]B. Malinowski, "The Problem of Meaning in Primitive Languages," suppl. I, in C. K. Ogden and I. A. Richards, *The Meaning of Meaning,* New York, 1923.

[24]The message on the greeting card was reproduced in *The New York Times Magazine,* April 3, 1960, p. 53. On "phatic communion" in other species, see F. Kainz, *Psychologie der Sprache,* vol. II, Stuttgart, 1943, p. 191; G. Revesz, "Contact Sounds," in *The Origin and Prehistory of Language,* New York, 1956, pp. 152–156. R. Jakobson, commenting upon the endeavor of "talking birds" to start and sustain communication, asserts that "the phatic function of language is the only one they share with human beings," and adds that it is also "the first verbal function acquired by infants. . . ."; see his "Linguistics and Poetics," in T. A. Sebeok (ed.), *Style in Language,* New York, London, 1960, p. 356. On the imitation of speech by birds, see especially the critical account by J. A. Bierens de Haan, "Animal Language in Relation to That of Man," *Biological Review,* vol. 4, pp. 249–268, 1928.

[25]For one summary of views, see "Die Appellfunktion in der 'Tiersprache'," in Kainz, *ibid.,* pp. 220–224.

selves conspicuous too by behavior known as 'mobbing.'" They point out the predator, so to speak, by addressing themselves to all and sundry. The jackdaw has two calls, transcribed *kia* and *kiaw,* said to mean *fly with me,* by which the bird beckons others in the flock.[26] In any case, encoder and decoder are often the same individual—as, for example, a blind man tapping with his cane. This may be observed in the manner in which electric fish distort their own high-voltage fields, by the striking acrodynamic sonar system in chiroptera, and by the even more sophisticated sonar system in cetaceans.[27] The fifth set, which aims toward the message (5) as such, is the poetic function of language, as has been illuminatingly discussed in this framework by R. Jakobson.[28] The last one, which focuses on the code (6), and which permits the rewording or translation of a linguistic sign into some further, alternative sign, is usually called the metalingual, or glossing, function of language.[29]

To summarize, of the six communicative functions, two—the emotive and the phatic—certainly occur in subhuman species as well; two others—the cognitive and the conative—probably occur; but the remaining two—the poetic and the metalingual—seem to be exclusively human.[30]

In the trenchant formulation of E. Stankiewicz, a human being may speak or may remain silent. If he does decide to speak, he has a freedom of choice in regard to the message to be transmitted. However, as to the code, his freedom is restricted: His selection must be made out of "prefabricated units" among sets of simultaneous binary distinctions,[31] elements in an algorithm (or decision procedure) concatenated into se-

[26]On the chaffinch, see W. H. Thorpe, "The Language of Birds," *Scientific American,* vol. 195, pp. 129–138, 1956; on the jackdaw, K. Lorenz, *King Solomon's Ring,* New York, 1952; more generally, P. Marler, "Specific Distinctiveness in the Communication Signals of Birds," *Behaviour,* vol. 11, pp. 13–39, 1957.

[27]See D. G. Griffin, *Listening in the Dark,* New Haven, 1958; W. N. Kellogg, *Porpoises and Sonar,* Chicago, 1961; J. C. Lilly, *Man and Dolphin,* Garden City, N.Y., 1961.

[28]R. Jakobson, "Linguistics and Poetics," *op. cit.,* fn. 24. The author is indebted to this essay for a formulation of the hexagonal model of language.

[29]*Cf.* C. Cherry, *On Human Communication,* New York, London, 1957, part 2, chap. 3. On interpretive recoding, see R. Jakobson, "On Linguistic Aspects of Translation," in R. A. Brower (ed.), *On Translation,* Cambridge, Mass., 1959, pp. 232–239.

[30]For an overview of the acoustic aspects only, *cf.* N. E. Collias, "An Ecological and Functional Classification of Animal Sounds," in *Animal Sounds and Communication, op. cit.,* fn. 8, pp. 368–387; and Marler's summary of "Developments in the Study of Animal Communication," *op. cit.,* fn. 8.

[31]*Cf.* M. Halle, "In Defense of the Number Two," in E. Pulgram (ed.), *Studies Presented to Joshua Whatmough on His Sixtieth Birthday,* 's-Gravenhage, 1957. On the principle of dichotomy, viewed in philosophical perspective, see C. K. Ogden, *Opposition,* London, 1932.

quential patterns. According to this selection, he varies the cognitive content, or meaning, of his messages. But, keeping the meaning constant, the speaker is also free to flavor and color his message in a variety of ways. This possibility of modulating his attitude toward what he speaks about is the pragmatic dimension of "emotion." Here again, the speaker has at his disposal features which are strictly conventional; but he is not necessarily forced to make binary or ternary choices, for by even a barely perceptible variation in the degree of the quality of such devices he can mirror a range of differences in his emotional intensity (associated, presumably, with a rising production of hormones).

A bird may likewise vocalize or remain silent and may, moreover, have a certain choice in regard to the message to be transmitted; thus crows have been reported to possess four or more distinct cries. Two of these can be identified and have been labeled the assembly call and the dispersal call. Furthermore, it has been shown that the reactions to the calls are only partly inborn; in part they seem to be the result of copying from other individuals. But once the contact has been established, the number of caws emitted will vary from one to five, their frequency being in direct proportion to the degree of excitement.[32] There exist, of course, other types of communicative situations where a frequency–intensity relationship may prevail such that even rather substantial changes in the frequency of a response are accompanied by only very small formal modifications, thus resulting in reduction of signal ambiguity. The difference may be summed up by this analogy: The harder a cyclist pedals, the faster his vehicle moves; but a telephone rings at a constant rate no matter how urgent the call (although it may ring commensurably longer).[33]

A human being may speak or may remain silent: the speech signal (like acoustic signals in general) is transient—that is, it can be altered rapidly and turned off entirely. This property is not necessarily shared, however, by communication in other modalities—for instance, the olfactory. Thus a skunk is able to emit a chemical signal very abruptly, but lacks the capability to shut it off: the message persists interminably, even in the sender's absence. Communication by smell therefore functions, in this and other respects, including especially the capacity for delayed feedback, like writing rather than like speech.

The symbolic information-bearing sound features of speech include the distinctive and configurative (or constructive). There are linguists who are convinced that all utterances can be dissolved into and characterized by sets of two-valued attributes,[34] while other linguists prefer to have recourse to more complex principles of patterning,[35] but all agree

[32]H. and M. Frings, "The Language of Crows," *Scientific American,* vol. 201, pp. 119–131, 1959.

[33]*Cf.* D. Morris, " 'Typical Intensity' and Its Relation to the Problem of Ritualisation," *Behaviour,* vol. 11, pp. 1–12, 1957.

that the coding of such features is digital. When, however, it comes to other information we know is carried in the vocal–auditory band, the nature of the coding is far less clear.

Charles Darwin was one of the first (he himself cited Herbert Spencer's essay "The Origin and Function of Music" in this context) to explore in methodical detail, as well as to provide with an evolutionary interpretation, what he called *The Expression of the Emotions in Man and Animals.*[36] In the fourth chapter, where he takes up specifically "a very obscure subject," the emission of sounds, he remarks pessimistically: "It is not probable that any precise explanation of the cause or source of each particular sound, under different states of mind, will ever be given." Half a century later, E. Sapir echoed Darwin's observation:[37] "The voice is a complicated bundle of reactions and, so far as the writer knows, no one has succeeded in giving a comprehensive account of what the voice is and what changes it may undergo. There seems to be no book or essay that classifies the many different types of voice, nor is there a nomenclature that is capable of doing justice to the bewildering range of voice phenomena." And more than a quarter of a century later, R. Jakobson and M. Halle are obliged to repeat that the systematic study of such "physiognomic indices," as they prefer to call them here, "still remains on the agenda."[38]

Linguists like Bally, Devoto, Spitzer, Von Wartburg, Vossler, and others, who insist—again to paraphrase Stankiewicz—on emphasizing the priority

[34]R. Jakobson and M. Halle, *Fundamentals of Language,* 's-Gravenhage, 1956.

[35]A. Martinet, "Substance phonique et traits distinctifs," *Bulletin de la Société de Linguistique de Paris,* vol. 53, pp. 72–85, 1957–1958.

[36]London, 1873; also in *The Descent of Man,* London, 1871. Darwin's observations were based, in the main, on domestic cats and dogs, and man. M. Mead, in her preface to a recent edition of the former book, stresses the relevance of Darwin's work to "the new science of kinesics. . . ." On Darwin and linguistics, see A. Schleicher, *Die Darwin'sche Theorie und die Sprachwissenschaft,* Weimar, 1873; and four recent discussions of the evolution of language as part of the evolution of communication: J. H. Greenberg, *Essays in Linguistics,* Chicago, 1957, chap. 5; L. F. Brosnahan, "Language and Evolution," *Lingua,* vol. 9, pp. 225–236, 1960; M. Critchley, "The Evolution of Man's Capacity for Language," in Sol Tax (ed.), *Evolution after Darwin,* vol. II, 1960, pp. 289–308; and R. L. Birdwhistell, "Implications of Recent Developments in Communication Research for Evolutionary Theory," *Report of the Ninth Annual Round Table Meeting on Linguistics and Language Studies,* Washington, D.C., 1960, pp. 149–155.

[37]E. Sapir, "Speech as a Personality Trait," *American Journal of Sociology,* vol. 32, pp. 892–905, 1927.

[38]*Op. cit.,* fn. 34. In *Preliminaries to Speech Analysis,* Boston, 1952, p. 15, Jakobson and his associates pair "expressive features" with "neutral, unemotional" features, where the former are said to present "a grading gamut" in contrast to the dichotomous scale of the distinctive features.

and esthetic superiority of the message over the code, have actually paid attention to aspects of the expressive language problem. But in structural linguistics, the expressive range of morphophonemic, morphological, and syntactic considerations—to say nothing of code-switching between a neutral and an emphatic style, between one social dialect and another—has been virtually ignored. Only on the phonemic level have a few structuralists touched on the notion of expressiveness, most originally among them Gy. Laziczius who was the first to insist on the conventional nature of the elements he designated "emphatics."[39] N. S. Trubetzkoy was of the opinion that data in this area are so meager and unreliable that one could only speculate about their role in language, and he ended by relegating them to a special branch of phonology which he wanted to be designated *Lautstilistik*.[40] Only during the last few years have linguists and psychologists alike made new attempts to disentangle the interwoven threads of the total ribbon of speech. We owe to J. Lotz the most comprehensive—if excessively laconic—typology of features, which encompasses invariants that are either socially determined or bound by the somatic characteristics of our organs and by our habits of speech, in addition to the variable pragmatic features said to be "continuous in the sense that a variation in the emotional expression indicates a difference in the intensity of the emotion, the louder one shouts, the angrier the impression one creates."[41] Socially determined features include the so-called vocalizations—vocal characterizers, qualifiers, and segregates—first specified by H. L. Smith, Jr.,[42] and then applied as a psychotherapeutic tool by some of his collaborators.[43] Another categorization entirely—in terms

[39]For a discussion of this notion and citation of the literature, see the obituary of Laziczius by T. A. Sebeok, *Word,* vol. 15, pp. 175–182, 1959.

[40]N. S. Trubetskoy, *Grundzüge der Phonologie,* Prague, 1939, pp. 17–29.

[41]"Speech and Language," *op. cit.,* fn. 12, and "The Structure of Human Speech," *Transactions of the New York Academy of Sciences,* ser. II, vol. 16, pp. 373–384, 1954.

[42]H. L. Smith, Jr., "An Outline of Metalinguistic Analysis," *Report of the Third Annual Round Table Meeting on Linguistics and Language Teaching,* Washington, D.C., 1952, pp. 59–66; R. E. Pittenger and H. L. Smith, Jr., "A Basis for Some Contributions of Linguistics to Psychiatry," *Psychiatry,* vol. 20, pp. 61–78, 1957.

[43]N. A. McQuown, "Linguistic Transcription and Specification of Psychiatric Interview Materials," *Psychiatry,* vol. 20, pp. 79–86, 1957; R. E. Pittenger, "Linguistic Analysis of Tone of Voice in Communication of Affect," *Psychiatric Research Reports,* vol. 8, pp. 41–54, 1958. See also the pioneer work of P. J. Moses, *The Voice of Neurosis,* New York, 1954; and R. E. Pittenger, C. F. Hockett, and J. J. Danehy's painstakingly detailed *The First Five Minutes,* Ithaca, New York, 1960. For a summary of the rapidly growing literature dealing with the reflection of psychological states in verbal behavior, see G. F. Mahl's "The Expression of Emotions on the Lexical and Linguistic Levels" (mimeographed), New Haven, 1960, footnote material, pp. 2–3.

of a series of dichotomous distinctions between learned versus unlearned, voluntary versus involuntary, and constant versus intermittent features—has been suggested by a team of linguists and psychologists.[44] Finally, two independent attempts at a unifying theory have lately been sketched out, one by G. L. Trager[45] and another by E. Stankiewicz.[46]

It is generally agreed among linguists that a consistent typology of the several kinds of features is one of the most urgent tasks to be accomplished. A reliable description and classification of the features across biological species would be no less useful. We already know that some subhuman communicative systems not only are diagnostic of the species but also allow for enough individual variation to yield, as in chaffinches, "very strange songs," or idiolects: the song of the chaffinches is so organized, we are told, "that individual birds are recognizable, even by human beings, by their personal signature tune," as a result of learning during the early life of a bird. Furthermore, a group of birds will, by mutual imitation, build into its over-all pattern a distinctive set of community traits, thus forming a dialect.[47] Little is known at present about how such networks are woven in different species, how they operate, and of what survival value they may be.

Most linguists who deal with expressive or paralinguistic phenomena appreciate that the coding of the features involved may be analog. Thus Trager writes: "These voice qualities as described seem to involve paired attributes, but the pairs of terms are more properly descriptive of extremes between which there are continua or several intermittent degrees." And Stankiewicz puts it this way: "The expressive elements are . . . in a binary relation to the neutral terms, and present a graded scale in relation to each other. Grading is not, however, a necessary characteristic of the expressive units. On the expressive level they may furthermore form binary relations to each other. . . ." Such features appear, in fact, to have but one attribute in common: they may not coincide both in form and in distribution with those features which possess distinctive, viz., cognitive function; in this sense, they are conditioned by the system, and we would therefore consider them a part of language. Graded elements may turn out to be formally identical with some distinctive elements in a given

[44]In Osgood and Sebeok, *op. cit.,* fn. 16, p. 76.

[45]G. L. Trager, "Paralanguage: A First Approximation," *Studies in Linguistics,* vol. 13, pp. 1–12, 1958; applied later in "Taos III: Paralanguage," *Anthropological Linguistics,* February, 1960, pp. 24–30.

[46]E. Stankiewicz, "Expressive Language," in T. A. Sebeok (ed.), *Style in Language,"* New York, London, 1960, abstract in Part Three.

[47]P. Marler, "The Voice of the Chaffinch and Its Function as a Language," *The Ibis,* vol. 98, pp. 231–261, 1956; more generally, H. Stadler, "Vogeldialekt," *Alauda,* vol. 2, (suppl.), pp. 1–66, 1930.

language, but then they must be distributed differently. Thus length in Hungarian is phonemic: ɛ (open e), as in *ɛl* (*away*) is opposed distinctively to *e•* (long close *e*), as in *e•l* (*he lives*); but long open ɛ• (with varying degrees of duration) may be opposed to short ɛ only affectively: *ɛmbɛr* (*man*) versus *ɛ•mbɛr* (*man!*) Or graded elements may differ formally, as does the vocoid in the Hungarian interjection *ɸɯ*, a global "gesture" no part of which recurs in that language.

Are such features a part of language or are they not? Some linguists favor an attitude of reductionism which attempts to oppose absolute (whether or not binary) categories, said to belong to language, to phenomena which they find they cannot describe precisely in such terms and which they therefore relegate as "non-linguistic elements of the real world," to be purged from a science of linguistics. Here is a dramatic statement of this position:[48]

> Ordinary mathematical techniques fall mostly into two classes, the continuous (e.g., the infinitesimal calculus) and the discrete or discontinuous (e.g., finite group theory). Now it will turn out that the mathematics called "linguistics" belongs in the second class. It does not even make any compromise with continuity, as does statistics, or infinite-group theory. Linguistics is a quantum mechanics in the most extreme sense. All continuity, all possibilities of infinitesimal gradation, are shoved outside of linguistics in one direction or the other.

Another linguist seems to oppose discreteness of contrast to continuity in scale as language versus the rest of culture:[49]

> The embedding medium of linguistic messages . . . shows a continuous scale of dynamics, organized to some extent in any given culture: one may speak softly, or more loudly, or more loudly still, or anywhere in between with no theoretic limit to the fineness of gradation. But . . . in general . . . if we find continuous-scale contrasts in the vicinity of what we are sure is language, we exclude them from language (though not from culture).

The two disciplines, considered by some to be separate from linguistics, to which continuity is most often consigned are semantics at one extreme and phonetics at the other. The following quotation illustrates the former:[50] "In some areas of lexicon, semantic structure may be so complex that it is impossible or unprofitable to approach it . . . with Aristotelian class logic and the "same or different" pragmatic test as the principal

[48]M. Joos, "Description of Language Design," *Journal of the Acoustical Society of America,* vol. 22, pp. 701–708, 1950.

[49]C. F. Hockett, *A Manual of Phonology,* Baltimore, 1955, p. 17.

[50]F. G. Lounsbury, "A Semantic Analysis of the Pawnee Kinship Usage," *Language,* vol. 32, pp. 158–194, 1956.

tools. . . . Continuous scales may be introduced in place of these sharp dichotomies. . . ." In the other discipline, phonetics, it is just the expressive elements of speech which are sometimes described as fluctuating phenomena beyond the reach of science. Thus one linguist writes:[51]

> . . . the rhetorical accent is subject to gradations: the length may be augmented and the intensity increased to convey overtones of awe, amazement, admiration, and many other subtle and elusive shadings in attitude. . . . Whether or not the linguist attempts to analyze and define the various types and styles of expressive accent, he must eliminate the phonetic increments introduced by such expressive factors in order to deal directly with the grammatically significant category of stress accents.

The same theme was sounded, perhaps more cautiously, in the conclusion of a monograph on American English intonation:[52]

> The most deep-seated cleft between groups of characteristics occurs between items which are organized into *systematic* contrasts and those which have merely *gradient* differences. . . . If linguistics is to classify only language structure, then it limits itself to describing only systematic contrasts. . . . The gradient items are usually excluded from linguistics as such. . . .

But, some sixteen years later, this same colleague wrote:[53]

> Voice quality would . . . in my view be considered linguistically relevant whether, on the one hand, unitized (i.e., "discretely coded") in contrastive phonemes or in componential systems such as whisper versus song, or whether, on the other hand, it is socially significant but gradient (i.e., "continuously coded" by degree) as may be rates of speed, degree of voice loudness, or general height of voice.

Students of verbal behavior, including linguists animated by an awareness of psychology, are more likely to use an expression such as *the flow of speech* and thus tend toward the other extreme. "It will be useful to replace" dichotomy with a continuum, a psychologist of language recently argued, and he goes on to speak of "the relative 'criteriality' of an attribute for a category."[54] A linguist and another psychologist more judiciously separate the spurious continuity of segmentable speech stretches from the functional continuity of hesitation phenomena, and

[51]S. S. Newman, "On the Stress System of English," *Word,* vol. 2, pp. 171–187, 1946.

[52]K. L. Pike, *The Intonation of American English,* Ann Arbor, 1946, p. 170. D. L. Bolinger also considers the views cited in fn. 48–52 above in his monograph, *Generality, Gradience, and the All-or-None,* 's-Gravenhage, 1961.

[53]K. L. Pike, *Language in Relation to a Unified Theory of the Structure of Human Behavior,* vol. III, Glendale, Calif., 1960, p. 52a.

[54]R. Brown, *Words and Things,* Glencoe, Ill., 1958, p. 10.

call for a statistical approach to complement, rather than to replace, the usual discrete one:[55]

> If we define *structure* as a list of elements and statements about the permissible relations among them it may be that the most acceptable compromise will involve reliance upon discrete assumptions to define units . . . and continuous statistical assumptions to state their rules of combination and distribution.

A shift in professional opinion is reflected, in this later prediction by another linguist:[56]

> Those factors of "rasp, overloudness, chuckling," and the like are still usually mentioned as being outside the field of linguistics proper—more or less as intonation was outside the domain some decades ago. However, even those who place the voice qualifiers outside are nowadays, I think, placing them "just outside." Their role in psychiatrically applied linguistic research shows signs of being so crucial that they may before long establish a status as describable elements of a speech system.

At least one prominent linguist, E. Sapir, has not hesitated to carry out an analysis of grading, however fragmentary, on the semantic level in an important but neglected paper. He discusses and exemplifies logical, psychological, and linguistic grading in language, and then summarizes as follows:[57]

> Logical grading is of the open-gamut type and may be with or without reference to an objective norm or statistical average, while psychological grading and linguistic grading tend strongly to emphasize closed-gamut grading, whether of the conjunct or disjunct type, and have difficulty in combining the notions of grading and norming into that of a normed field within which grading applies.

He also takes up the role of affect and kinaesthesia, and the use of polar terms, but he nowhere implies that his work is outside the realm of linguistics.

[55]H. Maclay and C. E. Osgood, "Hesitation Phenomena in Spontaneous English Speech," *Word,* vol. 15, pp. 19–44, 1959.

[56]W. F. Twaddell, "Linguistics Plus," *Report of the Tenth Annual Round Table Meeting on Linguistics and Language Studies,* Washington, D.C., 1959, p. 151. Problems in the transportation of a semicontinuous natural signal into a series of discrete elements are also discussed by G. E. Peterson in "The Discrete and the Continuous in the Symbolization of Language," in E. Pulgram (ed.), *op. cit.,* fn. 31, pp. 209–218; and G. Fant in his *Acoustic Theory of Speech Production,* 's-Gravenhage, 1960, also touches on some of these, especially in chap. 1, sec. 12, and chap. 3, sec. 1.

[57]E. Sapir, "Grading: A Study in Semantics," *Philosophy of Science,* vol. 11, pp. 93–116, 1944.

It is instructive to contrast Sapir's analysis of semantic grading in language with J. B. S. Haldane's terse conclusion, "Animal signals grade into one another," illustrated by an example in geese (*Anser anser*), cited after Lorenz:[58] A group of geese produce phrases of about ten "honks" when at rest. If moving on the ground the number diminishes as the speed increases, until in flight the "honk" is monosyllabic. Its pitch also alters.

In logic, at least since C. S. Peirce, and in linguistics, at least since F. de Saussure, it has been taken for granted that the connection between a speech-sign vehicle (or the signifier) and its meaning (or the signified) is arbitrary rather than iconic. According to Hockett:[59]

> The contrast between arbitrary and iconic is also exemplified by digital and analog computers. An analog computer is often beautifully adapted for a narrow function and worthless for anything else. Just so, bees can talk about nectar and hive-sites; human beings can talk about anything.

Now the most interesting point about the property of arbitrariness is that it is a logical consequence of digital structuring in the code. The connection has been demonstrated by a mathematician, B. Mandelbrot, who has further shown that the discrete character of linguistic units necessarily follows from the continuous nature of their substratum: If linguistic signs are discrete, Mandelbrot argues, this is just because they are, so to speak, "carried" by continuous sounds. The point of view which insists on expelling all continuous phenomena from language, furthermore, cannot allow for linguistic change, as Mandelbrot has also noted: A structural "internal diachrony" presupposes that the discreteness has not been established perfectly. Every diachronic law necessarily contradicts the rule of stability which motivates the characteristic of discreteness. This, moreover, is quite normal, since real diachronic effects appear only when the number of repetitions is extremely large and when the effect of "stability by repetition" can no longer be maintained.[60]

A series of fascinating experiments with the reactions of American and French crows and gulls to recorded communication signals, tested reciprocally, has led to the hypothesis that a change in the acoustical behavior of deviant individuals may also be the first step in the evolution of a new species among animals which use sound for sexual signaling; assuming that such patterns are genetically determined, they could result in selec-

[58] J. B. S. Haldane, *op. cit.,* fn. 15, p. 392.

[59] Hockett, *op. cit.,* fn. 7.

[60] B. Mandelbrot, "Structure formelle des textes et communication," *Word,* vol. 10, pp. 1–27, 1954. See also A. Martinet, *Économie des changements phonétiques,* Bern, 1955.

tive mating and thereupon a separate breeding population of individuals having a similar appearance.[61]

One might speculate that, from the standpoint of evolution, the function of an analog mechanism is to produce behavorial isolation leading, in due time, to other genetic changes and thus to formal diversity within the subpopulations. Digital mechanisms, on the other hand, were introduced later, when the scanning and integration of much larger quantities of information more exactly acquired adaptive value.

In her presidential address at the 1960 Annual Meeting of the American Anthropological Association, M. Mead singled out a number of areas where a failure to build appropriate cross-disciplinary bridges has tended to stunt the capacity of the science of linguistics for orderly growth:[62]

> There is one adjacent science which has developed enormously during the last three decades and now can provide us with highly variegated and well-established information about the behavior of living creatures that could be of the greatest fruitfulness for our own studies. This is the discipline called ethology in Europe and the comparative study of animal behavior in the United States. Here, the anthropologist and the ethologist, each with his wealth of detail, can communicate in the concrete terms so dear to both and no conceptual model is needed beyond some basic familiarity with biology. . . .[62]

With unfailing perception, she has identified a hitherto neglected research opportunity of considerable promise. However, if articulate transactions between two sciences of such differing content and varied traditions are to be carried out with reasonable sophistication, a unifying theory upon which both can agree, at least as a point of departure, will be a minimal requirement.

[61]H. and M. Frings, et al., "Reactions of American and French Species of Corvus and Larus to Recorded Communication Signals Tested Reciprocally," *Ecology,* vol. 39, pp. 126–131, 1958. See also P. Marler, "Bird Songs and Mate Selection," in *Animal Sounds and Communication, op. cit.,* fn. 8, 348–367.

[62]M. Mead, "Anthropology Among the Sciences," *American Anthropologist,* vol. 63, p. 479, 1961.

Mathematics and computation

W. KARUSH

On the use of mathematics in behavioral research

This discussion will describe some general aspects of mathematical methods to make possible better estimations of the potential value of mathematics in the development of fields that are new in the use of such methods. For the greatest value to be realized, it is also necessary to establish an improved basis for cooperation with mathematicians. The fields of main interest here are such domains as linguistics, language-data processing, decision making, learning and problem solving, group organization and behavior, and others which deal with phenomena of higher human behavior and invention. Our concern is especially with those areas related to the automation of human functions through application of the electronic digital computer. Where the use of mathematical methods is in a relatively early stage and there does not exist a widely accepted body of mathematical theory and concepts generally exploited by workers in these fields, it seems especially useful to examine the advantages of closer association with mathematics.

The current accelerated growth of research and development in the behavioral fields is resulting in a search for new scientific approaches to meet the stimulating possibilities of the automation of human processes. Mathematics seems a hopeful avenue in this situation, in view of its prestige and the success of its methods in the more traditional exact sciences. There are many attitudes toward the possibilities inherent in the use of mathematical methods, ranging from overenthusiastic expectation of immediate success to undue skepticism. In newly developing fields general agreement often does not exist as to the most promising directions of investigation and since the limitations of time and effort do not allow exploration of all directions, it is important to build as informed a basis as possible for the selection of alternatives.

This discussion is divided into six sections. The first deals with the classification of applications of mathematics into four types: direct application, inventive application, modeling, and theory construction. The second section treats the interplay of inductive and deductive processes in cooperative enterprises involving empirical domains and mathematical domains. The third section points up some features of the symbolic language of mathematics as a working instrument and as a method for ensuring sound deductions. The deductive nature of mathematical theories is discussed in the fourth section, which also explains the need for extramathematical considerations to establish validity within the context of the field of application. The fifth section is concerned with the motivation and manner of working of the research mathematician, and how the newer fields are beginning to turn traditionally pure mathematics into applied mathematics. The last section considers some of the new directions in mathematical work for applications to new fields, with particular attention to the central role of the computer.

In a discussion of this length it is possible to do no more than touch upon the various aspects of the general subject concerned. It should be mentioned that, in particular, mathematical statistics and its uses for inductive inference within a field are lightly treated; however, this subject is familiar to a great many workers in the behavioral sciences, and does not fall in the main stream of the discussion in this paper. (For a detailed discussion of statistics, see Edmundson, "A Statistician's View of Linguistic Models and Language-data Processing.")

TYPES OF APPLICATIONS

In a general way, the application of mathematics to a particular field involves the transformation of a problem expressed in the terms of that field into a problem expressed in mathematical terms. This transformation is accomplished by "mapping" contextual notions of the field into mathematical counterparts. The question can then be treated as a mathematical one and the consequences derived by mathematical techniques can be transformed back into the context of the field to shed light on the original problem. It is instructive to delineate several varieties of such work; we distinguish four types, which may be referred to as *direct application, inventive application, modeling,* and *theory construction.* These are to be regarded as suggestive, not categorical.

In a direct application, the transformation of the contextual question into mathematical form is immediate and produces a well-defined problem for which the means of resolution are available without mathematical innovation. Further, the mathematical conceptualization is accepted without question as being a "true" image of the real context. The subsequent mathematical work is essentially dictated by the statement of the problem and involves the execution of standard techniques of a largely manipulative nature. We may, for example, find ourselves dealing with more elementary notions and facts concerning numbers, algebra, geometry, or analysis, and the problem at hand might involve the solution of an algebraic equation or the determination of the maximum of an elementary function. On the other hand, a direct application may require advanced mathematics; also, it may call for the use of (known) approximate or computer techniques of solution. The degree of mathematical sophistication may be lesser or greater, but the essential features are that (1) the contextual problem translates directly into a well-defined mathematical problem; (2) the means of solutions are known; and (3) the empirical validity of the mathematical formulation is not in question. This might be called direct problem solving; it is illustrated in a simple form by the descriptive word problems of courses in mathematics and science.

In an inventive application, the mathematical counterpart of the original question is again accepted as a true representation of the real problem, but the means for the resolution of the mathematical problem are not immediately at hand. Thus, mathematical inventiveness is called for. A successful effort may come from a modification of existing methods, or it may call for a degree of novelty and ingenuity which marks it not only as a contribution to the area of application but also as a contribution to mathematical method. Its possible usefulness extends beyond the original application and it becomes "mathematically significant." Such a piece of work is a candidate for publication as mathematical research in order to make it generally available for other mathematical applications. The mathematics of the inventive type of application may range from an exercise in advanced problem solving to a research question whose resolution requires a significant extension of mathematical technique.

In modeling, the appropriate mathematical format for translation is not immediately at hand, and the major question concerns the validity of a possible mathematical representation, or "model," as a true representation of the real context. This difficulty occurs in a spectrum of applications, from the specific to the more general. If in a given problem, for example, the entities and relationships as known in the area of application (say, strings of words in natural language) are not representable as ordinary numbers and ordinary relationships between numbers, then the question becomes one of inventing the proper mathematical structure to impose on the given problem; this might be a sequenced structure such as a network or tree configuration, a topological structure, a stochastic process, etc. The modeling effort is often applied on a grander scale where an attempt is made to translate, say, the dynamic interactions of a real system involving a large number of variables; here, we may face the question of delineating basic elements of the system as well as hypothesizing on the nature of their interrelations. A model must be restrained by the requirements of realism, but it is also subject to the restraints of mathematical or computational feasibility. A model based on well-developed mathematical concepts is a more workable tool than a model whose formulation raises many difficulties of a mathematical or computational character. On the other hand, if it is necessary to overidealize in order to achieve an immediately workable model, then it may be advisable to concentrate on overcoming the mathematical difficulties for the advantage of greater empirical validity. In this connection the electronic computer is having an important effect; its use as an instrument of simulation has reduced the severity of the restraint of mathematical feasibility. In many applications, computer simulation and modeling have become synonymous.

Finally, in theory construction we have the most ambitious type of mathematical application. In this case, the aim of modeling generalizes into abstracting a deductive theory of fundamental concepts and first principles. Well-known examples are the theory of games (Von Neumann) and information theory (Shannon). The theory seeks to build a mathematical base of axioms and primitive terms whose deductive consequences are rich, conceptually and operationally, for the field of application. It unifies a host of disparate phenomena within a single framework of ideas and opens the door to the formulation and resolution of a wide variety of new important problems. In theory construction, the depth and generality of the mathematical conceptualization as a representation of real phenomena become essential elements. Success calls for creative imagination of a high order. What often is involved is abstraction which at the time is far removed from existing knowledge or immediate intuition (a famous example, in the exact sciences, is Einstein's creation of the special theory of relativity). If a proposed theory is judged to have serious possibilities in an important domain of application, again the difficulty of the purely mathematical questions it poses will not be cause for its rejection. It becomes the motivation for mathematical research proper which may enrich mathematical knowledge as much as it enriches the field of its origin. It is typical of successful theories that their impact is great in both directions.

The individual mathematician who is engaged in a problem area may be participating at several levels of work in one or more of the broad types of activities described above. The part of this general spectrum of applications to which a given mathematician is prepared to contribute most significantly is conditioned by his training, interest, and creative powers. The class of workers called "mathematicians" by the scientific community at large is commonly understood to include all those whose principal techniques are mathematical and whose contributions (elementary, advanced, research) fall anywhere in the spectrum. Traditionally, the great majority are engaged in work centered about direct application. The more creative workers and the researchers—those whom the professional mathematical community might label "mathematicians"—make their contributions in more advanced applications. We shall discuss later the important present need for modeling and theory construction in the newer fields of application; it may be remarked here that significant work of this kind depends upon mathematical talent of the rarer creative type, and we shall orient most of our discussion toward this kind of contribution.

INTERACTION WITH MATHEMATICS

The advance of a field as a scientific body of knowledge involves conceptualization at increasing levels of abstraction and generality. This is a process that interrelates and unifies separate segments of knowledge in a manner that permits further penetration into the field. Early abstractions are inductive inferences from direct observations on phenomena of the field; when accepted, these generalizations become working concepts for subsequent development. A next advance may involve unification at a higher level of abstraction, the new generalizations being inferred from increased knowledge expressed in terms of earlier concepts. This progression of consolidation by generalization continues, leading over time to a hierarchy of levels, each of which is rooted in preceding ones.

Mathematics provides a format for the expression of generalizations together with a body of relationships and deductive methods for the development of implications and further conceptualization in a field of application. The empirical validity of a given mathematical representation depends on the verification of its hypotheses, or consequences of these, within the field of application, and not on the complexity or subtlety of its deductive constructs. The possibility of successful mergers with mathematics is determined by the existing abstractions and generalizations of the field; theoretical knowledge must be ripe for meaningful representation by mathematical notions. Conversely, the search for mathematical formulations in meaningful association with the context of the field may suggest precision and abstraction within the field itself that can stimulate its theoretical growth. Either way, it is clear that a close exchange is called for, especially at early stages of cooperation.

A realistic image of this exchange is not a simple linear transition from empirical induction to mathematical deduction, but rather a continual interplay between these two processes, as illustrated in the figure. The exchange area shown involves several activities. For one, it involves the formulation of hypotheses or axioms for the initiation of deductive infer-

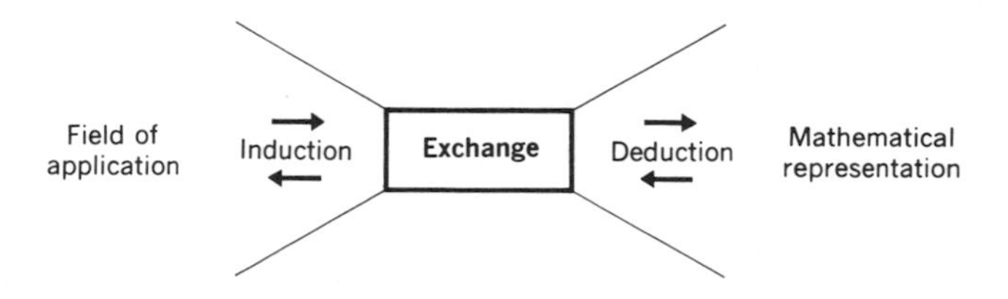

ences, the right-hand arrow (→) in the inductive region indicating the empirical basis for this formulation. The mathematician plays an equal role in this activity by delineating possible alternatives, putting intuitive notions in precise form, helping to clarify a partially stated problem, and so forth. Another direction of exchange is indicated by the left-hand arrow (←) in the inductive region. An exchange for the purpose of mathematical formulation, or for any reason, may lead to new inductive work, such as the search for evidence or more precise analysis of experimental data. When a tentative mathematical representation has been agreed on, deductive inference within the mathematical representation (→) can proceed on its own toward the contextual needs that motivated the representation. At some point, the results derived in the deductive region are fed back (←) into the exchange area in order to explore their implications for further inductive work (for example, experimental verification) or for further deductive directions. This latter feedback is essential, since the acceptance of a mathematical model or theory is commonly based upon verification of key consequences rather than of initial hypotheses.

It is worth comparing the situation in a nonmathematical field with that in a field of the exact sciences, say physics, where mathematics is well established. In the latter, concepts of mathematics are intimately connected with those of the field, and there are various mathematical models and theories identified with the field. There exists a large and effective group of mathematical workers, the mathematical physicists, who belong to the field itself and center their interest there. These individuals, and others in the field with lesser mathematical training, carry out the mathematical work; they also perform the functions, or are intimately familiar with them, on both sides of the above diagram. The bulk of the everyday mathematical work is of the direct- or inventive-applications type referred to earlier, resting upon models and theories firmly established in the past. Naturally, extensions and innovations of the latter type also go on, with advances occurring at rarer times.

The situation is different in fields new in the use of mathematics. Many present-day workers in such fields have the mathematical training to carry out the less-advanced aspects of direct application; but the exploration of more advanced methods would require collaboration with mathematicians primarily trained outside the field. The fountainhead of mathematical application is modeling and theory construction; progress in these areas will determine the significance of mathematics for the newer fields. Successful associations with mathematics in these areas could give rise to effective working mathematical tools and increasing numbers of applications of the direct and inventive types. There would evolve a new generation of experts trained in both the respective field and mathematics to carry out and develop further the mathematical work.

A field which is highly developed mathematically, such as physics, is a source of problems and motivation for the growth of mathematics proper; modern physics and modern analysis were born and grew together in the seventeenth century. The great variety of mathematical research carried on today has greater or lesser connection with its origin; it is recognized that freedom to pursue mathematics, as significant mathematics, to far-flung points is a necessary component of a total program arranged on a spectrum of correspondence with application. History gives many examples of how earlier abstract mathematics, sometimes generations later, becomes the essential means of applied innovations—witness the geometric theory utilized by Einstein in his special theory of relativity.

In nonmathematical fields, the need to discover the primary links with mathematics implies a close interdependence between empirical context and mathematical exploration. This should not be interpreted to mean limiting mathematics to traditional methods or small deviations from them. New methods are requiring fresh points of view in mathematics, and these require conditions of freedom to allow imaginative discoveries to be made, if they are to be made. New directions need to be developed in mathematics, as well as in the fields of application (see "Mathematical Theory and Verifiability" below).

LANGUAGE OF MATHEMATICS

It is common for the nonmathematician to regard mathematics as essentially a symbolic language—esoteric and useful perhaps, but a collection of marks and rules of manipulation far removed from imaginative processes of the mind. In many cases, educational training contributes to this view of mathematics as a kind of ritualism, and an untrained perusal of the work of the mathematician in its external aspect often reinforces this impression. For the mathematician, as with any scientific worker, technical language is a vehicle for thought and invention, and to identify the content of his domain with the vehicle for expressing that content is like identifying musical notation with music and grammar with writing. In practice, such an uninformed view can divert attention from the more fruitful possibilities of mathematical applications. For example, symbolic expression within a field of application does not automatically assure that methods of mathematics can be brought usefully into play; further connections are needed than these, which may require deeper study to define and validate a relevant system of relations among the entities named by the symbols.

At the same time, it would be a mistake not to appreciate the importance of the notational apparatus of mathematics. Leibniz's invention of the symbolism of calculus is regarded as a principal contribution to the subject. Notation that is suggestive and conveys the essential in its simplest form greatly affects the use and development of mathematics. Good notation conveys much information in compact form and it exposes new possibilities by being convertible to many forms; it "automates" mathematical processes safely at one level by rules of manipulation of symbols, thereby freeing thought for exploration and invention at a higher level. As a part of mathematics becomes traditional and widely applied, and as mathematical research moves beyond it, the line between manipulation and meaning fades and notation carries more and more of the burden of content. This process undoubtedly accelerates the wider use of mathematics by making techniques available to a larger audience. However, it must be recognized that the uncritical use of traditional rules in nontraditional contexts may lead to difficulties, which can call for a close reexamination of buried assumptions.

There are problems in fields of applications which by their nature are essentially questions of symbol manipulation or representation. These can arise, for example, in connection with the symbolic representation of information or with computer processes, and they can give rise to questions of serious mathematical meaning. It is worth noting that the natural methods for studying the structure of symbolic arrays are more likely to be found in the purer branches of mathematics, including mathematical logic, than in branches traditionally regarded as applied.

We can follow this theme of mathematical language into a deeper aspect of mathematics, namely, its deductive character. The rigorous syntax of mathematical statements is a mode of communication designed to expose the deductive sequence of steps from hypothesis to conclusion so as to provide a high degree of assurance of the logical validity of an argument. Mathematical validity rests on sound deduction, and workable means of avoiding error and checking correctness of inference must be available to temper the free exercise of imagination. The mathematician makes full use of intuition, imagination, guessing, and all the other aspects of creative thought in his work; to allow these and yet meet the required standards of rigor which guarantee his work, he uses an appropriate mode of discourse. The published, external aspect of his work is an organization of it in this discourse which rarely reflects the actual process of its creation; an analog is the relationship between a musical score and the inventive processes of the composer. It might be mentioned that the development of mathematical logic in the twentieth century is closely allied to the analysis of mathematical discourse and, more generally, to the study of the methodology of deductive theory ("metamathematics").

MATHEMATICAL THEORY AND VERIFIABILITY

The basic structure of mathematical, or deductive, theory is expressed by the familiar ideas of undefined term, axiom, proof, theorem, and definition. The axioms are the unproved statements of a theory; they specify relations among the undefined terms which tell all that may be logically assumed about them within the theory. Theorems, proved by deductive inference, provide new relations among these and other terms that have been introduced by definition. A theorem will typically contain assumptions, other than the axioms, which are conditional and specific to the theorem; for example, in a theorem *If P then Q*, conditional assumptions occur in the hypothesis *P*.

A mathematical theory does not commonly occur in this pure form. A particular theory ordinarily presupposes other mathematical theories. For example, if certain undefined entities are taken to be real numbers, then the theory of real numbers becomes available in dealing with these entities in the given theory. By carrying the concepts of one theory over into those of a new theory, we implicitly build the second theory upon the first; the more fully developed the presupposed theories are, the more apparatus there is available to make headway in the new theory. This process is not generally spelled out in practice; in principle, it can be. If this interdependence were carried back to theories which lie at the foundations of mathematics, we would find the following: A typical theory is a collection of theorems which, apart from the foundational terms and axioms, share a common set of additional terms and assumptions that have been gathered together to pursue some definite purpose. The new deductive organization of terms and assumptions singles out a set of ideas designed to explicate and develop some category of mathematical structure. The process of structuring one theory on another is in many ways an analog in mathematics of the process of successive abstraction in an empirical field described above.

Sometimes a theory in mathematics is referred to as an "abstract" theory. This is not a precise methodological term, but it is intended to convey the idea that the theory is built on formal abstractions out of other concrete, or familiar, mathematical contexts; the latter provide particular interpretations that satisfy the axioms of the abstract theory. The theory is developed without commitment to a particular interpretation (proving a theorem in the abstract proves it simultaneously, so to speak, in all interpretations); the abstract theory lays the groundwork for the discovery of unifying relations for a variety of particular cases. For example, the abstract "group" is a theory that unifies and generalizes certain features of such diverse elements of mathematics as operations on numbers, permutations, geometric symmetry, and transformations of spaces. New interpretations of a theory may emerge later; one measure of the significance of a theory is the variety and significance of its interpretations inside and outside mathematics.

The following feature of a theory is important in applications: Two particular instances, s_1 and s_2, of a general theory T are indistinguishable in terms of T. Nothing can be discovered in T which will mark off s_1 from s_2; their distinctive features must be found outside of T (for example, an oval and a circle are the same in the topological theory of the plane). One means of judging to what extent T embodies meaningful features of an empirical context s_1 is to compare s_1 with alternative interpretations s of T and decide whether s_1 may be reasonably treated by a theory that does not distinguish it from s.

Let us consider further the matter of mathematically derived relations and their validity as images of real relations within a field of application. A mathematical deduction establishes that if a certain hypothesis (or set of hypotheses) H is granted, then a certain conclusion C logically follows. The verification of C in the real context may thus be achieved by checking whether H holds in the same context. This principle is self-evident, but in practice it is often overlaid with difficulties. The clarification of hypothesis H may call for considerable exchange with the mathematical expert. The following incident illustrates the point in a simple situation. The author of this paper was recently asked, "If a sphere is put on a plane, how much of the surface of the sphere makes contact with the plane?" The answer was given as, "One point, of course." This did not satisfy the inquirer because he felt this was not the correct problem. He was asked, "Well, by a sphere do you mean a solid homogeneous ball of perfect elasticity on an unyielding plane surface and acted on by the vertical pull of gravity?" When he indicated that this might be the question of interest, he was referred to the mathematical theory of elasticity. Further exchange revealed the possibility of an infinitely thin elastic material bounding a gas under pressure; and so the process of mutual understanding developed.

Conversely, a deduction H *implies* C may be used as evidence for the theory whose axioms gave rise to this deduction. For example, an experiment designed to mirror the conditions H and yielding C as an observed consequence provides such evidence. It is to be emphasized that a mathematical theory does not itself establish the validity or significance of its interpretation in an extramathematical context; methodology outside the theory is required for this. The validity of Euclidean geometry as a description of the real world ultimately rests on observational corroboration, not upon mathematical deduction. The greater the number of corroborations and the wider the variety of deductive predictions which are corroborated, the more firmly established a theory becomes. The essentially hypothetical and tentative nature of axiomatics for the explanation of extramathematical phenomena is generally accepted in scientific work today. A classical example is the introduction of non-Euclidean space in relativity theory to replace Euclidean space, for an appropriate range of physical phenomena.

Mathematical statistics addresses itself to problems of inductive inference within the context of a field of application. Although this aspect of mathematics is not being explored here, it may be remarked that the justification of mathematical assumptions is equally important in the use of statistical methods. Perhaps it should be said that the question is especially critical here; the familiar remark that statistics can "prove" anything expresses the skepticism that may sometimes be felt about statistical inference.

The newer fields of application can present unusually difficult problems of observational verification of mathematical consequences. In a more classical field, such as physics, where experimental science is closely linked with precise theoretical concepts, it is frequently possible to make measurements and impose controls which accurately reflect the hypotheses H of a deduction and permit verification or rejection of a conclusion C. In other fields, where measurement and experimental control are difficult and mathematical conceptualization is new, there may be a need for considerable development before theory and observation can be accurately associated. It was mentioned earlier that modeling and mathematical theory construction will provide the principal basis for a growing alliance of application and mathematics. The tentative acceptance of a mathematical representation may need to rely upon intuition and informed judgment, and be tested by its eventual usefulness over time, rather than by immediate exact evidence. A plausible criterion would be whether a model or theory presents notions and relations that are fruitful, say, by suggesting new workable concepts in the field and opening up promising research questions. The theory of games, for example, has had an important impact in various fields in this way, rather than as a mathematical copy of actual phenomena; this may be regarded as its chief contribution, and continuing mathematical work may lead to still greater conceptual use of the theory.

THE WORKING MATHEMATICIAN

The division of research mathematicians into applied and pure is a qualitative separation described in a general way as follows. The applied mathematician is principally interested in answering questions in a field of application, and uses mathematics as a means to this end; he may even be trained as a specialist in the field. He is interested in applying and developing effective methods of solution—analytical, approximate, or computational. His results may have interest as mathematics, but his motivation lies in application. The direction of his work is conditioned by the changing needs of the field of application. On the other hand, the work of the pure mathematician is understood to come mainly out of mathematics itself; as in any discipline, good mathematics opens new avenues of investigation and builds upon itself. What is done is conditioned by the methods at hand and the judgment of what is significant; new results give rise to new methods and new possibilities.

Applied mathematics provides motivation for research in pure mathematics; reciprocally, pure mathematics creates methods for applied mathematics. Historically, the tie has been a strong one and most present-day mathematics has its origins in applications to "real" problems, with this part or that being carried on closer or farther from its beginnings. The separation of these activities began chiefly in the twentieth century, with the rapid proliferation and specialization of science and the formalization of mathematics. The great mathematicians of the past were at once applied and pure; it is interesting that this holds for a number of outstanding individuals in our own century.

The needs of the newer areas of application are laying the basis for a return of parts of pure mathematics to empirical problems. This is so because much of traditional mathematics is not suited to these novel areas (see the last section below). We therefore must think not so much in terms of a traditional division into applied and pure, but in terms of new applied mathematics, drawing on any mathematics which can be useful, whatever its present label. We turn to some features of mathematical research work pertinent to our interest, regardless of its classification.

The type of activity which might be called "library research" is not characteristic of the work of the creative mathematician. A problem which can be resolved by looking through books and finding the right recipe is "trivial," in the parlance of research mathematics. For the purposes of application, such contributions are not necessarily "trivial," and the mathematician can serve a useful function in this regard, as one familiar with established techniques, especially those of advanced mathematics. But his main interest is in questions requiring some mathematical imagination, that is, in mathematically "significant" problems.

A mathematical investigation involves the formulation of a problem. There is an aspect of this in which the mathematician, as any good scientist, is well trained: to view a problem as properly stated only when its statement suggests means of resolving it. An objective without a practical conception of means is not a design for research, but an expression of hope. A problem statement, for example, should point the way to connections with other problems and existing methods. We may illustrate this by some recent work of the author. In explaining a new mathematical result to a colleague, he expressed it in a certain form. This suggested to his colleague the possibility of finding a method of solving a certain class of optimization problems. The problem was more explicitly formulated as one of finding a functional transformation having a certain property, which we labeled a "maximum transformation"; this was guided by analogy with the classical theory of the Laplace transform.

The analogy also provided the necessary clues to conjecture what the maximum transform might be; the conjecture was then established by methods of proof based on another part of analysis—the theory of convex functions. This satisfactory completion of the initial problem became the starting point for two directions: (1) to look for other fields of application of the maximum transform; and (2) to study the transform in a more abstract mathematical setting with the idea of exploring further general properties.

The mathematician deals with precise notions but is pragmatic in his approach. Like any scientific worker he breaks down a main area into workable subareas by considering special cases, introducing tentative hypotheses, and so on. The result of concentrating on a subproblem may be to reject it, succeed in it, or refine it further. When a subarea has been successfully illuminated, the region may be enlarged to a broader subproblem, or an overlapping subarea may be attacked. Gradually the illuminated region of partial results grows and, hopefully, reveals the solution of the original question.

One characteristic of the mathematician is his freedom of choice of tentative hypotheses in defining these subareas. He, too, is an experimenter, but his laboratory and raw material being mental, he may explore more freely than one who is committed more closely to the realities of external data and experimentation. The actual experimenter, however, has independent observation as a tool of verification, while the mathematician must count on precise statement and rigorous deduction as the guarantee of validity. In practice, the mathematician may also exercise greater freedom at a more general level. When a path of investigation fails to resolve an original problem but reveals the possibility of success in an alternative area, he is in a position to revise the original problem and proceed from there, hoping that this larger strategy proves successful in the long run. An unexpected turn may lead to success in an unanticipated area, much like what occurs in any scientific work.

The mathematician's training in rigor makes him a useful partner and critic in activities of clarification and formulation within the context of a field of application itself. In new enterprises of abstraction and generalization, this can be a principal contribution of the mathematician. In addition, such preliminary work sets the stage for eventual mathematical representations of significance.

There is a function that the mathematician fulfills in science that may be mentioned here, namely, the refinement of theory. When a theory of initial success and promise is introduced into a field, its methods are exploited freely in any part of the field where it leads to advance; as long as the methods work, they are used, even uncritically. The theory is pushed to the limit, and eventually ambiguities or contradictions can arise in attempts to apply it to more difficult problems at the frontier of the field. If so, the foundations of the theory must be reexamined; the mathematician has found inspiration for research in such situations. A classical example is the rigorization of the calculus in the second half of the nineteenth century, following 200 years of widespread use after Newton and Leibniz. A modern example is found in the mathematical foundation of quantum mechanics developing from twentieth-century physics. Efforts such as these inspire a major development in mathematics. Often, the connection between the developing research and its discernible application is stretched thin, as investigators in the field of application turn to ad hoc methods or to other problems, and the mathematician is led deeper into mathematical considerations. The value of major mathematical development of this kind is to be measured on a long time scale, and judgment of ultimate value is not easily rendered.

NEW DIRECTIONS

Much of mathematics has its historical roots in the physical sciences and its applications, accordingly, are oriented toward problems in such fields. The needs of newer fields concerned with phenomena of human behavior and their automation suggest that a significant impact of mathematical method will go hand in hand with new developments in mathematics. Although it is to be expected that the new will build on the old, it would seem that a reorientation of mathematical interests is needed. This is complicated by the early state of precise conceptualization in these fields, which often raises questions of the appropriateness of the deductive formalism of mathematics. Also, the difficulty and novelty of the problems require attracting mathematical talent of a high order at a time when mathematics is flourishing as never before and finding increased applications in areas where the extension of methods is in a more direct line with tradition. Nonetheless, the change has begun and is increasing. In this section we shall briefly describe a few new directions of mathematical activity indicative of the change.

The theory of games belongs in the list. There originally were great hopes for this theory in explaining economic behavior, which, it is fair to say, have not been realized; but the theory has had a widespread effect as a means of conceptualization in many fields. The theory belongs to the class of theories of conflict of opposing interests, which are promising avenues of research. Present work in game theory (for example, in many-person games) is directed toward widening the scope of the theory. Related to game theory, and other areas, are theories of utility and decision making that treat problems which are pertinent to newer applications.

Information theory is another important development. Although its original motivation and use was in communication engineering, its ideas have found their way into many other domains of interest. Once again the chief impact has been as a stimulant and a means of conceptualization. What is needed for a more direct influence is the theoretical treatment of information as a semantical notion rather than as a symbolic code, and ideas of this sort are being explored in various quarters.

It was mentioned earlier that an inversion of pure and applied mathematics is occuring, whereby the tools of the former seem to have more direct relevance than those of the latter in the new problem areas. We find, for example, a wider exploration of methods of combinatorial theory, network theory, theory of linear graphs, finite algebras, etc. Problems requiring such methods have attracted a number of research mathematicians.

Modeling frequently calls for the description of processes which are dynamic and involve random elements. Here, the work in multistage decision processes, such as dynamic programming, is pertinent, as are Monte Carlo techniques and adaptations of the mathematics of stochastic processes. Again, modeling is often confronted with processes involving many variables in a complex of interactions; progress in this work has been made, largely because of the possibility of simulation on a large-scale digital computer.

The computer is the focal point of many of the new directions. It provides a powerful experimental instrument of flexibility, speed, and capacity, and its exploitation is in an early stage. The development of heuristic or adaptive research methods of problem solution, in which the computer seeks out solutions unaided, or in close coupling with a human experimenter in real time, is an important direction of research. Another is the development of a flexible symbolic representation of performable functions of the computer, at some appropriate level of aggregation, which would allow combinations of these functions to be manipulated symbolically with pencil and paper. With such a tool, computer processes could be interwoven with the language of mathematical relations in a single analytical format and lead to richer mathematical-computer models. This is related to work in higher-order-programming languages which attempts to bring the language of problem formulation and the language of the computer closer together. What is needed, however, is an intermediate logical-mathematical format for modeling which is adapted to research and the search for methods of solution; the result might be a procedure which could be transformed into a programming language for execution on the computer (See "Computer Languages" by Melkanoff).

The development of an integrated language of mathematical and computer operations is part of a more general problem associated with the automation of control functions. This is the problem of formalism which embraces both mathematical representations of systems and representations of the processes of actual execution of systems, by computer or otherwise. Such a formalism must deal, for example, with properties of information about a system, as well as with the system in the abstract, so to speak. By and large, a conceptual distinction exists between theoretical formulation and its integration into an operational context; automation of decision making is breaking down this separation. What is called for is a formal metalanguage, adapted to research needs, treating relationships *within* a system and operations *on* a system.

Various aspects of research on computers have brought methods of mathematical logic into prominence. It seems striking at first that mathematical logic, which grew out of attempts to formalize mathematical foundations and which is traditionally regarded as "purer" than pure mathematics, should now provide some of the most promising directions of applied research. Yet the fundamentally logical structure and operation of the digital computer suggests that the connection is a natural one. The use of Boolean algebra in computer design work is one familiar application of mathematical logic. Another connects the description of computer algorithms with the theory of recursive processes, a very active part of present-day research in logic. The investigation of higher-order-programming languages to simplify the problem of human communication with the computer is leaning heavily on symbolic methods of modern logic. Studies of computer processing of natural language and of other symbolic structures relate to this branch of mathematics.

The theory of automata has emerged as a mathematical and logical theory to describe the over-all behavior of a computer as a sequentially functioning mechanism. The study of self-adaptive (learning) features is of especial interest in relation to future possibilities of computer automation. The theory of control and communication processes as expressed in cybernetics provides a conceptual framework for exploiting the behavior of biological organisms in the study of self-adaptive and intelligent behavior of computers.

An interesting speculation emerges from consideration of the computer as a logical machine. The finite nature of the machine leads to the description of its behavior in terms of "constructive" processes. On the other hand, the logical structure of most mathematics rests upon nonconstructive notions. These nonconstructive concepts of infinity have given mathematics great scope and permitted its far-flung development. They have also given rise to paradoxes in the foundations of mathematics which are unresolved; for example, the consistency of the real-number system itself is not settled (and, in a certain logical sense, is unresolvable). The difficulties have not interfered with the development of mathematics and its uses, but they have led to a special school of intuitionistic mathematics which insists on finite, constructive methods and thereby rejects much of mathematics. It would be ironical if the intuitionists emerged as the true believers in the next millennium.

The scientific development of the fields of knowledge of main interest here, for which mathematics may prove to be an important tool, is at an early stage. These fields must look toward attracting scientists of various technical backgrounds, mathematicians among others. Success depends on the talents and interests of the individuals engaged in the work; growth should carry with it the setting of high standards of scientific ability and accomplishment where traditional criteria are lacking or are inappropriate.

MICHEL A. MELKANOFF

Computer languages

Before discussing artificial languages, and more specifically computer languages, let us briefly define machine language. The modern digital computer may be considered as a machine capable of carrying out a sequence of operations upon a set of data. The operations performed by the computer are determined by the fixed hardware, by a set of instructions, and by the data themselves. The operating computer may thus be said to obey a sequence of instructions that are programmed by the coder. Let us define an admissible instruction as part of a set built into the computer by its designer. The execution of an admissible instruction is unambiguously defined in terms of a sequence of events which take place within the machine. The total repertoire of admissible instructions forms a finite, precise vocabulary which may be considered as a particular computer language in terms of which the programmer can communicate with the machine.

MACHINE LANGUAGE

We shall now examine this computer language in accordance with an analysis by C. B. Tompkins (private communication and seminar notes). The obedience to individual commands causes the computer to carry out two distinct types of processes: (1) an operation is performed upon the data, and (2) the next command is selected either unconditionally or in a manner which depends on the data. In the computer language, we can consider each individual command as a sentence containing two clauses: (1) an operational clause specifying the operation to be performed, and (2) a sequential clause specifying how to select the next sentence.

Note that the word *instruction* or *command* implies an imperative form to which the logical attribute *meaningful* is not applicable. This might appear to restrict our analysis, but we can easily transform every imperative sentence into a declarative sentence which describes the state of the computer upon execution of the command. This in turn implies that we can depend upon our computer to obey every admissible command precisely; fortunately the reliability of modern machines warrants this assumption.

Let us now consider a peculiar feature of the computer language which distinguishes it radically from natural languages. While the topological structure of a string of sentences in a natural language is a straight line, a string of sentences in a computer language admits a more complex topology. Indeed, it is imperative that such sentences be modifiable and reusable at will to permit efficient utilization of the computer. This is achieved through the presence of the sequential clause, which permits return to previously used sentences, and through the common storage for, and deliberate lack of formal distinction between, instructions and data, which permits modification of a command. As a result, the original program prepared by the coder contains only a small fraction of the commands actually obeyed by the computer. In fact, the coder's main job is to produce a program which will generate, rather than contain *ab initio,* the series of commands required to solve a given problem.

We shall now consider the individual constitutents which make up a clause of the computer language.

Admissible Numbers An admissible number is one that is susceptible of unambiguous representation within the computer. The format of such a number may, for example, be binary or decimal, using fixed- or floating-point representation. The range is limited by the number of digits available on the machine. The format and range of the admissible numbers by which to represent the data is specified by the machine design. Usually, the computer language refers indirectly to these numbers through admissible symbols, but occasionally they may appear explicitly in one of its sentences.

Admissible Operations These are the operations which the computer was designed to perform, and strict adherence to the list of admissible ones is essential. In some machines, it is possible to specify nonadmissible operations, but the results are then unpredictable (or more correctly, can only be predicted after an exhaustive and rarely practicable analysis). Since it is practically impossible to verify the truth or falsehood of the corresponding declarative sentences, sentences containing inadmissible operations may be considered meaningless.

Admissible Symbols These are the numerical designations (or addresses) of either admissible numbers or instructions stored in the memory. The format of admissible symbols is determined by the machine design, while their range is limited by the capacity of the memory.

In order to permit proper control of the flow of the computation, the admissible numbers must consist of at least two disjoint classes, such as the positive and nonpositive numbers. Furthermore, commands must be provided which can detect these differences, and which contain the sequential clauses needed to branch (select two more different paths) accordingly. If such commands are not available, it is impossible to break away from a closed loop (a series of computer commands which are obeyed in infinitely repeated sequence). It might be possible to break away from a closed loop by taking advantage of special commands peculiar to a specific computer, but such commands are not considered here as part of a general computer language.

There is usually no valid reason for attempting to use inadmissible operations or symbols, but inadmissible data such as overflowed results, which occur when the result of an operation exceeds the capacity of the computer to store a piece of data, can be generated during certain operations. Such contingencies must be detectable and sequential clauses must again be available to furnish proper branching.

EVOLUTION OF HIGHER-LEVEL LANGUAGES

Computer languages may be classified into levels according to their relation to the basic computer instructions. The further a computer language is removed from these basic instructions, the higher its level.

As long as the programmer limits his vocabulary to the use of numbers, symbols, and operations admissible to the machine, we say that he is using an *absolute machine language,* which may be classified as a *first-level* language. Such a language can be particularly onerous when addressing a binary machine where every command must be laboriously prepared as a long string of 1s and 0s. This may be remedied by providing a more convenient numerical language admitting the use of other bases, such as decimal, hexadecimal, or octal. We shall call such a language an *absolute language.* Instructions phrased in this absolute language must now be translated to binary format before they can be accepted by the computer. One naturally turns to the computer itself to perform the translation by means of a conversion routine specifically coded for the purpose. In the early days, when the memory capacity of the computer was limited, the conversion routine was loaded into the machine separately (in absolute machine format). The absolute-language instructions were then input as pseudo-binary data, and under the control of the conversion routine the computer would output a set of instructions in absolute machine language which could then be loaded directly into the machine after clearing out the conversion routine. As memory sizes increased, it became customary to keep the conversion routine in the computer at all times, permitting the coder to load and execute immediately a program prepared in absolute language. While this procedure can hardly be said to imply a higher-level language, it presents the first case, where the coder is addressing a "software computer" within the original hardware computer.

The next extension of the computer language was introduced to widen the list of admissible operations which in early computers were quite limited. Interpretation routines were constructed as software computers which admitted both normal and coded commands. The coder could now speak to the computer in an interpretive language, and the interpretation routine would decode the coded commands and translate them into a string of normal commands executed by the computer. Advances in computer art have rendered this language somewhat obsolete, as modern computers are provided with a large and powerful set of admissible operations and with sufficient memory capacity to store an adequate number of subroutines.

Computer languages have also evolved by widening the class of admissible symbols. The absolute languages, which referred to the data and instructions by their storage address, were both inconvenient and conducive to clerical errors. A first improvement was achieved by the introduction of relative addresses, which were then transformed into absolute addresses under the control of special conversion routines. An absolute address designates the specific location of a piece of data in the memory of the computer with respect to a fixed reference point. A relative address designates the location of a piece of data with respect to some arbitrary point, which must, of course, be specified in order that the conversion routine operate properly. These *relative languages* were again of short duration and have been replaced by the *symbolic languages* which are in almost universal use today. These languages embody all the worthwhile extensions discussed above and present a sufficient departure from absolute machine language to justify their classification as *second-level* languages. The coder now addresses a symbolic assembly program[1] and his vocabulary has been extended as follows:

1 The admissible symbols now include alphanumeric characters, which bring a new convenience to the coder by letting him address the data and instructions by almost any name he chooses. He may even address them by reference to some neighbor.

2 The admissible operations are now specified by a succinct mnemonic set of characters, which speeds up programming and reduces errors. Furthermore, a new set of admissible operations is usually available in the assembly program. For example, the input-output system of a modern computer is often so complex that it requires elaborate machine-language coding, and the symbolic language will usually admit simple statements to bring about the execution of certain standardized input-output operations.

[1]A symbolic address refers to a piece of data by an alphabetic or other symbol (such as DOG, X, etc.) as desired by the programmer. All reference to this data must, of course, continue to use the same symbol. A symbolic assembly program is a program used to assign absolute addresses to symbolically addressed data.

3 A new type of sentence is admissible (and sometimes required) by the assembly program. These so-called "pseudo-operations" are not considered commands which must be sequentially obeyed, but are accepted instead as information to be used by the assembler during the generation of the final machine program. Such a pseudo-operation may specify, for example, that a certain piece of data must be treated as a Boolean variable.

This new flexibility is obtained at the cost of a fairly complex assembly program and requires a fairly elaborate set of rules for proper usage.

In spite of their complexity, the symbolic languages still resemble very closely machine languages and may be said to be largely machine-oriented. The heavy use of computers in scientific work, where the required operations can be described in terms of well-defined arithmetic steps and algebraic formulae, has led to the introduction of problem-oriented languages. We shall refer to them as *algebraic languages* and classify them as a *third level.* Specifications for such languages include the following:

1 They must provide a convenient way of coding algebraic formulae.

2 They must be easy to learn.

3 The computer which accepts this language must produce a reasonably efficient machine language program.

4 Errors must be quickly recognized and easily corrected.

The algebraic languages available today generally satisfy these requirements. They consist of a series of executable statements which can still be described in terms of operational and sequential clauses, and nonexecutable statements or declarations which correspond to the pseudo-instructions used in symbolic languages. To illustrate such a language, consider some statements in IBM's FORTRAN (formula translating system), which is in wide use today.

Arithmetic Statements These are the fundamental statements of the language. The sequential clause is implicit and always leads to the next statement in sequence. The operational clause appears explicitly in the typical form

X = A + (CBAR/2.5)

This signifies that the quantity on the right side of the equals sign must replace the quantity on the left. Such a statement resembles a conventional arithmetic formula, but differs in the interpretations of the equals sign. Thus the arithmetic statement A = A + 1 is permissible in the FORTRAN language but is obviously unacceptable as an arithmetic formula. The right side of the statement can take on a variety of forms, which makes a large number of operations admissible in this language.

Control Statements These statements control the flow of the calculation and usually consist primarily of a sequential clause. For example, the statement GO TO 37 signifies that the statement labeled 37 must be executed next.

Other such control statements are available which permit single and multiple branching in a variety of forms.

Declarations These are nonexecutable statements which sometimes must appear in a definite part of the program. For example, the statement END, which signifies the termination of a program or subprogram, must appear as its last statement. On the other hand, the statement 32 FORMAT (F 3.5), which specifies a certain type of input or output format, may appear anywhere in the program.

These brief examples will suffice to illustrate the power and the convenience of algebraic languages. The compiler program to which the language is addressed performs the following operations:

1 It translates the algebraic language into symbolic and machine language with a considerable degree of efficiency.

2 It monitors the instructions programmed in the algebraic language and is capable of detecting most "barbarisms" and "solecisms" whereupon it generates a diagnostic output of considerable value.

"Barbarisms" and "solecisms" appear as such to the compiler program. For example, the symbolic designation A $ B violates the rules for symbol designation, for it contains the forbidden symbol $. Since it cannot even be accepted by the compiler program, it might be called a barbarism. On the other hand, the symbolic designation PAF (I) will be misinterpreted by the compiler program as a request to form a mathematical function (through improper use of the letter *F*); we might call this a solecism.

Needless to say, the compiler program is itself a formidable code. The 704 FORTRAN, for example, consists of some 24,000 machine instructions and required 18 man-years to develop. Since algebraic languages were developed for the specific problems of applied mathematics, it is not surprising that they do not prove equally convenient for data-processing problems.

Third-level languages oriented toward the above problems are beginning to appear. As an indication of some of the difficulties which may arise, consider a simple logical problem such as the old puzzle of the three missionaries and the three cannibals who must cross a river in a single boat two at a time without ever allowing more cannibals than missionaries to be present at the same place. While this problem can be stated very simply in natural language, an exacting and relatively complicated description must be given in mathematical form before the problem can be coded for a computer. The coding itself then requires a new approach which is not easily carried out within the presently available computer languages. This is due to the fact that modern computers, as a result of their historical development, are generally more oriented toward arithmetic than logical problems. Thus, a vast number of arithmetic problems can be concisely and explicitly described within a relatively narrow and well-understood arithmetic language. Such is not generally the case in logical data-processing problems, which are often poorly defined and where few algorithms are available. Despite these difficulties, the applications of computers to business are growing so rapidly that third-level data-processing languages should soon come into wide usage.

Having considered third-level languages, we might speculate on languages of fourth or higher levels. Such languages could permit the programmer to simply state, for example, a differential equation to be solved under certain boundary conditions. This might perhaps be done as follows:

Given the differential equation

$$\frac{d^2y}{dx^2} + \left(\frac{dy}{dx}\right)^2 x^2 = (x + y)^3$$

with the boundary conditions

$$y = 0 \; at \; x = 0 \qquad \frac{dy}{dx} = 7 \; at \; x = 0$$

the programmer might write in the fourth-level language

DE (*d*2*y* (*x*) /*d*2*x*) + (*d*1*y* (*x*) /*d*1*x*) * (*x***2) = (*x* + *y*) ** 3

*BC*1 *y* (0) = 0

*BC*2 *d*1*y* (0) /*d*1*x* = 7

A sufficiently powerful program would then examine the differential equation and boundary conditions, perhaps search its memory for suitable numerical techniques, decide on a scheme for numerical integration, produce the necessary algorithms, rewrite the differential equation as an iterated set of arithmetic statements, and translate these statements into machine language. Some laboratories are working on this type of problem. It seems clear, however, that generalized higher-level computer languages require such formidable programs as to make them impractical for the present.

COMMUNICATION BETWEEN COMPUTERS

A problem of considerable importance in the field of computer languages and one which presents some interesting similarities to the problems faced in linguistics is that of communication between various computing machines. This problem arises because of the diversities of equipotential computers and their rapid turnover. Computers manufactured by various firms utilize quite different machine languages in spite of their similarities, and unless two computer installations own the same type of machine their programs are not interchangeable. This leads to an unfortunate duplication of effort, as the problems are often similar in many places.

Furthermore, even if the various firms could agree on a single machine language at any one time, the rapid introduction of new machines would reactivate the problem. Computer installations are thus periodically faced with the prospect of recoding all their programs as a result of having purchased a new computer. Various approaches have been taken to cope with these problems. Some installations may refuse to purchase the new machines and will thereby suffer from the obsolescence of their equipment. On the other hand, some computer manufacturers go to considerable effort to maintain compatibility among successive models. This may be a risky policy, for the later models may thereby be deliberately prevented from acquiring the more powerful structure which competing firms are offering. Thus, while the IBM 704, 709, 7090 series offers extensive compatibility, the 7090 has been held down to 36 bits per word and 3 index registers, which is less powerful than comparable features of competing machines.

Another possible way to salvage on computer y a program constructed for computer x is to simulate on y the operation of x. But this can only be considered as a temporary stopgap, for it may seriously impair the power of y, and the resulting difficulties and inefficiencies will usually outweigh any advantage gained from the reprogramming effort.

A further possibility is to create a program for translating one computer language into the other. This is an interesting problem which requires comparative analysis of computer languages. Consider some definitions suggested by C. B. Tompkins (unpublished research paper). He starts by defining an elementary sequence as follows:

> ***Definition*** An elementary sequence is a set of commands (or sentences) to be executed (or read) sequentially. Each command in the sequence, except possibly the first, has a unique predecessor; each command in the sequence, except possibly the last, has a unique successor.

An elementary sequence is thus a set of commands which has the topology of a straight line, allowing no branching within the sequence. In particular, a single command always constitutes an elementary sequence. Next we define an efficient code:

> ***Definition*** A set of commands (or sentences) is efficient if no set with fewer written commands (or sentences) in the same language could attain the same arithmetic effect.

Now we are in a position to describe a partial ordering of the power of computer languages:

> ***Definition*** Two computer languages are equivalent if any sentence in either is expressible as an efficiently coded elementary sequence in the other.

The above definition of an efficient code is admittedly somewhat vague. Except for the simplest codes, it may be practically impossible to prove that a code meets this criterion for efficiency. Furthermore, more practical definitions of efficiency might measure coding time or machine time. Still, our definition provides us with a structural yardstick such as the one used in the definition of equivalent languages. Here too the definition is a structural one, for we are not inquiring into the relative complexity of the elementary sequences; our concept of language power is based on the elementary sequence as the basic unit.

> ***Definition*** A language A is said to be at least as strong as a language B if every sentence in B is expressible as an elementary sequence in A.

Note that while there exist language pairs where one is stronger than the other, this is not necessarily the case.

Now consider the problem of translation from one computer language to another:

> ***Definition*** If a is a set of commands (or sentences) in computer language A and b is a set of commands (or sentences) in computer language B, then b is a translation of a if a and b attain the same arithmetic effect.

We shall also be interested in efficient translations which we define as follows:

> ***Definition*** If a is an efficient set of commands (or sentences) in computer language A and b is a set of commands (or sentences) in computer language B, then b is an efficient translation of a if a and b attain the same arithmetic effect and b is efficient.

The two relations *translation of* and *efficient translation of* are obviously symmetric and transitive.

Turning to the practical side of the problem, our goal is presumably to generate efficient translations by means of a computer. It is clear that if the requirement of efficiency is abandoned, translations are always achievable, since in the worst case we can always resort to simulation. On the other hand, it is not clear that we can always achieve efficient translations. In the following discussion we shall assume that the source programs which we wish to translate into object programs are efficient sets of commands. Although this is only approximately correct in reality, it will not seriously detract from practical application.

Two given computer languages must be related in one of three possible fashions:

1 A is equivalent to B.

2 A is stronger than B.

3 A is not equivalent to B, A is not stronger than B, and B is not stronger than A.

In the first case, we can achieve efficient translations, since we can always construct a two-way dictionary in terms of efficiently coded elementary sequences. We shall indicate this fact as follows:

Case 1: $A \rightleftarrows B$

In case 2 we can achieve efficient translations from A to B by providing an efficient set of commands in B for every sentence in A. However, we cannot guarantee efficient translations from B to A, since an exhaustive analysis of every loop in B would be required to make certain that the loop could not be replaced by an elementary sequence in A. Thus, we have the result that efficient translations from a weaker to a stronger language are impractical if not impossible. We summarize these results as follows:

Case 2: $A \underset{\leftarrow \cdots\cdots\cdots}{\overset{\longrightarrow}{}} B$

Finally, case 3 may be described by stating that certain parts of A are stronger than parts of B and vice versa. Therefore, our analysis of case 2 permits us to conclude that efficient translations in either direction are impractical, that is:

Case 3: $A \underset{\leftarrow \cdots\cdots\cdots}{\overset{\cdots\cdots\cdots \rightarrow}{}} B$

In practice, case 1 is exceedingly rare. On the other hand, case 2 often represents the situation where computer A is more modern than computer B. Finally, case 3 represents two contemporary computers of different manufacture. Since the dashed arrow indicates a nonefficient translation and thus an inefficient use of the computer toward which the arrow points, it is clear that all cases of real interest lead to a loss of efficiency.

We might next inquire about the possibility of translation at higher levels. Our definitions become even more tenuous when we wish to compare two computer languages of different levels, but for certain classes of problems the advantages of third-level languages are so evident that, although the technical criterion for efficiency is not met, we can accept translations from third- to first-level languages as relatively efficient from the standpoint of over-all usefulness. We can therefore suggest that communication between computers can be achieved with relative efficiency by translations from third-level language of computer *A* to first-level language of computer *B*. Such processes are indeed now under development.

We might also consider communication between the third-level languages of two different machines. Here is appears that case 1 holds to a fair degree of approximation. It is therefore hardly surprising that a number of translation routines at that level are under development.

The widespread use of third-level languages and their strong resemblance to each other clearly points the way to a universal third-level computer language. Vigorous steps have recently been taken in that direction and have resulted in the creation of ALGOL (algebraically oriented language). At the present time ALGOL compilers are under preparation for several computers, and the ACM (Association for Computing Machinery) has announced that it will publish only that language. ALGOL itself has undergone several modifications and really seems to be catching on. The future of ALGOL depends on its ability to meet the general requirements of any universal third-level computer language:

1 It must be sufficiently strong to take full advantage of both present and foreseeable computers.

2 It must not be so strong as to require excessively complex compilers.

3 It must be consistent and unambiguous.

4 It must be easy to learn and easy to use.

5 It must have the ability to grow and evolve.

For the computer, natural languages play a role entirely different from that of computer languages. The latter are used to formulate instructions; it is inconceivable that the natural languages could be used for that purpose. The vagueness, ambiguity, and richness of natural languages preclude their use for addressing the computer directly. The natural languages appear instead as data which must be translated, abstracted, sorted, and so on. Still we saw that computer languages may also appear as data which must be translated by the machine. There is a tempting inference to be drawn from the evolution of computer languages toward a universal third-level language, and one might inquire as to whether a natural interlingua might prove useful in the translation problem. Such an international language would certainly cut down the number of translational programs required for complete communication, but the labor of constructing and learning this new language does not seem to justify it.

L. C. RAY

Programming for natural language

Computing machines are becoming more more and more readily available for research purposes. Their areas of application are seemingly endless. The main objectives of this discussion are to acquaint the reader with the availability of these important new tools; to point out their potentialities; to explain in general terms how one applies these tools; and to emphasize the challenge to researchers in the comprehensive advance planning, the thorough analysis of procedures, the painstaking evaluation of applicability, and the detailed problem definitions and specifications that are essential to the successful utilization of these tools.

Basically, a computing system is a collection of machines and communication and control devices that is able to transmit, store, and process information. These attributes have inspired some to call computers "giant brains." But a computer is not a brain; it is a tool and does only what it is directed to do.

Since many different types of information can be received, stored, and processed, these new tools have wide applicablility. Computers can handle statistical work, engineering calculations, accounting operations, and a wide range of logical operations. They can be turned from one type of processing task to another with ease.

These new tools are important in research because they promise significant economies, especially in terms of time, in operations involving massive paperwork. They are equally important in that they can be utilized to carry out tasks that are not now being done because other means cannot accomplish the job or cannot do it in time for the results to be of use.

CHARACTERISTICS OF COMPUTERS

Computers have the following major characteristics:

They are automatic; that is, they are capable of self-sequencing through long series of varied processing operations in accordance with a specified processing plan.

They are capable of very high speeds of operation with high reliability.

They are able to communicate with the outside world via electrical signals.

They are capable of carrying out simple types of yes/no decisions or of taking an alternate next course of action in accordance with prespecified criteria.

They are capable of using large-capacity, very compact data-storage media.

They provide high-speed selection and retrieval of information that is stored.

They are adaptable to a wide variety of conditions affecting the origination of data, the accumulation of data, the transmission of data from point to point, and the processing of data for many purposes.

When we say that a computer is automatic, we mean that it can be sequenced by a program through a long and varied series of operations on the data it receives for processing. It is automatic in that once the machine has been started no human intervention is required in carrying out these long sequences of operations.

In accordance with the procedural plan initially fed into the computer, it can direct itself through these typical steps in the processing of natural language:

Reading in a batch of running text in natural order
Forming word records for the batch of text
Sorting word records alphabetically
Calling up dictionary records from a file stored on magnetic tape
Collating or merging the word records with the dictionary records
Removing dictionary records not matched by word records
Re-sorting a merged file into the original text order
Repeating the same processing cycle for the next batch of text

In the accomplishment of this automatic processing, the computer combines different kinds of operations in a single processing run and carries out repetitive cycles of specified operations upon different batches of data. The human operator does not have to give new or revised processing instructions nor need he physically move records back and forth between different parts of the computer system during the processing run.

In addition, the automatic self-sequencing characteristic of the computer means that the system itself keeps track of where it is at any given time in such a processing cycle, so that if the process were interrupted, it could be resumed at a later time at exactly the point at which it had been interrupted.

The high speed of computers is probably their most frequently publicized characteristic. It is this speed which enables them to take in and digest enormous volumes of information and prepare results in a fantastically short period of time. Presently available computers can perform, at rates of several thousand operations each second, arithmetic operations such as addition and subtraction, or logical operations such as comparing two sets of data to determine whether or not they match. Moreover, these operations are carried out with a high degree of reliability.

This high-speed, high-reliability characteristic can be used to save enormous amounts of elapsed time. Some computers can perform as many numerical calculations in an hour as a man can do in six months or more. The cost of operating a computer for an hour is considerably less than a man's salary for six months (even at "coolie" wages). Even more important, however, is the fact that computers can be used to do jobs where there is not enough skilled manpower to accomplish the task in the time available.

The information received, stored, and processed by a computer is expressed in a machine code or language. Internally, this "language" is composed of electrical signals. Information in other forms—for example, the patterns of holes on a punched card—is converted by the input devices of computers into the appropriate patterns of electrical signals to be used inside the machine. The output devices of the computer can use the electrical signals that come out of the central processing portion of the system to cause the printing of the proper symbols, and thus convert the information back to a form that can be read directly by the human eye. Other types of output devices can convert the electrical language into holes in punched cards, magnetized spots on magnetic tape, or even displays on the face of a tube like those used in television sets.

The ability of the computer to communicate with the outside world in the form of electrical signals implies that this new kind of processing system can readily accept information coming to it from a variety of sources and from a variety of media. The ability to communicate via electrical signal further implies that one can communicate with a computer between different buildings by cables, or over any distance through various communication links.

The computer is able to make certain elementary types of decisions. It may not exercise judgment, but it may determine whether or not selected criteria apply in a given case, and decide what to do next (choosing from several prespecified alternatives) in accordance with these determinations.

The decisions that are made by a computer are made solely on the basis of the rules that the human planner and programmer provides in advance. It is able to carry out what it is programmed to do, including making choices between alternate courses of action depending on tests that it makes on the data being processed. It furthermore is able to make these limited decisions consistently.

The ability of the computer to make routine yes/no decisions gives it significant flexibility, permitting it to carry out different processing operations in accordance with its previous results. Thus, if a word cannot be found in a dictionary, the program can direct the computer to the sequence of processing operations that will cause this fact to be printed.

The computer provides for large-capacity and compact data storage. For example, less than one inch of magnetic tape will hold processed information equivalent to that which can be stored in the 80 columns of a punched card. A typical reel of magnetic tape used with many present-day computers is ½ inch wide and 1 foot in diameter, yet it stores the same amount of information as 30,000 to 50,000 punched cards. The contents of the present volume could easily be stored on one of these reels.

There is therefore a definite reduction in the space necessary to store information now contained in files and records of all types. The reels are lightweight, can easily be carried from place to place, and, if dropped, do not require the reassembly or checking of the order to be sure that none of the individual records has been lost or misplaced, as would be the case if a tray of punched cards had been dropped.

In addition to providing large-capacity data-storage media, the computer also provides high-speed selection and retrieval of the information. For information that is stored in the high-speed internal storage portion of the computer, typically about 100,000 characters of information at any one time, a desired record can be selected in a few millionths of a second. For information stored in auxiliary external storage such as on a magnetic drum, a desired record can be selected in a hundredth of a second or less. For information that is stored on magnetic tape, one or more desired records located at random on the reel can be retrieved in two or three minutes. In some computers, there is provision for tape search to proceed concurrently with other operations on the central computer until the desired records have been found. There may also be provision for simultaneous search of several units.

Finally, the characteristics of the computer together produce a major feature: its adaptability to a wide variety of conditions affecting data origination and accumulation and to a wide variety of processes that can be combined and consolidated in the efficient transmission and utilization of data to serve many organizational objectives. Related to this adaptability is the computer's versatility in the multitudinous processing tasks that can be performed by a single system, ranging from file maintenance and routine computations to the syntactic and semantic analysis of language for translation purposes. The computer is also capable of fast changeover from one task to another or taking on peak workloads by extra shift operation, and it can be expanded through the addition of components in an integrated system.

ADVANTAGES OF COMPUTERS FOR NATURAL-LANGUAGE-DATA PROCESSING

The characteristics of the computer—its self-sequencing ability, high speed, ability to carry out routine decisions, ability to receive and transmit information in a variety of media and formats, ability to select and retrieve stored information at high speed, and its multipurpose adaptability—have many important implications for natural-language-data processing.

In general, the benefits that may be expected from a carefully planned and carefully organized application of computers may be outlined as follows:

Increased speed
- By providing faster, more accurate and more pertinent data, designed to meet specific requirements
- By increasing the rate of information flow

Increased accuracy
- By having more data accessible
- By having pertinent data accessible sooner
- By reducing human handling and therefore human error
- By leaving fewer routine decisions to clerical personnel
- By relieving the language specialist of routine work and making more of his time available to handle more challenging problems

Increased economy
- Single runs yielding a variety of products such as translations, abstracts, and indices at minimum processing cost
- Reduction in number of operating steps

CODED REPRESENTATION OF INFORMATION

The binary number system is fundamental in the operation of all computers. This is because simpler and more reliable circuits can be built with two-state devices (e.g., diodes) than with multistate components. In many computers, all numbers are represented by their binary equivalents, and operations on the numbers are performed on the binary equivalents. Although from an engineering standpoint such operations are simple, the process of converting problems stated in decimal language to their equivalents in binary language is not by any means a trivial programming task. It is largely for this reason that many computers use what is called a binary-coded decimal language for representing numbers.

With four bits (i.e., binary digits) we can represent 16 quantities (the numbers 0 to 15). Suppose, then, that we want to represent some decimal number in a binary-coded decimal computer. Let us agree that for every decimal digit we shall use the corresponding four binary digit representation. A number such as 529 would then become

```
0101 0010 1001
  5    2    9
```

in a binary-coded decimal computer. The electronic circuitry for operating on such a coded representation of a decimal number is considerably more complicated than that needed for operating on a straight binary number.

One of the important characteristics of a computer is its ability to process alphabetical information as well as numerical information. Numerous coding systems can be devised for representing alphabetical as well as numerical information. If we allow six bits for each alphanumerical character (i.e., a decimal digit or a letter), then we can have up to 64 symbols represented. This is done as follows: If the first two bits are 00, then the remaining four constitute the binary-coded decimal representation of a number as described above. If the first two bits are 01, the remaining four bits represent the first nine letters of the alphabet; if they are 10, the next nine letters of the alphabet; and if they are 11, the last eight letters of the alphabet.

We are all familiar with many applications of computers. Generally, these applications involve operations that are arithmetic in nature; however, this should not lead us to conclude that it is possible only to do arithmetical operations with a computer. In fact, some of the greatest flexibility of the system may be demonstrated by its capacity to manipulate not only numerical information but also, for example, alphabetic information or combinations of the two.

As described above, the computer can represent strings of alphabetical symbols by binary numbers. These binary numbers can be manipulated in many useful ways. For example, a computer can sequence alphabetical entities. To do this, the computer need only compare the two numerical representations of alphabetical entities. Suppose we had the words BOY and BOYS. These two words are unequal numerically. That is, the word BOY when represented as a binary number would be a smaller number than the word BOYS. Therefore, the computer could be used to indicate that the word BOY is to occur earlier in an alphabetical sorting (if that is what is to be performed).

Although the most common use of a computer is for the manipulation of alphabetical and numerical quantities, the computer can also manipulate any other symbols representable by binary numbers.

DECISION-MAKING OR LOGICAL OPERATIONS

The most important operation that a computer can perform for language-data processing is that of making an elementary decision. In the operation of a computer, instructions are processed at an exceedingly fast rate. Therefore, it is very often important that the computer be able, at any point in its computation, to decide between alternative courses of action. For example, in a scientific computation, it is often necessary at a certain point to inspect a numerical quantity and to perform one of two alternative actions depending on whether the quantity lies within or outside a given range.

This decision-making operation can be accomplished quite simply. Suppose two numbers are to be compared. If the first number is less than or equal to the second, we want the computer to perform one course of action, and if the first number is greater than the second, we want it to take a second alternative. The computer can determine this in a very simple way. For example, it may subtract one number from the other and inspect the answer, noticing whether it is positive or negative. Depending on whether the sign is positive or negative, the computer takes one or the other of the two available courses of action.

We must emphasize here the importance of this decision-making or logical operation in a computer. It is generally not possible to anticipate the exact condition that will exist at a specific point in a computation. Almost always, however, when planning a computation for the system to perform, it is possible to set up certain criteria which the computer can use for determining its course of action. Therefore, decision-making operations are used where the programmer knows ahead of time the conditions under which he wants the computer to perform specified sets of actions. He intersperses among the data-generation operations the decision-making operations that tell it under what conditions to do different types of actions and generate different types of data. It is the combination of the elementary arithmetical operations with, perhaps, elementary information-handling operations, all under the control of decision-making operations, that enables the computer to perform long computations automatically without the necessity for intervening and stopping the computation at each crucial or test point.

PLANNING THE USE OF A COMPUTER

Presently available computers can be used to solve a large class of problems well. But the application of these new tools can be ineffective and costly unless the particular problem has been carefully planned and defined, analyzed and organized in the light of both the advantages and limitations of the new equipment. In particular, the premature "computerization" of procedures, far from bringing about the benefits that might be expected, may actually set back progress for several years.

There are four steps to be followed in planning the utilization of a computer for a research program. As a first step we should perform a detailed examination of our basic needs to provide a sound over-all knowledge of both the basic objectives of the program and of the interrelationships of the functions that will produce these objectives as a guide to establishing a comprehensive development program. Secondly, effective utilization will require the systematic exploration of the possible areas for introduction of the new tools, with some idea of what these tools can do and how they do it. Third, detailed consideration should be given to the consolidation of functions, procedures, and data so as to provide maximum utilization of information each time it is handled. Finally, we should look for those things which we cannot do effectively at present, and determine whether they can be achieved as products of a coordinated processing system.

One should not attempt to use a computer until the problem has been analyzed in terms of a well-defined, detailed, and specific set of steps to take for a solution. One should also be wary of using computer hardware without first having some factual basis for anticipating a direct or indirect saving in time, cost, or manpower, or for expecting some other benefits.

EXPRESSING THE PROBLEM TO THE COMPUTER

In expressing any problem to a computer, it is necessary to select and define the problem, to analyze and reorganize it for solution by automatic processing techniques. The problem must be broken down into the detailed steps which would enable fifth graders to solve it, the conditions for processing must be specified, the methods, techniques, and equipment to be used must be selected, and finally the problem in all its detail must be expressed in the specific language of the selected processing system.

The first phase of expressing a problem to the computer, the planning of the work, is the most challenging to the researcher. While he may never need to know much about the logical design or the components of a computing system and may never be required to prepare a machine program, the researcher will necessarily be faced with the question of how best to utilize the equipment. There is an inescapable management responsibility in planning the work and in appreciating the time and effort that is required to translate the plans into specific procedures and programs leading to productive runs.

PROGRAMMING

Once the rigorous work of problem definition, analysis, and specification has been carried through to the point of identifying the machine processes involved, the problem must be expressed in the detailed language appropriate for the computer system selected. This process, called *programming,* is best discussed in parts: program planning, flowcharting, and the actual composition of the program.

Program planning is concerned with defining the computation objectives, data formats, and operational sequences to be achieved in the various runs. Next, a list of required programs is developed. Each program in turn is examined to determine whether there are operations or functions that are used repeatedly. To avoid writing a routine for this type of operation each time it appears, a single subroutine is prepared, if not already available in a program library, and used whenever required.

Then, for each program, a program flowchart is developed. This sets forth in diagrammatic form the sequence of computer operations. From the flowchart one can see the actual sequence of operations to be performed by the computer and their relationships to each other. The flowchart is of great use in composing the sequence of machine instructions.

We shall illustrate the process of developing sequences of machine instructions with a simple example. The programs will be shown as they might be written for the IBM 7090 computer systems. Instead of using 7090 machine language, we shall use the standard symbolic language for this machine (*cf.* "Computer Languages"). Although this language is not the actual machine language, it is easier to use because the symbols involved are more easily assimilated by humans than the numerical machine code. In practice, such symbolic coding is transformed into machine language (code) by a program called a compiler. As our example we will assume that 10 pairs of numbers stored in memory locations DATA through DATA + 19 are to be added and the sums placed in locations SUM through SUM + 9. (For a similar discussion, *cf.* "Programming Aspects of Machine Translation" later in this volume.) A possible program to accomplish this task is shown in Table 1.

TABLE 1

Memory location	*Operation*	*Address*
START	CLA (clear and add)	DATA
	ADD (add)	DATA + 1
	STØ (store)	SUM
	CLA	DATA + 2
	ADD	DATA + 3
	STØ	SUM + 1
	CLA	DATA + 4
	ADD	DATA + 5
	STØ	SUM + 2
	CLA	DATA + 6
	ADD	DATA + 7
	STØ	SUM + 3
	. . .	. . .
	CLA	DATA + 18
	ADD	DATA + 19
	STØ	SUM + 9

However, computers have the important property of allowing the program to modify the command list. If we exploit this feature, we can obtain the more compact list of instructions shown in Table 2.

TABLE 2

Memory location	*Operation*	*Address*
START	AXT (set index register)	10, 1
	AXT	20, 2
	CLA	DATA + 20, 2
	ADD	DATA + 21, 2
	STØ	SUM + 10, 1
	TXI (modify index register)	START + 6, 2, —2
	TIX (transfer on index)	START + 3, 1, 1

The first two instructions set the values 10 and 20 into index registers 1 and 2 respectively. The next three instructions (CLA, ADD, STØ) perform the desired operation, except that specifying an index register causes its contents to be subtracted from the address of the operand before the operation takes place. Thus the first time through, these instructions are interpreted as follows:

START + 3	CLA	DATA [(DATA + 20) — 20]
+ 4	ADD	DATA + 1 [(DATA + 21) — 20]
+ 5	STØ	SUM [(SUM + 10) — 10]

The next instruction lowers the value of index register 2 by 2. This will cause the third and fourth instructions to operate on the next two data items. The final instruction in the sequence checks to see if index register 1 is still greater than 1. If it is, the value of index register 1 is reduced by 1 and the instruction transfers to START + 2. If it is not, then all the additions have been performed and the computer proceeds to the next instruction.

This simple example illustrates modification of instructions, a conditional transfer of control, and one form of an iterative loop.

The straightforward approach to the problem yielded thirty instructions to be stored and executed. The iterative approach produced seven instructions to be stored and fifty-two instructions to be executed. In general it is possible to exchange computing time for storage space and vice versa. Evaluating the relative merits of efficient storage versus minimum running time requires a detailed knowledge of both the problems to be solved and the machine to be used.

We have attempted here to condition the researcher in linguistics to think of computers as valuable tools for handling a very broad class of problems. With the proper approach and handling these tools are capable of producing remarkable results. The machines are not magical and are not "geniuses." They are better classified as high-speed, reliable "idiots." They must be carefully instructed on every step of their computation. They have no insight into the problems they are solving except that which the human mind can codify in a form that the machine can utilize. This places a heavy burden on the researcher to design his study with enough detail and completeness so that valuable machine resources are not wasted. If we ignore the contribution computers are making to linguistic studies, the deep analysis of problem areas that is necessary to permit automatic processing would still be a highly desirable end in itself.

Language-data processing

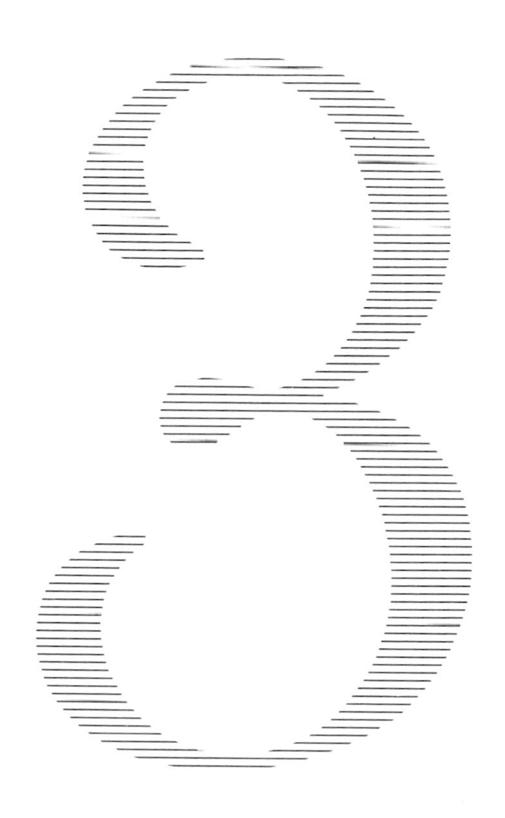

PAUL L. GARVIN

A linguist's view of language-data processing

Language-data processing is a relatively new field of endeavor. As with all new fields, the exact area it covers is not completely defined. Even the term *language-data processing* is not yet generally accepted, although its use is increasing.

The definition of the field of language-data processing given here includes the application of any data-processing equipment to natural-language text—that is, not only the application of computing machinery, but also the application of the less powerful punched-card and tabulating equipment. It may even be reasonable to say that a purely intellectual procedure for the treatment of language data, which by its rigor and logic attempts to simulate, or allow for, the application of data-processing equipment, is a form of language-data processing, or at least a data-processing approach to language analysis.

From a linguist's standpoint two purposes can be served by language-data processing:

The first of these is linguistic analysis, which will ultimately and ideally include the use of data-processing equipment to obtain analytic linguistic results.

The second purpose is the use of language-data processing in information handling, where linguistics is auxiliary to the major objective. Here language-data processing is of interest for applied linguistics. It is also of interest as an area in which the usefulness and perhaps even the validity of analytic linguistic results can be tested.

Concretely, language-data processing for linguistic analysis will primarily include *automatic linguistic analysis* or at least automatic aids or automatic preliminaries to linguistic analysis. Language-data processing for information handling includes such fields as machine translation, information storage and retrieval (if based on natural language), automatic abstracting, certain intelligence applications, and the like. All these activities can be summed up under the heading of *linguistic information processing*. The two aspects of language-data processing are related in that the results of the former can be utilized in the latter. Sometimes this is not only desirable but necessary.

The area of linguistic information processing can be divided into two major subareas: (1) machine translation; and (2) information retrieval, automatic abstracting, and related activities, all of which may be summarized under the heading of *content processing*. There are two criteria for this division. One is the degree to which the results of linguistic analysis are considered necessary for the purpose. In machine translation none of the serious workers in the field will deny the usefulness of linguistic analysis or linguistic information; on the other hand, a number of approaches to information retrieval and automatic abstracting are based on statistical considerations, and linguistics is considered a useful but not essential ingredient.

Another criterion by which to distinguish between the two subareas of this field is more interesting from the linguist's standpoint. This is the manner in which the content of the document is to be utilized. In machine translation the major objective is to recognize the content of a document in order to render it in another language. In content processing the recognition is only the first step. The principal objective here is to evaluate the content in order to process it further for a given purpose. This evaluation requires the automatic inclusion of some kind of relevance criterion by means of which certain portions of the document can be highlighted and other portions can be ignored. The criterion for such an evaluation in the case of information retrieval seems to be the comparability of each particular document to those of a related set; common features and differences can serve as a basis for an index in terms of which information can be retrieved in response to a request. In automatic abstracting, various portions of the document are compared and on the basis of their relative significance are retained or omitted from the condensed version.

It is apparent that the evaluation of content poses a somewhat more complex problem for the investigator than its mere recognition. It is not surprising, therefore, that the linguistic contributions to content processing have so far been much less conclusive than the contributions that linguists have made to machine translation. It is on the other hand equally apparent, at least to the linguist, that a linguistic approach has an important contribution to make to content processing, especially if a product of high quality is desired.

It is also worth noting in this connection that important negative opinions have been voiced with regard to both aspects of language-data processing. N. Chomsky, whose approach to language was presented earlier by Stockwell in "The Transformational Model of Generative or Predictive Grammar," takes the strong position that a discovery procedure—that is, a fixed set of rules for the discovery of relevant elements—

is not a realistic goal for a science such as linguistics. This implies, of course, that automatic linguistic analysis also is an unreasonable proposition. Y. Bar-Hillel, a well-known symbolic logician and a philosophical critic of language-data processing, takes an equally clear-cut position. In a survey of machine translation in the United States conducted on behalf of the Office of Naval Research, he made the well-known statement that fully automatic, high-quality machine translation is impossible.[1] He has voiced a similarly negative view in regard to other aspects of practical language-data processing.[2]

Needless to say, in spite of the need for objective criticism and an awareness of the difficulties involved, a more positive attitude toward the field is a prerequisite for active participation in the research.

The present discussion concerns the problems of language-data processing in both senses as related to the assumed properties of natural language. We shall follow the problem through the system by going from input to internal phase. We shall not consider the mechanics of the output, since at present linguistics has little or no contribution to make to this question. More detailed attention will be given to those areas of the field which are not covered elsewhere in this volume.

AUTOMATIC SPEECH RECOGNITION AND CHARACTER RECOGNITION

All present-day language-data-processing activities use the conventional input mechanisms of punched card, punched-paper tape, magnetic tape, or the like. This is generally considered to be a major bottleneck in terms of practicality since the cost, especially for the large quantities of input that are desirable for eventual production, is prohibitive. A good deal of effort in various places is therefore directed toward automating the input.

To accommodate the two usual manifestations of the sign components of languages—the phonetic and the graphic—efforts toward automating input proceed in two directions: *automatic speech recognition* and *automatic character recognition*. The purpose is to design a perceptual device which will be capable of identifying either spoken or written signals for transposition into the machine code required by a computer. Needless to say, this objective is of considerable interest to the linguist, and linguistics has a significant potential contribution to make, especially in the case of speech recognition.

The problem in speech recognition is one of identifying, within the total acoustic output of the human voice or its mechanical reproduction, those elements which are significant for communication. The difficulty

[1] Y. Bar-Hillel, "The Present Status of Automatic Translation of Languages," in F. L. Alt (ed.), *Advances in Computers*, New York, London, 1960, pp. 91–163.

[2] Y. Bar-Hillel, "Some Theoretical Aspects of the Mechanization of Literature Searching," in Walter Hoffman (ed.), *Digital Information Processors*, Interscience Publishers, New York, 1962, pp. 406–443.

of the problem becomes apparent when one realizes that most phoneticians agree that only a small portion of the total energy in the human voice output (some claim as little as 1 per cent) is utilized for purposes of the linguistic signal proper. The remaining energy serves as a signal for such nonlinguistic elements as the identification of the sex and individuality of the speaker, his state of health (whether or not he has a cold), his emotional state, and a large number of other behavorial indices. Thus, the acoustic power available for purposes of speech recognition appears to be rather small. The significant fact here is that this small percentage tends to be masked by the rest. The second difficulty is that the natural vocal signal is semicontinuous; that is, the number of physically observable breaks in the continuity of the stream of human speech is much smaller than the number of discrete elements into which the signal may be decomposed in either alphabetic writing or linguistic analysis.

The problem in phonemic analysis is one of transposing a semicontinuous natural signal into a series of discrete elements. To give an example, a short utterance such as *time* is revealed by acoustic instruments to consist of essentially two distinct physical portions: a burst following a pause representing the element /*t*/, and a set of harmonic elements extending over a given period and with no observable major interruptions. In terms of phonemic analysis, on the other hand, the utterance *time* is usually interpreted to consist of four discrete units: the phonemes /*t*/, /*a*/, /*y*/, and /*m*/. The method by which the phonemic analyst arrives at this decomposition of the continuous span into its presumed underlying components is one of comparison, based on his assumptions about the dimensional structure of language. The /*t*/ is isolated by comparing *time* to *dime;* the /*a*/ is isolated by comparing *time* with *team;* the /*y*/ is isolated by comparing *time* to *town;* and the /*m*/ is isolated by comparing *time* to *tide*. The analyst gains his initial knowledge of the speech signal from his interpretation of what he hears. Not until an initial description of the elementary discrete units has been obtained does the analyst proceed to investigate the structure of phonemic fused units of a higher order of complexity such as syllables or the phonemic analogs of orthographic words.

It is not unreasonable to suppose, on the other hand, that an ideal speech-recognition device may deal directly with the semicontinuous *phonetic stretches* that are observable in the stream of speech, and that may turn out to correspond, roughly or precisely, to the fused units of phonemic analysis. The preceptual mechanism which would constitute the first component of such a device would then have to meet two objectives: first, to recognize pertinent points of interruption in the stream of speech in order to find the boundaries of the phonetic stretches; and second, to recognize, within the total energy spectrum of the human vocal signal, those particular acoustic features of each stretch that are relevant to the transmission of the spoken message.

The present state of speech recognition resembles the early stages of phonemic analysis in the sense that experiments so far have been largely limited to machine perception of short isolated stretches comparable to the short isolated examples elicited by an analyst in the beginning of his work. Just as in phonemics these short examples are used to determine an initial inventory of vowels and consonants, so the present speech-recognition work on short stretches is directed toward an identification of vocalic and consonantal features. Even in this limited framework, progress has so far resulted in the identification of only some of the gross acoustic features, such as the break between syllables, the friction component of certain consonants, and the voicing component of vowels and certain consonants. More refined identifications can be expected as acoustic research progresses, and an adequate capability for identifying isolated phonetic stretches is quite conceivable.

Little attention has been given so far to machine recognition of the interruptions in the continuity of the stream of speech that linguists call *junctures*. Linguistic and acoustic research on the phonetic characteristics of junctures will undoubtedly make significant contributions to this aspect of speech recognition.

Assuming that a perception mechanism can acquire the capability of recognizing both the boundaries and the characteristic features of the phonetic stretches of normal speech, there still remains a significant phase of speech recognition which goes beyond the perceptual. From the stretches that have been recognized, the complete device must in some way compute a linguistically relevant input for the internal phase of the data-processing system; that is, the speech-recognition device, after having identified phonetic stretches on the basis of their perceptual characteristics, must transform them into strings of linguistic signs—morphemes. For practical purposes the device might have to transform sound types not into morphemes, but into printed words or their binary representations.

Consider the problem in terms of an immediate application of speech recognition: the *voicewriter*. This device is intended to transmit the spoken message to a typewriter to obtain as output a typewritten version of the message.

It is clear that a good many of the pecularities of a typewritten document, even not counting problems presented by orthography in the narrower sense, are not directly contained as vocal signals in the spoken message. These details would include paragraphing, capitalization, and punctuation. In dictation such features of the document are either left to the secretary or indicated by editorial comments. Thus, even assuming a functioning perception mechanism, some provision would have to be made for details of this type—for instance, a capacity for receiving and executing verbal orders similar to the editorial comments for the secretary.

The problems posed by the orthography in the narrower sense—that is, the actual spelling conventions for particular words—vary to the extent that the writing system deviates from the spoken form of the language. It becomes a translation problem, comparable to the problem of translating by machine from one language to another. The same spoken form may well correspond to more than one written form, and this ambiguity then has to be resolved by context searching, which is a syntactic operation analogous to its equivalent in machine translation. Thus, assuming that the perception mechanism has identified a phonetic stretch */riyd/*, the voicewriter may have to represent it in typescript as either *reed* or *read,* depending on whether it occurred in a sentence dealing with *a reed in the wind* or a sentence dealing with *reading.*

An additional context-searching routine, comparable to the "missing-word routines" used in machine translation for dealing with words that are not found in the machine dictionary, will probably have to be included for the identification of "poor" phonetic stretches—that is, those that do not have enough signal strength or are not pronounced clearly enough to be recognizable by the perception mechanism.

At the present state of the art is appears that it may not be necessary to go through a three-step computation sequence from phonetic stretches to phonemes to morphemes or written words, but that a direct computation of morphemes or written words from phonetic stretches can be envisioned. This computation would be carried out by means of a dictionary of phonetic stretches stored in memory, to be processed by appropriate ambiguity-resolution and missing-form routines. (This conception of the linguistic aspects of the speech-recognition problem stems from Madeleine Mathiot, personal communication.)

The problem of character recognition is by comparison somewhat less complex, because—unless one thinks of a device for recognizing handwriting—the visual input into the device is discrete—that is, it can be expected to consist of separately printed or typed letters or characters. Thus, the very difficult speech-recognition problem of recognizing the boundaries of stretches within a semicontinuous signal does not exist for character recognition. On the other hand, the problem of recognizing what particular features of the signal—in terms of strokes, angles, curves, directions, and the like—are relevant to the function of the character is similar to the problem of recognizing the linguistically relevant acoustic features of speech. A further advantage of character recognition is that no computation is required to give orthographic representation to the visual signal, since the signal is orthographic to begin with. Linguists have generally given much less thought to the structure of writing systems in terms of their differentiating characteristics than they have to the phonological structure of speech and its relevant distinctive features. Thus, the linguistic contribution to the field of character recognition has been quite trivial so far. It seems that the recognition of relevant properties of shape such as the ones enumerated above is closely related to the problem of recognizing visual shapes in general, and therefore is less closely related to linguistics than is the problem of speech recognition.

Where linguistics can make a contribution is in the recognition of poorly printed or otherwise unrecognizable characters, for the gaps in the recognition string will have to be filled by a context-searching routine similar in principle to that required for speech recognition.

One of the fundamental difficulties in the area of character recognition seems to be variety of fonts that are used in ordinary print and typing. Devices which are limited to a single font—particularly if that font has been specifically designed to facilitate the operation of the device—are now in an operational stage. On the other hand, devices which can deal with a multiplicity of fonts, particularly fonts with which the device has had no prior "experience," are still in their infancy. Some experiments have already yielded data about those characteristics which different fonts have in common and on which a common recognition routine can be based. Work is in progress on the particular perceptive mechanisms which could optimally serve to recognize these characteristics. In this respect, the field of character recognition appears to be closer to practical results than the field of speech recognition.

AUTOMATIC LINGUISTIC ANALYSIS

From a linguist's standpoint, the internal phase of language-data processing involves two types of activities: automatic linguistic analysis on the one hand and linguistic information processing on the other.

An automatic linguistic-analysis program is here defined as a computer program which, given as input a body of text, will produce as output a linguistic description of the system of the natural language represented by the text. A corollary capability of such a program will be the capacity for deciding whether or not a given input indeed constitutes a text in a natural language.

As discussed earlier in "The Definitional Model of Language," we can conceive of the system of a language as an orderly aggregate of various kinds of elements, each of which has a finite and typical set of cooccurrence possibilities with regard to other elements of the system. The elements are of different functional types and orders of complexity, as exemplified by such elements of written English as letters, syllables, words, or phrases. These elements recur in texts in a regular way, so as to form *distribution* classes in terms of shared cooccurrence characteristics.

Here the purpose of linguistic analysis is to specify the nature and boundaries of the various types and orders of elements, as well as to describe the cooccurrence patterns serving as the criteria for the definition of the distribution classes, and to list the membership of these classes. The former aspect of linguistic analysis is often termed *segmentation,* the latter is called *distributional analysis.*

Linguistic segmentation is the first step in the analysis of raw text—that is, spoken messages recorded from native informants. Segmentation procedures are based on the relation between the form (i.e., the phonetic shape) and the meaning (in operational terms, the translation or possible paraphrase) of the message. Their mechanization thus would require the comparative processing of two inputs—one representing the phonetic shape of the raw text and the other its translation or paraphrase.

A program designed for a single rather than a dual input hence cannot be expected to accomplish segmentation. We can therefore suggest that the initial inventory of elementary units not be compiled automatically, but that the automatic processing of the text for purposes of linguistic analysis use a previously segmented input consisting of units already delimited. This could be a text segmented into morphemic segments by a linguistic analyst or, the more practical alternative, a text in conventional spelling with orthographic word boundaries marked by spaces, and punctuation indicating certain other boundaries. The type of linguistic analysis to be performed on this previously segmented input would then be one of classifying the elementary input units on the basis of their relevant cooccurrence properties. That is, automatic linguistic analysis would essentially be a distributional analysis by a computer program.

The intended output of such a distributional analysis program would be a dictionary listing of all the elements (for instance, all the printed words) found to recur in the input text, with each element in the listing accompanied by a grammar code reflecting the distributional description of the element in terms of the distribution class and subclass to which it belongs. Since the purpose of the program thus is to produce a grammar-coded dictionary listing, it is logically necessary to require that the program itself initially contain no dictionary or grammar code, but only the routines required for their compilation.

The basic question of distributional analysis is: does unit *a* occur in environment *b*? This question can be answered by a computer program. The problem is primarily one of specifying automatically what units *a* the question is to be asked about, and what environments *b* are to be considered in arriving at an answer.

In ordinary linguistic analysis, informant responses are evaluated and text is examined "manually" in order to arrive at distributional descriptions by using the diagnostic contexts which are discussed in "The Definitional Model of Language." The difficulty of informant work, as all linguists know, is the element of subjectivity inherent in the use of a human informant. This subjectivity is maximized by using one's own self as an informant; it may be minimized by circumscribing the test situation very narrowly and by using a variety of informants, as well as other controls. However, as the questions become more sophisticated, the informant's responses become more and more difficult to control and his memory becomes less and less reliable. Thus, even in ordinary linguistic analysis one reaches a point where informant work has to be combined with the study of text.

The basic difficulty in the use of text for purposes of linguistic analysis is that large samples are required. This is understandable if one takes into account the inverse ratio of the recurrence of elements to the size of sample: The less frequently an element recurs, the larger the sample required in order to study its distributional properties. Data-processing equipment allows the processing of very large bodies of text using the same program. At the present time, lack of speech- or character-recognition devices is the greatest practical bottleneck requiring considerable expense at the input end for keypunching or related purposes.

From the linguist's standpoint, these difficulties are balanced primarily by the advantage of the increased reliability of data-processing equipment and the possibility of attaining a rigor hitherto not customary in the field. Once costs can be brought down, there is the promise of an ultimate operational capability for processing much larger samples of language than the linguist can ever hope to examine manually. Finally, even without access to extensive programming and computer time, a partial implementation of automatic analysis can be expected to yield interesting results.

A fully automatic distributional analysis program can be looked upon as a heuristic rather than a purely algorithmic problem. A. L. Samuel has set forth some of the characteristics of an intellectual activity in which heuristic procedures and learning processes can play a major role. As applied to the problem of playing checkers, these are as follows:[3]

1 The activity must not be deterministic in the practical sense. There exists no known algorithm which will guarantee a win or draw in checkers, and the complete exploitations of every possible path through a checker game would involve perhaps 10^{40} choices of moves which, at 3 choices per millimicrosecond, would still take 10^{21} centuries to consider.

2 A definite goal must exist—the winning of the game—and at least

[3]A. L. Samuels, "Some Studies in Machine Learning Using the Game of Checkers," *IBM Journal of Research and Development*, pp. 211–212, July, 1959. Quoted by permission.

one criterion of intermediate goal must exist which has bearing on the achievement of the final goal and for which the sign should be known. . . .

3 The rules of the activity should be definite and they should be known. . . .

4 There should be a background of knowledge of the activity against which the learning progress can be tested.

5 The activity should be one that is familiar to a substantial body of people so that the behavior of the program can be made understandable to them. . . .

The above criteria seem to be applicable to automatic linguistic analysis as well, paraphrased as follows:

1 Linguistic analysis is not deterministic in the practical sense. There exists no known algorithm which will guarantee success in linguistic analysis, and the complete exploitation of every possible combinatory criterion might involve an equally astronomical number of steps as the number of moves to be explored in a checkers algorithm.

2 A definite goal does exist—a detailed distributional statement—and criteria can be formulated for intermediate goals that have bearing on the achievement of the final goal. These would be the broader distributional statements from which the ultimate, more refined classifications can be derived. Unlike checkers, the final goal can not be formulated as simply.

3 The rules of the activity are definite and can be formulated. This, of course, presupposes that one accepts as a basic assumption the possibility of linguistic discovery procedures. The procedures discussed in "The Definitional Model of Language" are those of substitution and dropping; they can be made computable, and they may be introduced into the heuristic linguistic-analysis program after certain necessary preliminary steps have been completed. Other equally computable procedures can be formulated.

4 There is, of course, a background of knowledge of the activity against which the machine results are tested: Linguistic analysis is, or can be made into, an established field and machine results can be compared to human results.

5 Although the activity of linguistic analysis is not one that is familiar to a substantial body of people, its results nonetheless can be compared to the intuitive behavior of an entire speech commuunity, and the behavior of the program can be explicated in terms of this observed intuitive behavior.

It is thus possible to envision a computer program which will process the initially segmented text by applying to it a variety of linguistic analytic procedures, and will evaluate the results of each trial on the basis of certain built-in statistical or otherwise computable criteria. The program, operating in an alternation of such trial and evaluation routines, can be expected to accept certain trials and reject others on the basis of these criteria. The results of the initial tests performed by the program can then be utilized for the automatic formulation of additional tests leading to a more refined classification, until the potential of the program is exhausted and the output can be printed out for inspection by a competent linguistic evaluator.

Such a program will be particularly interesting for the analysis of languages in which word classes—that is, parts of speech—are not easily definable and where conspicuous formal marks of syntactic relations are either absent or infrequent. Examples of such languages are Chinese and English.[4]

MACHINE TRANSLATION

Let us now turn from automatic linguistic analysis to linguistic information processing. The activities in the latter field can be divided into two major categories: machine translation on the one hand and content processing on the other.

Prior to machine translation, descriptive linguists were mostly concerned with the formal features of language and considered linguistic meaning only to the extent to which it has bearing on formal distinctions. In translation on the other hand—both human and machine translation—meaning becomes the primary subject of interest. Relations between forms are no longer dealt with for their own sake; they are now treated in terms of the function they have as carriers of meaning. Meaning is granted an independent theoretical existence of a sort, since it is only by assuming a content as separate from the form of a particular language that one can decide whether a passage in one language is indeed the translation of a passage in another language: they are if they both express the same, or at least roughly the same, content; they are not if they do not.

In the process of translation the expression of the content in one language is replaced by the expression of an equivalent content in another. To mechanize the process, the recognition of the content in its first expression, the *source language,* must be mechanized; then the command can be generated to give the same content another linguistic expression in the *target language.* A machine-translation program must therefore contain a *recognition routine* to accomplish the first objective, and a

[4]For the detailed discussion of a proposed program of automatic linguistic analysis, see Paul L. Garvin, "Automatic Linguistic Analysis—a Heuristic Problem", *1961 International Conference on Machine Translation of Languages and Applied Language Analysis,* vol. 2, pp. 655–669, London, 1962.

command routine to accomplish the second. Since the command routine presupposes the recognition routine and not conversely, a "recognition grammar" of this sort is more essential for purposes of machine translation than a "generative grammar."

For recognition of the content of the source document, the machine-translation program has to take into account, and can take advantage of, the structural properties of the language in which the content is originally expressed. In a sense, one structural property has already been accounted for by the nature of the input: the two levels of structuring, the graphemic and the morphemic, are utilized in the input by sensing the text letter by letter and recognizing spaces, punctuation marks, and special symbols. The graphemic input then has to be processed for morphemic recognition: the program has to ascertain what content-bearing element is represented by each combination of letters—that is, printed word between spaces—that has been sensed at the input. In order to effect this identification, the program can and must draw on the other two sets of levels of natural language: the two levels of organization, and the levels of integration.

The two levels of organization, those of selection and arrangement, are represented in the program by the *machine dictionary* and the *translation algorithm* respectively. It is obvious that in order to produce a non-ridiculous translation, a program must contain not only a dictionary but also an algorithm. The function of the algorithm is dual: it must select from several possible dictionary equivalents that which is applicable to the particular sentence to be translated; it also must achieve the rearrangement of the words of the translation, whenever this is necessary in order to give the appropriate expression to the content of the original. To make possible the generation of these selection and rearrangement commands, the algorithm must be capable of recognizing the syntactic and other conditions under which these commands are necessary and appropriate. For this recognition to be effective, the levels of integration of the language—that is, the fused units of varying orders of complexity—have to be taken into account. Fused units have to be identified as to their boundaries and functions. The details of this problem are discussed later in "Syntax in Machine Translation."

In an early theoretical paper on machine translation by this author[5] the statement was made that "The extent of machine translatability is limited by the amount of information contained within the same sentence." Since the sentence is the maximum domain of necessary linguistic relationships, a translation algorithm based on fixed linguistic rules appears to be limited to this domain. Later experience has shown that such

[5]Paul L. Garvin, "Some Linguistic Problems in Machine Translation," *For Roman Jakobson,* 's-Gravenhage, 1956, pp. 180–186.

deterministic rules are, however, not the only possible translation rules. In order to deal with relations across sentence boundaries, it is necessary to assume that in addition to deterministic rules, *probabilistic rules* can be found, the span of which is not limited to the sentence. To make the distinction clear: a deterministic rule is one which under one ascertainable set of conditions comes up with a *yes* branch, under another set of conditions with a *no* branch; a probabilistic rule is one which bases its decision on a tabulation of a set of factors and branches off into *yes* or *no* depending on relative percentages rather than absolute conditions. Broadly speaking those translation decisions which are based on primarily grammatic conditions—that is, conditions of the cooccurrence of linguistic forms—will be largely deterministic. Decisions that are based on other conditions will be largely probabilistic. It is clear again that in terms of the actual design of a program, deterministic routines should be given precedence over probabilistic ones.

CONTENT PROCESSING

As indicated above, the field of content processing differs from machine translation in that it requires not merely the rendition of the content of the document, but its evaluation according to some relevance criterion. Evaluation in turn implies comparison of elements in terms of this relevance criterion; such a comparison then presupposes some orderly classification within the frame of which units can be selected for their comparability. The principles of classification will be discussed further below.

At several points in the flow of an information-retrieval or automatic abstracting system one may reasonably speak of the processing of the content of natural-language messages. At the input of an information-retrieval system is the user's *request for information*. If this request is phrased in natural language, it will have to be processed for transmittal to the internal phase. Systems in which the request is either stated in some *standardized language* or is reformulated manually, will not require language-data processing at this point.

The internal phase of a retrieval system consists of information from which portions relevant to the request are selected for display at the output end. The ordering system used for the storage of this information can be called a system of *indexing*, since it is comparable in purpose—though not necessarily in structure or efficiency—to the index of a file or library. This indexing system can be prepared manually, in which case only the actual searching operations within the memory are automated; if it is not prepared manually—that is, if the system is equipped for *automatic indexing*—natural language has to be processed. In this case it is the natural language of a series of documents, the informational content of which is to be stored in the memory. Needless to say, systems are possible and have been devised in which neither the formulation of the request in machine language nor the storage in indexed form is done by machine, but such systems—although of unquestioned utility for a number of purposes—are of no interest in the present framework.

Automatic abstracting by the nature of the process uses documents in natural language at the input, and the system must therefore be capable of recognizing content indices in natural-language text in order to yield at the output the required condensed representation.

In all the above it is again possible to divide the automatic process into a recognition phase and a command phase. If this is done it becomes apparent that the automatic processing of the natural language of informational requests, the automatic processing of natural-language documents for indexing, and the automatic processing of natural-language documents for abstracting all fall under the same heading of being recognition operations, with similar requirements for a recognition routine. Where they differ is essentially in their command routines. The command routine for the processing of the informational request will have to include commands for translation into a search language to be used during the search. In automatic indexing the command routine will have to consist of commands for the storage of portions of documents in appropriate memory locations corresponding to the index terms under which they can be retrieved during the search. In automatic abstracting the command routines will have to consist essentially of *accept* and *reject* commands for individual sentences, if—as is the case at the present state of the research—abstracting is in effect an activity of extracting. It is possible that a future automatic abstracting system may be capable of rewording the sentences extracted for retention in the abstract by generating natural-language text on its own in order to approximate more closely human abstracts, which have certain characteristics of continuity and readability that are absent in mere extracts. This particular final phase of automatic abstracting is the one area of language-data processing in which at the present we can visualize a genuine practical way of sentence generation by machine. This is, of course, as yet for the future, but it may turn out to be an important area of application for some of the efforts of linguists today in the formulation of generative grammars.

From the linguist's point of view, the major purpose of language-data processing as discussed above is the recognition of content for purposes of comparative evaluation. The program must ideally be capable of doing two things: it must first recognize an individual *content element* in the natural-language text (a single word or a relevant combination of words); second, it must be able to decide on some comparability criterion for each of the content elements that it has found.

In order to meet the first of these requirements, the program will have to include some features comparable in nature to those of the algorithms used in machine translation. Something like an *idiom routine* is necessary to recognize word combinations that represent single content elements, as well as provisions for the recognition of the syntactic units and relations relevant to the objective. In technical terms, the system must contain a machine dictionary equipped with a grammar code capable of calling appropriate subroutines for idiom lookup and syntactic recognition.

An additional area of the application of syntax routines to content processing has been suggested by one school of linguistics: the automatic standardization of the language of the original document. The purpose of such a set of routines would be to transform all the sentences of a document into sentences of a type exhibiting a maximally desirable structure, namely kernel sentences, as discussed earlier by Stockwell. The work now in progress under the direction of Professor Z. S. Harris at the University of Pennsylvania's Transformation and Discourse Analysis Project is, as far as I know, primarily concerned with the application of transformation theory to this objective. The aim of the work is to be able to reduce the sentence of natural-language documents to a standardized kernel shape. The assumption is that storage in this kernelized form will significantly facilitate retrieval.

To meet the second requirement, the dictionary will have to include, in addition to a grammar code, a semantic code capable of calling appropriate subroutines for content comparison and evaluation.

SEMANTIC CLASSIFICATION AND SEMANTIC CODE

In order to compare content elements to each other in terms of some relevance criterion related to the goal of the operation, whether it is processing of the request, assignment to index terms, or acceptance or rejection for the extract, these elements must be classified in terms of the content which they represent, rather than in terms of their formal co-occurrence characteristics. The semantic code will thus have to be able to refer each dictionary entry to the appropriate area of content representation—that is, to the semantic class to which it belongs. For optimal efficiency such a semantic code ought to be based on a systematic classification of content elements. Classifications of a kind can be found in existing thesauri and partial classifications can be found in synonym lists. There are two major defects in thesauri of the Roget type: one is that they usually do not contain enough of the technical terminology required for most practical content-processing purposes; the other, more serious from a linguistic standpoint, is that they are compiled purely intuitively and without adequate empirical controls, sometimes on the basis of an underlying philosophic assumption, and do not necessarily reflect the intrinsic content structure of the language which they represent. Most synonym lists have similar weaknesses.

These criticisms are based on the assumption that there may exist for each language a system of content in the same sense in which there exists the formal system that linguists deal with when they treat the various levels of a language. This assumption is not unreasonable in view of the intuitive observation that the meanings of content elements are not unrelated to each other. It is, after all, from a similar assumption of the systematic relatedness of formal elements that modern descriptive linguistics has derived its results.

It is thus possible to envision a systematization of content, or meaning, not unlike the systematization of linguistic form for which today we have the capability. It is likewise not unreasonable to assume that some of the methods which have allowed us to systematize formal linguistic relations may contribute to a systematization of content relations. The following linguistic considerations have bearing on such a systematization:

First, the basic assumption that there exists for each language a system of meanings comparable to the system of forms allows application of linguistic methods to the problem of meaning.

Second, two methodological assumptions can be made that allow the formulation of linguistic techniques for the treatment of meaning: (1) that, irrespective of theoretical controversies about the "nature" of meaning, there are two kinds of observable and operationally tractable manifestations of linguistic meaning—translation and paraphrase; and (2) that linguistic units with similar meanings will tend to occur in environments characterized by certain specifiable similarities.

The first assumption allows the formulation of techniques for semantic classification based on similarities in the translation or paraphrase of the content-bearing elements in question. In a monolingual approach, which most workers in the area of content processing would consider the only reasonable one, these would be paraphrasing techniques.

The second assumption permits the extension of linguistic techniques of distributional analysis from problems of form to problems of meaning.

In order for either type of linguistic techniques to yield significant and reliable results, the conditions affecting their application will have to be controlled and the appropriate comparison constants specified. If this is done, one may reasonably expect to arrive at a semantic classification of the content-bearing elements of a language which is inductively inferred from the study of text, rather than superimposed from some viewpoint external to the structure of the language. Such a classification can be expected to yield more reliable answers to the problems of synonymity and content representation than the existing thesauri and synonym lists.

Two directions of research can be envisioned at present: the application of a technique of paraphrasing, and the investigation of the role of context in the definition of meaning. Both lines of study can be based on prior linguistic research experience.

The paraphrasing technique can most usefully be applied to the study of the verbal elements of a language such as English. It can be based on the use of replacement predicates, limited in number and of the required semantic generality, which can be substituted for the original verbal elements found in the sample text that is to be processed.

The following example illustrates how such replacement forms can serve to define the potential semantic features of a given original form:

First rephrasing operation

Original statement: The induction and the confirmation of the theory depend on experience.

Original form: depend on

Replacement form: be based on

Resultant statement: The induction and the confirmation of the theory *are based on* experience.

Comparison property: semantic similarity

Semantic feature induced from operation: basic relation

Second rephrasing operation

Original statement: In all other cases, the magnitudes of the elements *m, r,* and *t* of the problem depend on the motion of the observer relative to point P_0.

Original form: depend on

Replacement form: vary with

Resultant statement: In all other cases, the magnitudes of the elements *m, r,* and *t* of the problem *vary with* the motion of the observer relative to point P_0.

Comparison property: semantic similarity

Semantic feature induced from operation: covariance

These operations have yielded a crude first-approximation semantic spectrum of the verbal element *depend on,* which can be represented in a manner suitable for adaptation to a semantic bit-pattern code:

Lexical unit	*Semantic features*		
	basic relation	*constituency*	*covariance . . .*
	be based on	consist of	vary with . . .
depend on	1	0	1

It is assumed that the successive application of paraphrasing operations to a large sample of text will serve to establish a series of semantic features for each verbal element that has occurred. On the basis of similarities and differences in their respective sets of features, the verbal elements can then be arranged in a systematic thesaurus. Such a thesaurus would have been inductively derived from the processing of text, and thus could be considered empirically more reliable.

Once a thesaurus of verbal elements is available, the nominal elements of the language can be classified semantically on the basis of their co-occurrence with semantic classes of verbal elements. Each nominal element in a text can then be assigned semantic features, depending on whether or not it has been found to occur as the subject or object of members of the various classes in thesaurus. This research can ultimately be automated, but first the detailed requirements for such a program must be worked out.

The application in content processing of such an empirically derived systematization of meaning is outlined below as it would apply to information retrieval.

As mentioned above, natural language has to be processed at two points in the flow of an ideal system: the inputting of requests, and the automatic assignment of document content to index terms. The latter further implies the systematic storage of the indexed information, based on a systematization of the terms to which the information has been assigned. The processing of the request, finally, has to be related to the ordering of the stored terms to permit retrieval of pertinent information. Thus, both language-data-processing operations are ultimately referred to the same semantic system. It is possible to envision this semantic system as a set of thesaurus heads and subheads, with the individual content-bearing elements of language classed under the lowest subheads, each of which will include under it a number of elements which for all operational purposes can be considered synonymous.

The semantic classes and subclasses subsumed under the heads and subheads will have been derived inductively by the linguistic techniques suggested above. They will have been based on a finite set of semantic features ascertained by these techniques. These features would be classified so that the broadest classes would be defined by shared features that are few in number and more general in scope, the narrowest subclasses by features that are many in number and more specific.

The criteria on which to base these semantic features and the techniques for ascertaining them could be related even more specifically to the purposes of automatic indexing or abstracting than the techniques described above. In the case of information retrieval it might be reasonable to base equivalences on reference to the same subject-matter area rather than on some simple relation of synonymity based on sameness of content.

The information derived from such an analysis of the semantic system of the language can then be incorporated in the semantic code, which is part of the machine dictionary. In the indexing phase of a retrieval program, the document can be run against the dictionary; the semantic code would then assign its contents to the appropriate index terms, which can be stored in memory in the ordering derived from the semantic system on which the semantic code is based. In the request-reading phase, the request can be run against the dictionary, and the semantic code could serve to extract the index terms by means of which the required information is retrieved from storage and furnished in answers to the request.

In summary, it is worth noting that the major difference between a linguistic and a nonlinguistic approach to content processing is that the former ideally requires the inclusion of a previously prepared machine dictionary with a dual code: a grammar code and semantic code. To offset this added complexity, a linguistic approach should contribute increased accuracy and reliability.

This discussion has been limited to some of the areas of linguistic contribution, both theoretical and methodological. This is not intended to imply that techniques based on nonlinguistic assumptions and approaches, whether statistical, logical, or philosophical, are in any way considered potentially less significant. On the contrary, the rules which may be derived for content processing from a linguistic analysis of content systems might well turn out to be largely probabilistic rather than deterministic in the sense these terms are used in the above discussion of machine translation. If this is so, the linguistic classifications will indeed have to be meaningfully related to the statistical, logical, and other considerations which are now being set forth in other areas of language-data processing.

M. E. MARON

A logician's view of language-data processing

A natural first step in presenting a logician's view of automatic language-data processing is to focus on the logician's particular frame of reference. This means that we must first discuss the nature of logic and examine, however briefly, its scope, methods, and limitations. However, more is needed than a description of logic and a clarification of its methods. It is of primary importance to examine the intimate relationship which logic enjoys with natural language and, more specifically, to consider the role of logic in the analysis of language. Furthermore, we must show how much the computing machine functions as a language transducer and consider the application of machines to the processing of data formulated in ordinary language.

One of the crucial areas for language-data processing is the field of automatic information storage and retrieval. Using the tools of inductive logic, we shall analyze the problems of document identification and retrieval and present a probabilistic interpretation of the information-retrieval problem. Hence, this discussion will be not only a tutorial survey and an examination of logic and its role in language-data processing, but also an example of the application of logical analysis to one of the major language-processing problems—the automatic information-retrieval problem.

THE NATURE OF LOGIC

The Two Branches of Logic Logic is the study of correct inference, and since there are two basic kinds of inferences, strict and probabilistic, we see that logic branches into two major parts: deduction and induction. The key concept of deductive logic is *implication*; deduction is the study of those inferences for which the premises of an argument logically *imply* the conclusion. In a valid deductive argument if the premises are true, the conclusion *must* be true. However, although the conclusion must necessarily follow from the premises, the conclusion never tells us anything new. That is, the conclusions are already contained in the premises, and deduction merely allows us to make explicit what is already implicit in the premises. Psychologically speaking, the conclusions may appear surprising, new, or different, but from a logical point of view, they are always there in the premises. Thus, all the hundreds of theorems of Euclidean geometry are contained implicitly in the initial postulates; deduction merely unwraps the postulates and shows us their contents in more detail. As we shall see, every valid deductive argument is a tautology—it is logically empty.

The conclusion of an inductive argument, on the other hand, tells us something new—it goes beyond its premises. However, new information is gained only at the sacrifice of certainty, since the conclusions of inductive arguments can be asserted only with a probability: to extend our knowledge, we give up the certainty of deduction and resort to induction. This characterization of inductive logic shows that its key concept is *probability*.

Logic and Language How does a logician analyze reasoning, argument, or knowledge in general? He cannot examine such psychological entities as ideas, concepts, or judgments; he can analyze only their linguistic counterparts. That is to say, the analysis of reasoning, of inference, etc., implies the analysis of language, and since only the linguistic formulation of an argument can be subjected to analysis, the logician's concern with language becomes obvious.

This allows us to see the difference in the field of inquiry between the physical scientist, on the one hand, and the logician on the other. The scientist looks at the world in order to describe and explain it; the logician looks at language. The logician is one step removed from the world in the sense that he attempts to clarify the structure and relationships of linguistic expressions. He applies his tools of analysis to the *language* of science and of mathematics.

The distinction between empirical science and logic leads us to the differentiation of different *levels* of language. The scientist observes the world and formulates his results in a language which may be called the *object* language. The logician, on the other hand, examines language and formulates his results in a higher level of language, which is called a *metalanguage*.

One of the important contributions of Bertrand Russell is the distinction between levels of language (all of which are confused and mixed together in ordinary discourse). Russell demonstrated that if we use language on a particular level to describe that same language we get into paradoxes. Thus, the paradox asserted in the sentence

This sentence is false.

is prevented once we recognize that there are distinct levels of language and that it is improper to allow a sentence to talk about itself.

Logic and Linguistic Form From a logician's standpoint, the basic unit of language, and therefore of knowledge, is not the sign or the word, but the sentence. Only a sentence can have a *truth* value; *words* of themselves cannot be true or false. When we say that only sentences can be true or false, we see that truth is a property of linguistic expressions. (Modern philosophers are not concerned with *The Truth,* which is alleged to be a property of the world, but rather in the kind of *truth* which is a property of sentences.) Before a sentence can be said to have truth value, we must first establish that it is meaningful. Meaning is logically prior to truth. For a sentence to be meaningful, requirements beyond those of grammar and logic must be satisfied. However, the problem of meaning is extremely complex, and an analysis of adequate criteria for meaningfulness would take us far beyond the scope of this discussion.

The concepts of meaning and truth belong to semantics, which studies the relationships between language and what the language purports to denote. But linguistic expressions also enter into relationships other than to the things that they describe. Sentences enter into relationships with facts, and we say of this relationship that if a sentence describes the facts correctly it is true; if not, it is false. Sentences may also enter into relationships with *other* sentences. Consider, for example, the following relationships which may hold *between* the sentences *A* and *B*: *A* implies *B*; *A* is implied by *B; A* and *B* are contradictory, independent, or consistent, and so on. The question whether or not any of these relationships hold between any set of sentences is not decided by reference to the facts described by the sentences in question. Rather, the question is decided by an analysis of the linguistic form of the sentences. The task of the logician is to clarify the nature of these relationships between linguistic expressions and to provide rules for deciding whether or not the relationships hold.

As indicated above, logic is the study of linguistic forms. This statement may be clarified by considering a simple example involving the relationship of implication. The stock example is the following one:

All men are mortal.
Socrates is a man.
Socrates is mortal.

To be more precise we must indicate that the truth of the conclusion may be asserted only on the assumption that the premises are true: therefore put *if* before the premises and *then* before the conclusion. Now if the inference is valid, then the *form* of the argument should allow us to reason not only about men and mortals, but also about dogs, engineers, etc. Thus, for example, we should be allowed to assert the following arguments:

If *all dogs are faithful*
and *Fido is a dog*
then *Fido is faithful.*

If *all engineers are clever*
and *Jones is an engineer*
then *Jones is clever.*

Thus the relationship of implication which holds between the premises and conclusion is independent of the facts described by the corresponding sentences, and we may omit their actual content. The relationship of implication is a function of the linguistic form alone. We may therefore represent the form of the argument as follows:

If all α *are* β *and* γ *is an* α*, then* γ *is* β.

The validity of the above argument is independent of what we substitute for α, β, and γ. Thus, we see that the logician is interested in the linguistic form as opposed to the content and, furthermore, the linguistic form is a function of the kind and position of the small words such as *if, all, and, then,* etc.

Logical (Formal) Languages In order to analyze logical relationships so as to justify, clarify, and make reasoning rigorous, logicians have developed a variety of precise artificial languages. These languages are similar to the language of mathematics, but they are more general and usually more rigorous. The simplest of these languages is the calculus of sentences—often called the *sentential calculus* or the *propositional calculus.* In order to analyze the internal structure of the sentence itself, we must go to a more complex language such as the *lower-order predicate calculus.* There is also a *higher-order predicate calculus.* Also there are multivalued logics where the truth value of a sentence may take on more than the customary two values of truth and falsity. There are also modal logics. To describe a logical language so as to indicate more clearly the role of logic in the analysis of linguistic forms, let us consider the sentential calculus in more detail.

A formal language can be described by enumerating the primitive variables (basic building blocks) which make up its vocabulary, and by enumerating those connectives that are provided for combining the basic units in order to construct new expressions. For example, in arithmetic we have variables symbolized by x, y, z, etc., which take on the values of the real numbers. There are also the usual operations of addition, subtraction, and multiplication, and relationships such as equality, etc., which allow these variables to be connected in order to form new expressions such as $x + y = z$, $x \cdot y = z - x$, etc.

Similarly in the sentential calculus there is a set of variables denoted by the letters p, q, r, etc., but these variables may take on only one of two possible values. Thus, when we interpret the variables as sentences, these two values may be either truth or falsity. In addition, these sentences may be joined by the logical connectives of *not; and; or; if, then; if and only if,* etc. These connectives are symbolized as follows: *negation* $(\bar{p})$, *conjunction* $(p \cdot q)$, *disjunction* $(p \vee q)$, *conditional* $(p \supset q)$, *biconditional* $(p \equiv q)$.

The rules which specify how the variables may be connected to make new expressions are called *formation rules,* and these rules are analogous to the rules of grammar. If these rules are not satisfied we say that the expression in question is not well formed; in other words, it is logically meaningless.

In addition to formation rules, we must have *truth rules.* These are the rules which, in a sense, explain the meaning of the connectives. They can best be represented in the form of a truth table, which is similar to a multiplication or subtraction table in arithmetic. The truth table for the operation of negation is shown in Table 1. The truth table for the operations of conjunction, disjunction, conditional, and biconditional is shown in Table 2, where A and B stand for arbitrary expressions, and T stands for true and F for false.

TABLE 1

A	$\bar{A}$
T	F
F	T

TABLE 2

A	B	$A \cdot B$	$A \vee B$	$A \supset B$	$A \equiv B$
T	T	T	T	T	T
T	F	F	T	F	F
F	T	F	T	T	F
F	F	F	F	T	T

Given the formation rules and the truth tables, we may do the following things:

1 Construct any arbitrary expression of any complexity by combining variables and connectives. Thus, we may construct a *molecular* sentence from the atomic sentences p, q, and r using negation, conjunction, and disjunction as follows:

$$(p \vee q) \cdot \bar{r}$$

2 Assign truth values to the basic variables and using the tables compute the truth value of the complex expression. For example, in the molecular sentence given above, if we assume that p and r are true and q is false, we compute the truth value to be false.

Now the class of all possible (well-formed) expressions may be divided into three distinct categories which are:

1 *Tautologies,* whose truth value is always true, regardless of the truth values of their components. For example, $p \vee \bar{p}$ is a tautology because no possible assignment of truth values to its components will allow the expression as a whole to be false.

2 *Contradictions,* whose truth value is always false, regardless of the truth values of their components. For example,

$$\bar{p} \cdot \bar{q} \equiv \bar{p} \supset q$$

is a contradiction since no possible assignment of truth values for p and q will make the whole expression true.

3 *Synthetic* or *factual sentences,* whose truth value can be either true or false, depending on the truth values of their basic components. An example of a factual sentence is the one considered above,

$$(p \vee q) \cdot \bar{r}$$

which is sometimes true (when r is false and either p or q is true) and sometimes false (when r is true or when both p and q are false).

The important point here is that the truth tables allow us to decide in a mechanical way to which of the above classes an arbitrary expression belongs.

This mechanical procedure may be described as follows: If the expression in question contains n basic variables, then there are 2^n different combinations of truth and falsity which they can have. Now consider separately each of the 2^n cases and use the truth tables to determine whether or not that combination makes the expression as a whole true. If in every one of the 2^n cases the whole expression comes out true, then it is a tautology. If in every one of the 2^n cases the expression is false, then it is a contradiction. If in some of the 2^n cases it is true and in other cases it is false, then the expression in question is factual or synthetic.

To illustrate the nature of a tautology, let the expression $p \vee \bar{p}$ stand for the sentence

Either it will rain today or it will not rain today.

This sentence is true regardless of the weather. It is true by virtue of its form alone, and its truth can be decided by an analysis of its form alone. Tautologies or logical truths are the theorems of logic, and the task of the logician is to find such expressions and establish that they are, in fact, theorems.

The Concept of Implication The key concept of deductive logic is implication. To say that an argument is valid is to say that the premises logically imply the conclusion. To say that the premises imply the conclusion is to say that the form of the argument makes it impossible to argue from true premises to a false conclusion. This means that if we construct a conditional sentence, for example, $P \supset C$, with the premises P as the antecedent and the conclusion C as the consequent, then that new conditional sentence must be a tautology if the argument is valid.

For example:

p implies $p \vee q$

because the conditional statement

$$p \supset (p \vee q)$$

is a tautology. This justifies our earlier remark that to assert a valid deductive argument is to assert a tautology, and makes clear why deduction never provides us with new information.

THE DIGITAL COMPUTER AND MECHANIZED LOGIC

Since we are concerned primarily with the problem of automatic language-data processing, let us now look at the digital computer from a logical point of view, so as to understand its role and limitations in handling natural language. We are very familiar with the successful application of computers to those problems in which the data processing involves information formulated in the language of mathematics. The problem now is to apply these same machines to the problem of processing information formulated in natural language. Our interest in this question springs from some very urgent practical considerations.

We are constantly faced with increasing numbers of new and different problems involving information. We are flooded with papers, reports, books, and documents of all sorts and in many languages, and we look to the computing machine to deal with this mass of data. Ideally, we would like to have a machine which would not only accept and store the contents of the incoming literature, but also read and "understand" the material, and retrieve relevant information for us on request. We might like to have our automatic information system remove redundant information, detect and bring attention to inconsistencies, derive relevant conclusions, verify hypotheses, etc. As a realistic beginning, we must determine in what possible sense a digital computer can operate as a general-purpose inference-making machine. Let us see what, in essence, a conventional computer can and cannot do with information.

The Nature of a Computer A computer is an information machine. It can accept, store, transfer, rearrange, and print out information. The critically essential characteristic of a conventional computer is that it can interpret and execute a set of orders (instructions) and modify them during the execution of a problem. It can solve complex problems because the transition from problem to solution can be described completely and unambiguously in terms of a sequence of basically elementary operations. These operations are performed when the machine instructions are interpreted and executed.

Information is usually represented in a digital computer in terms of a two-valued (binary) language consisting of words from an alphabet consisting of either pulse or no pulse—"signal" or "no signal," "voltage" or "no voltage," etc. The machine operates on the words in this binary language by performing operations which correspond to the basic logical connectives of the sentential calculus. It is because all the complex operations of mathematics can be reduced to sequences of operations of arithmetic and because these arithmetic operations, in turn, can be reduced to operations of logic, that a computer can solve complex mathematical problems. Furthermore, this reduction of mathematical operations to operations of logic allows us to consider a computing machine as a complex logic machine.

Again, the essential point to remember in considering the nature of a digital computer is the fact that it solves problems by interpreting and executing a sequence of rather elementary operations. A machine will do what you tell it to do, provided the set of instructions given it is unambiguous, precise, detailed, and exhaustively complete. Any given problem which allows its method of solution to be so described can be processed automatically on a machine.

The Automatic Processing of a Logical Language Given this understanding of a computer as an information machine which can interpret and execute a sequence of precise rules, we see immediately that a computer can be programmed to decide automatically whether or not an arbitrary expression in the language of the sentential calculus is a tautology. And, since the problem of deciding whether some given information logically implies some other information can be solved in a purely mechanical fashion, it is possible for a machine to tell us whether a particular statement is a logical consequence of some other given set of statements. This presupposes that the information can be properly formulated in the language of the sentential calculus.

Thus, whenever information can be formulated in the language of the sentential calculus—whether it be a set of tax rules, legal rules, business information, etc.—it can be programmed for a computer which can then determine whether there is a contradiction; whether a given sentence logically follows from the input information; whether two sets of sentences are logically equivalent, etc. The heart of the matter is to determine to what extent a computer can process information which is formulated in *natural* language. More specifically, to what extent is the sentential calculus adequate as a model for ordinary language?

LOGIC AS A MODEL FOR THE PROCESSING OF NATURAL LANGUAGE

Natural Language Language is a wonderfully powerful and versatile instrument, and it is used for a wide variety of purposes. The language of the poet functions to evoke our emotions; the language of the huckster is used to persuade us; the role of social language, so-called "small talk," is often merely to help us keep our lines of communication open. There are other functions of language, but the one we are most concerned with is the role of language in conveying information.

Even when language is used primarily to convey information, we find that it is often vague, ambiguous, imprecise, changeable, idiomatic, and, above all, exceedingly complex. Ordinary language has no explicit rules—neither formation rules, truth rules, nor transformation rules—for telling us that certain kinds of words when used in particular ways will convey various kinds and shades of meaning. The most amazing aspect of language is the fact that in spite of its vagueness, ambiguity, and imprecision, human beings are able to use it with success. Somehow or other we learn to use language to communicate with one another. Furthermore, no matter how new or different a situation is, we are able to choose our words and form sentences to describe the situation. When our friends and children and colleagues talk to us, we understand what they are saying—we see the implications and consequences of their remarks. And now we ask the question: "To what extent can a machine also handle ordinary language?"

The Mapping of Natural Language onto a Logical Language Let us look first at the problem of having a computing machine draw logical consequences from information formulated in ordinary language. Consider as the first step paraphrasing the information in the language of modern logic. A brief look at the problem involved will indicate that this is *not* the way to proceed. If we want a machine to operate on information formulated in ordinary language, we should not attempt to translate ordinary language into a logical language for subsequent processing because we would then be faced with three extremely difficult, if not insurmountable, problems:

1 The mapping of ordinary language onto a logical language
2 The problem of supplying the suppressed premises
3 The formulation of decision rules

To illustrate the first problem, consider the following sentence:

John Kennedy is President ***and*** *he is a Democrat.*

This is a conjunction of two elementary sentences which can be easily translated into the sentential calculus as

$p \cdot q$

where p = John Kennedy is President, q = John Kennedy is a Democrat, and $\cdot$ denotes the logical operation of conjunction.

Now consider another sentence:

Come to the dance ***and*** *bring a date* ***or*** *come stag* ***and*** *have a good time.*

This molecular sentence is made up of atomic sentences which we can symbolize as p, q, r, and s. There are two choices in grouping these atomic sentences. First

$$(p \cdot q) \vee (r \cdot s) \tag{1}$$

means

(Come to the dance and bring a date) or (come stag and have a good time).

The second

$$p \cdot (q \vee r) \cdot s \tag{2}$$

means

Come to the dance and (either bring a date or come stag) and have a good time.

In this particular case, common sense suggests that the second interpretation is the correct one—but it might not have been intended in this way. The point is that in many cases it would be very difficult to determine which is the proper interpretation, and the conclusion would certainly hinge on the interpretation and resulting grouping.

Now consider another sentence:

Jones died ***because*** *he ate fish with ice cream.*[1]

Here we have a molecular sentence with *because* as the major connective. But we cannot translate this sentence into the sentential calculus since *because* is not a truth-functional connective—the truth value of the sentence is not a unique function of the truth values of its atomic components. In some cases we would say that if p and q are true p *because* q must be true; and in other cases, if r and s are true r *because* s must be false, depending on the meaning of p, q, r, and s.

Consider the following inference:

If   *Jack is the brother of John*
and   *John is the brother of Arthur*
then   *Jack is the brother of Arthur.*

[1]W. V. Quine, *Methods of Logic,* Holt, New York, 1952, p. 8.

How can this be mapped onto the sentential calculus? If we represent each of the three sentences as atomic variables p, q, and r, then it is impossible to show that the argument is valid. The validity of the inference can be justified only if we consider the *internal* structure of the sentences in question. The sentences express relationships and must not be construed simply as sentential variables p, q, and r. We need a more complex logic that allows us to express a relationship, which means that we must go beyond the sentential calculus.

Examples could be multiplied at great length to show that the sentential calculus lacks the "richness" needed to paraphrase ordinary language. We use ordinary language to discuss and describe all of the complexities and intricacies of the world around us. We talk about things and their properties and relationships. We talk about properties of properties, properties of relationships, and classes of classes, etc. Increasingly complex logics would be required for proper "translation," and for some expressions there are no known logical counterparts. In addition, translation into a logical language presupposes that the truth values of the sentences in question are definite; it is assumed that the sentences are either true or false. In ordinary language, however, we express all degrees of uncertainty. Therefore, no two-valued logic could be used as the artifical counterpart in such cases.

Although logic is concerned with linguistic form alone, to understand the relevant forms we must understand the content of the initial sentences, and if there are vagueness, ambiguity, and lack of precision in ordinary language, we cannot hope to map it precisely. When we go from information which is inherently vague to a translation which is rigidly precise, we can never know whether or not our proposed translation is correct.

Another aspect of the problem is that of suppressed premises. When we communicate with one another, we assume a certain general background of information. We assume one knows that there are seven days in a week, that Wednesday follows Tuesday, that outer space is cold and dark and lacks oxygen, etc. If we attempt to convey information even to a very bright individual who has no background information, we have to supply all the relevant details or he can not properly understand our reasoning. And if we want a machine to derive conclusions from given information, we must be sure that it is supplied with all the relevant (and ordinarily suppressed) premises necessary for deriving the logical consequences.

Assume for the moment that we have managed somehow to cope with these problems. Assume that we have mapped ordinary language, correctly and completely, onto a suitable logical language, and that we have supplied a machine with all the relevant background information, also formulated in a suitable logical language. There still remains the problem of the decision rules. That is, if we want a *guarantee* that the machine will derive logical consequences, we must provide it with a set of rules to follow and interpret in order to go from initial information to implied conclusions. With the sentential calculus we have such rules, but in general, for more complex logics no such rules exist. In fact, we can prove that it is impossible to find such rules. Furthermore, even in those very limited parts of modern logic where they do exist, they are so complex that it would require an impractical amount of computing time and storage to implement them.

Thus the goal of processing ordinary language by translating it (first) into a logical language brings with it more problems than prospects, and raises more questions than it answers. What then are the alternatives?

LOGIC AND THE METHODOLOGY OF INFERENCE MAKING

Proof by Free Derivation There are two basically different methods to prove that an expression is a theorem of logic. The first technique, *proof by evaluation,* involves a truth-table type of evaluation to determine for the sentential calculus whether the truth value of the given expression could be false regardless of the truth values of the independent variables which constitute its component parts. The second proof procedure, *proof by free derivation,* is the method with which we have become familiar in elementary geometry. In order to describe proof by free derivation, we must consider an axiomatic formulation of logic, just as we would consider an axiomatic formulation of elementary geometry. In this approach to logic we start with a small set of initial expressions which, of course, are tautologies, since we are dealing with logic and not physical geometry or mechanics. For the sentential calculus the following four axioms are sufficient to prove all the theorems of this logical language:

Axiom 1 $(A \vee A) \supset A$

Axiom 2 $A \supset (A \vee B)$

Axiom 3 $(A \vee B) \supset (B \vee A)$

Axiom 4 $(A \supset B) \supset [(C \vee A) \supset (C \vee B)]$

In addition to the initial axiom set, we are provided with a set of transformation rules or rules of inference. These rules describe how to manipulate the axioms in order to generate new expressions which are theorems. One may consider, by analogy, that the transformation rules correspond to the rules of a game such as chess, which describe the legal moves of the game. One of the basic transformation rules in logic is the rule of detachment, called *modus ponens,* which states that if A is an axiom or a theorem, and if $A \supset B$ is an axiom or a theorem, we are allowed to assert B as a new theorem. Another transformation rule is the rule of substitution, which states that any expression may be substituted for any variable in a theorem so long as the substitution is made uniformly—i.e., so long as the identical substitution is made for every occurrence of the variable in question. Thus, for example, if

$$p \supset (q \vee p)$$

is a theorem, we may substitute $p \vee \bar{r}$ for p, which results in

$$[(p \vee \bar{r}) \supset (q \vee p \vee \bar{r})]$$

It is important to point out that the transformation rules of logic are not arbitrary, but their use carries with it the guarantee that the property of truth will be preserved in the derivation of new expressions. That is, if we start with expressions which are true and apply the transformation rules to operate on these initial statements, then all the other statements which we may generate must also be true. The sequence of steps leading from axioms to a new expression (which, of course, is a theorem) is called a *proof,* or a correct logical derivation, if at each step in the sequence there is a justification of that step by reference to one of the given transformation rules.

The Role of Logic Notice that transformation rules do not prescribe how to step from initial statements to a conclusion. Rather, they are descriptions of the steps which are allowable, without any reference to the sequencing of the steps. The transformation rules of logic do not prescribe how one should proceed in order to prove a given expression—they only describe what is allowable. They are analogous to the rules of chess which describe the allowable or legal moves but assert nothing about how one should sequence his moves in order to play a winning game. As in chess, there are no rules in logic which supply an optimal strategy or even a good set of tactics. The competent logician will find a sequence leading from axioms to theorems which obeys the rules, but finding such a sequence requires ingenuity, insight, intuition, luck, and skill.

The emphasis so far has been on deductive logic, and we have been considering one of its key problems—to prove that a given expression is a theorem. In inductive logic, one of the key problems is to find a probable conclusion. That is, given some experimental data, we must find a hypothesis which accounts for those data. Can logic supply the scientist with rules for finding hypotheses? Or if a scientist does find a hypothesis, can logic supply rules by means of which to determine the probability of that hypothesis relative to some given evidence? Again, as in deductive logic, the answer is no. Logic is not a tool for the discovery of conclusions—it is a tool for justification.

Logic has no rules that guarantee that following them will lead to the desired conclusion. If there were such rules, there would be no unsolved problems. Logic is not concerned with the art of making inferences, but is the science of justifying them. In the same sense that the rules of the game of chess are used to decide whether or not a sequence of moves is legal, so also are the rules of logic used to enable one to decide whether or not the steps in an inference are correct.

Returning to the initial problem, we ask the following question: If computers need rules to solve problems and if logic can supply no such rules, how do we proceed along the road toward automatic language-data processing?

Logic versus Methodology The logician cannot supply rules which guarantee that their use will carry one from premises to conclusions, but this does not mean that matters are hopeless or that we may not expect computers to aid us in the automatic handling of language-data problems. Much can be done in the way of automatic language processing, not only for problems formulated in the artificial languages of logic and games, but also for problems expressed in natural language.

In order to clarify the direction in which we must travel, consider, for example, the problem of learning how to prove theorems in logic. After the instructor of a logic course presents the fundamentals of logic, he begins to suggest ways to prove theorems. Experience would have provided him with a number of methods, approaches, clues, tricks, heuristics—aids for discovering proofs. This assortment of clues and hints, when properly organized, might be called the "methodology" of proving theorems, and it would include, for example, suggestions as to when to work backwards, when to try a reductio-type proof, when to stop and try another attack, etc. Naturally, these heuristics carry no guarantees, but experience has shown that they are useful and do, in fact, aid in discovering proofs.

These heuristics could be organized, clarified, and incorporated into a computer program so that a machine could interpret and execute them in order to prove theorems by free derivation. Such a computer program would differ from conventional programs in that it might never solve a given problem. Instead, it would simulate human problem-solving behavior in the sense that it would use similar sorts of problem-solving methods. It would grope, use trial and error, set up goals and subgoals, give up after a while on a fruitless line of attack and go back to try an alternative, etc.

Automatic Theorem Derivation As early as 1955, Newell, Shaw, and Simon initiated a project at the RAND Corporation to study automatic problem solving using logic as a specific problem area.[2] Although the

[2]A. Newell, H. A. Simon, and J. C. Shaw, "Empirical Explorations of the Logic Theory Machine," *Proceedings of the Western Joint Computer Conference, IRE*, February, 1957.

sentential calculus has a decision procedure, i.e., an effective method for deciding whether or not an arbitrary expression is a theorem, Newell, Shaw, and Simon nevertheless attempted to program a computer to find proofs by free derivation. They used an axiom set from Whitehead and Russell,[3] and in addition to these transformation rules they supplied the machine with a set of heuristics for finding proofs.

To illustrate their approach, we will assume that the machine is instructed to prove that some given expression, say, B, is a theorem. The machine is programmed to search among the list of axioms and theorems already proven to see whether or not there is an expression $A \supset B$. If there is, it is instructed to look at the same list to see whether or not there is an expression A and, if so, to use *modus ponens* and assert B as a new theorem. If the machine finds $A \supset B$ but not A, then it is to look for some expression C which is "similar" to A. The machine is given rules for determining whether, and under what conditions, two expressions are similar. If C is similar to A, it operates on C and attempts to transform it into A. Again, the machine has rules for attempting such a transformation. If successful, given A and $A \supset B$, it can assert B. If not, other rules, guides, and heuristics are attempted.

If after some time the machine cannot prove B, it would stop and print out that it was unable to solve the problem in question. By and large, however, as the program was extended and as heuristics were refined and improved, Newell, Shaw, and Simon found that the computer could do surprisingly well. In fact, it was able to prove automatically a rather large number of the theorems which Whitehead and Russell had proved in *Principia Mathematica*. The success of this approach to automatic problem solving shows that one can use a computer to solve problems by methods similar to those used by humans.

Automatic Game Playing As one might expect, there is a strong analogy between the type of problem solving involved in games and the type of problem solving involved in proving theorems in logic. In order to make the analogy explicit, consider again chess versus logic. In chess the initial board configuration of the pieces corresponds, by analogy, to the axioms of, for example, the sentential calculus. The rules of chess which describe how each piece may legally move (e.g., the king may move one square in any direction, rooks may move only on horizontal or vertical, bishops may move only on diagonals, etc.) correspond by analogy to the more complicated transformation rules such as *modus ponens,* substitution, etc. Thus, just as the rules of chess describe how one may go from initial position to a subsequent board position, so the transformation rules allow one to derive new expressions from the initial axioms. Hence,

[3]B. Russell and A. N. Whitehead, *Principia Mathematica,* vol. 1, Cambridge, England, 1910.

by analogy, subsequent board positions correspond to derived theorems, and the tactics of a chess player (e.g., protect the king, gain center control, etc.) correspond to the heuristics, clues, guides, etc., which comprise the methods used to prove theorems.

Since there is such a strong analogy between logic and chess, we would expect to be able to program a machine to play chess by heuristic methods similar to those used by Newell, Shaw, and Simon in their work on automatic theorem derivation. And in fact, they and others have been conducting such work.

Automatic Problem Solving Just as the experienced logician has a set of suggestions, guides, and clues to aid the beginning student in discovering proofs, so also does an experienced chess instructor have such a set of methods and tactics for teaching chess. Another analogy can be made to a language teacher who is attempting to teach students to translate Russian to English and who employs methods that go beyond the vocabulary and basic rules of grammar. These guides for language translation, when properly organized, could be programmed on a machine. Indeed, in recent years computers have been programmed to do a surprisingly adequate job of translating scientific Russian into reasonably passable English. As time goes on, and as the translation rules are improved through experience, we may expect automatic language translation to improve.

Just as we can translate languages by machine, so also can we automatically classify documents on the basis of their content. That is to say, we can program a machine to read a document and decide, on the basis of the occurrence of certain word patterns, to which information category the document in question most probably belongs. Such work represents a giant step in the direction of a fully automated information-storage and -retrieval system.

And finally, we consider automatic problem solving in general. Problems would be solved not by following rigidly a set of rules supplied by the logician, but rather by heuristic techniques. And, of course, with experience these rules can be improved and hopefully generalized. We should look in this direction to see how computers of the future will help us in our efforts to mechanize language-data processing.

Prospects and Conclusions We would favor an empirical, inductive approach to automatic language-data processing, in which we would look for rough rules and guides for solving the information problems in question. We would not attempt to translate ordinary language into a logical language for subsequent processing, but rather seek heuristic-type rules for handling natural language. We would abandon any search for absolute certainty and settle for approximate methods which could be refined and improved through experience. We would consider methods of approximation in the same manner as one would consider a theory in science, where modifications and improvements to the theory are made on the basis of data generated by experimentation. Functioning in this way, the computer becomes an excellent research tool. It performs experiments at very high speeds and provides data for subsequent modification of the rules, and thereby approaches closer and closer a desired solution.

We believe that the role of logic in mechanizing language processing is that of a tool for linguistic analysis, as it is effective in analyzing natural language and thereby in formulating and clarifying the approximate methods of language processing. An outstanding example of the use of modern logic for the analysis and clarification of ordinary language is the work of Reichenbach on tense analysis.[4] The prospects for automatic language-data processing are very good, but the role of logic in this research is limited. However, as a tool for linguistic analysis, as opposed to providing rules for deriving conclusions, logic offers real promise.

A LOGICAL ANALYSIS OF THE INFORMATION-RETRIEVAL PROBLEM

Our view of language-data processing has concentrated on the problem of establishing certain logical relationships between sentences. But before we can properly talk about deriving conclusions—by whatever means—we are obliged as a first step to assemble all of the relevant data. This step suggests that the problem of information storage and retrieval is, from a practical point of view, prior to automatic language transforming, and the problem is now one of mechanizing a library.

Among the many difficult problems encountered under the general heading *library automation* are those of storage space, access time, updating, purging, etc. However, from a logical point of view, the most basic problem concerns the proper *identification* of the subject content of the documents which make up the library—that is, the problem of deciding whether or not (or to what degree) some item is relevant to a given request for information.

The following analysis is based on the assumption that the core of the problem is the identification of information and that the interpretation of this problem must be probabilistic. The following sections describe a way of viewing the library problem based on some work of the author in collaboration with J. L. Kuhns.[5] This interpretation involves a technique called *probabilistic indexing* which introduces arithmetic (as op-

[4]H. Reichenbach, *Elements of Symbolic Logic,* Macmillan, New York, 1947, chap. 7.

[5]M. E. Maron and J. K. Kuhns, "On Relevance, Probabilistic Indexing and Information Retrieval," *Journal of the Association for Computing Machinery,* vol. 7, no. 3, July, 1960.

posed to logic alone) so that a machine can compute a number, called the *relevance number,* which is a measure of the probable relevance of a document to a request.

The Conventional Approach to Mechanization The basic problem associated with an automatic library system is, of course, to devise a mechanical method for identifying the class of documents which will satisfy an arbitrary request for information. In the conventional approach to the problem, the information content of every incoming document is represented by one or more index tags. These index tags are, figuratively speaking, the hooks used by the system to pick up the desired documents. The index tags may be considered as a shorthand representation of the content of the corresponding documents.

An indexer identifies the subject content of a document by a set of index tags, just as a library user, in making a request for information, must identify the information he needs in terms of a set of index tags. One might think of the class of all the index tags that identify documents, as well as requests, as constituting the vocabulary of a primitive language that permits the communication between the indexers and the library users.

Notice that in this approach the indexer must decide whether or not each of the tags from the library vocabulary applies for a given document. The symmetry of the library system is reflected at the user end by the fact that here also a request must be represented by the assignment of index tags on a go or no-go basis. There is one difference, however, which is that the request message may consist not merely of a vocabulary but also of syntax. That is to say, one may represent a request as a Boolean function of index terms. Thus, he may ask for all information on subjects *A* and (*B* or *C*).

Once the documents have been indexed by assigning to each its proper set of tags, these data are represented in digital form for subsequent machine handling. Each incoming request for information is digitally encoded, and then an automatic searching and retrieval system operates on the request essentially as follows.

The system matches the tags associated with each document to the tags and logic representing a request. In those cases where the set of tags of a document are logically compatible with the tags and logic of the request, the system retrieves the document in question. The set of documents whose tags are compatible with the request are then presented to the user as those items which will satisfy his information need.

Once the documents and requests are represented by terms from the common library language, the data can be encoded in digital form, and the actual mechanization consists merely of a logical matching procedure. This mechanical matching can be done on a variety of machines, for example, the IBM sorter, magnetic-tape system, Minicard system, Rapid Selector, etc. Regardless of the sophistication of the hardware, the logic of the searching strategy is always the same—a simple matching of document tags with tags and logic of a request.

Consider now the relationship between any document and the set of index tags that purports to identify its subject content. It is obvious, of course, that because the index for a document provides less information than the document itself, the correspondence between the two cannot be very exact. It is, therefore, extremely difficult to specify precisely the information content of a document in terms of one or even several index tags. It is not uncommon to find that a single tag can be used to characterize many possible subjects (to a greater or lesser extent) and, conversely, for any particular subject, one could find different tags for indexes. The correspondence between index tags and what they purport to denote is not strict.

There is a kind of semantic noise associated with index tags. They are semantically noisy in the sense that there is an uncertainty about what, in fact, they denote; it follows that just as there is noise in the tags as they are used to identify documents, so also is there noise in the tags as they are used to identify the user's information need. And now we see that the conventional search strategy consists in the logical matching of essentially noisy messages. It is not surprising that retrieval effectiveness is less than satisfactory.

The Concept of Weighted Tags. To say that index tags are noisy is to say that there is an uncertainty in the relationship between the tags and what they purport to denote. More precisely, there is only a probability that a person interested in the information content of a given document will use a particular tag in requesting that information. These considerations strongly suggest that it would be more reasonable and realistic to replace the conventional two-valued tags with weighted tags. That is, instead of asserting that a tag either holds or does not hold for a given document, it is better to recognize that a tag can hold to a degree—with a weight.

Thus, we could say of a tag relative to a given document that it holds with weight of 0.9 or 0.8 rather than 1. Or, we might wish to assign a low weight, such as 0.2 or 0.3, rather than decide that the tag in question should not be assigned to the document at all. Clearly, the use of weighted tags in indexing allows an immediate increase in precision and, as we shall see, it opens the door for the use of suitable mathematical machinery to compute values of probable relevance.

The Explication of the Concept of Relevance The key concept of any proper theory of information storage and retrieval is that of relevance. The problem is to explicate the concept of relevance and, hopefully, to arrive at a procedure for actually establishing a quantitative measure for relevance. Or, to lower our sights somewhat, we would like at least to obtain a comparative explication of relevance which would allow us to order (rank) documents according to some comparative measure. Consider the probability expression

$$P(D_i|A \cdot I_j)$$

which reads:

> The probability that if a library user makes a request using the index tag I_j, then he will be satisfied with document D_i.

We now assert:

> If $P(D_1|A \cdot I_j) > P(D_2|A \cdot I_j)$, then document D_1 is *more relevant* than document D_2 relative to the given request. (3)

Thus, we may say of the two documents that if there is a higher probability that D_1 will satisfy a request for information, then D_1 is more relevant than D_2. We must now compute the values of these probabilities so that a ranking by relevance will be possible.

According to the rules of the elementary calculus of probability, expression (3) can be transformed as follows:

$$P(D_i|A \cdot I_j) = \frac{P(D_i|A) \cdot P(I_j|A \cdot D_i)}{P(I_j|A)} \tag{4}$$

For any request I_j, the denominator $P(I_j|A)$ is a constant, and therefore we may rewrite (4) as follows:

$$P(D_i|A \cdot I_j) = k \cdot P(D_i|A) \cdot P(I_j|A \cdot D_i) \tag{5}$$

where $P(D_i|A)$ is the a priori probability that D_i will satisfy the request, and $P(I_j|A \cdot D_i)$ is the probability that if a user desires the information contained in document D_i, then he will use index tag I_j in formulating his request. Given the values of the probabilities represented on the right-hand side of (5), we can compute the values of $P(D_i|A \cdot I_j)$ for a given I_j, and thus, by statement (3), we can rank documents according to their relevance to the request in question.

Library statistics on document usage coupled with feedback from users concerning their satisfaction with retrieval documents can provide estimates for the values of $P(D_i|A)$. It is possible to estimate the values of $P(I_j|A \cdot D_i)$ by a statistical-sampling technique, but such a procedure would be rather involved and, as it turns out, quite unnecessary. When an indexer decides whether or not to assign a particular index tag I_j to a given document D_i, he estimates $P(I_j|A \cdot D_i)$ intuitively, and in the conventional library system, he converts his intuitive estimate to 0 or 1. We now contend that the weight of a tag for a document can be interpreted as an estimate of $P(I_j|A \cdot D_i)$. Thus the weights, in addition to library statistics, provide the data needed to compute $P(D_i|A \cdot I_j)$ for any given request. Given the values of $P(D_i|A \cdot I_j)$ for any request I_j, we can select and rank the proper documents, thus providing the user with a list of documents ordered according to probable relevance.

If an indexer is required to estimate the value of $P(I_j|A \cdot D_i)$, can he not estimate $P(D_i|A \cdot I_j)$ directly, since this is the goal of the computations? The answer lies in the fact that the general goal of the computations is the determination of $P(D_i|A \cdot R)$, where R is a truth-functional expression of index terms. That is, in the general case, a request for information would be represented not by a single tag I_j, but rather by a logical function of such tags, such as, for example,

$$I_j \cdot (I_k \vee I_l)$$

Thus we see that the indexer cannot make a single estimate of $P(D_i|A \cdot R)$, since there are as many values of this as there are different request forms R. The problem is solved, however, as soon as we transform $P(D_i|A \cdot R)$, so that R goes from the reference class to the attribute class. We may then obtain $P(R|A \cdot D_i)$ whose value we can compute, given the respective values of $P(I_j|A \cdot D_i)$, as j varies over the range of the tags contained in R. Thus, we see that although $P(D_i|A \cdot R)$ cannot be estimated directly, we can easily compute its values given the weights. In any case we need the weights, which are the estimates of $P(I_j|A \cdot D_i)$, and all other estimates are superfluous.

Two other points to be mentioned are that there are rules for computing $P(R|A \cdot D_i)$, given the values of $P(I_j|A \cdot D_i)$, and that the initial estimates of $P(I_j|A \cdot D_i)$, that is, the weights provided by the indexer, can be improved and smoothed by proper use of library statistics.

As mentioned earlier, conventional mechanized library systems are plagued by two almost complementary defects—complementary in the sense that as we improve one we aggravate the other. In one case the computer retrieves too much material, much of which is irrelevant, and in the other case the computer fails to retrieve some of the relevant documents. Correcting these two types of "errors" would contribute greatly to progress in achieving an effective information-retrieval system.

Given the weighted tags of probabilistic indexing, plus the logical and mathematical machinery for computing a relevance number, documents may be ranked by probable relevance. We have a solution, then, for the error of retrieving irrelevant data, since one may merely disregard those documents at the bottom of the list and thus avoid low-relevance material.

One way to deal with the problem of failure to retrieve relevant material is to establish measures of "closeness" between requests, so that given a particular request R one can determine what other request R' is closest to R and will "catch" relevant documents not selected by R. Since a request is usually a truth-functional combination of variables which take on the values of index tags, one way to proceed from R to R' is first to establish measures of closeness between index tags.

One may think of index tags as constituting points in a many-dimensional index space. Two different kinds of relationships existing between and among points of this space immediately suggest themselves: semantic and statistical relationships. Semantic relationships are those based on the meanings of the terms in question; the primary semantic relationship is synonymity. The statistical relationship is based not on the meanings of the terms, but rather on the frequencies with which they cooccur as tags for the same document. For example, although *logic* and *switching theory* do not mean the same thing and hence are not semantically related, one would find (at least in an engineering library) a high frequency of occurrence for documents which are indexed under both terms. Several different kinds of measures of statistical closeness can be defined, involving either conditional probabilities or correlation coefficients.[6]

Once statistical measures of closeness between points of index space are established, an automatic system could determine mechanically which of the index tags to consider in searching for relevant information. The request would be automatically elaborated to increase the probability of finding some documents which are relevant but which would not have been selected by the initial request. Clearly, the elaborated request retrieves more documents, but again they are ranked by probable relevance, and the user may wish to ignore low-relevance items if the list is too long.

The statistical measures of closeness between index tags, the procedure for computing a relevance number, statistical data on library usage, the ability to weight tags used in request formulation, etc., constitute techniques to be used in searching for the best output list. These techniques can be organized into a set of tactics, guides, or heuristics for automatically searching a library—a situation similar to other kinds of problem-solving activity.

In this probabilistic approach to the problem of information storage and retrieval, the library would consider the user's request as a clue. On the basis of this clue and statistical data which constitute other evidence, the library system would employ heuristics to search for a satisfactory list of documents ranked by their probable relevance to the request.

In conclusion, logic is the instrument for analyzing inferences and for justifying them; generally, it has no rules for making inferences—for discovering conclusions. There is no logic of discovery, and there are no guaranteed rules for processing language in order to make inferences, whether deductive or inductive. At best, the logician can provide advice

[6]*Ibid.*

and some tools for analyzing linguistic structures. His advice is that rough rules be formulated, then refined and improved as their use suggests; often it is necessary to settle for something less than an optimal solution and live with solutions that are good while not necessarily the best. In this empirical approach the computer can be used as a research tool for experimentation with rules at high speed.

Machines of the future will be designed in radically different ways. They will not be based on present design techniques which use formal logic. We will be able to communicate with future computers more effectively than is now possible. They will learn from experience and eventually, if we are ingenious and diligent enough, they will be able to handle natural language as we do—given the proper educational period. As we learn more about language and machines for handling language, we shall learn more about the whole problem of knowledge itself, and out of this type of research may grow a science of knowledge.

H. P. EDMUNDSON

A statistician's view of linguistic models and language-data processing

In this discussion, we shall survey the theory and application of statistics to the modeling and processing of natural language by a computer. Statistics is an instrument for making decisions since it has prescribed rules for drawing inferences. In processing language to draw inferences, the statistician can provide advice and techniques for analyzing linguistic structures, and the computer can be used empirically as a research tool to discover and test hypotheses at high speed. Computers thrive on statistical data, and language abounds in empirical statistics; but most needed are precise formulations of interesting linguistic hypotheses, clear inferential procedures for the linguist, and statistical methods for handling the evidential value of linguistic phenomena.

We shall examine the theory and application of probability and statistics to research involving natural language and the computer. Little knowledge of probability and statistics is presumed, hence, a condensed exploration is presented further below. The skilled mathematician will recognize those places where simplification has overruled rigor and completeness. The non-mathematician will recognize other places where notation has been used to overcome the redundancies and inaccuracies of natural language.

The concepts and methods developed by statisticians[1] are essential to linguistics and language-data processing. An impressive array of techniques awaits proper application—techniques that range from elementary considerations in probability to advanced results in decision theory and stochastic processes. This is not to say that statistics is the sole key to linguistic research, but without its use, the intrinsically stochastic be-

[1]See B. Lindgren and G. McElrath, *Introduction to Probability and Statistics,* Macmillan, New York, 1959; P. Hoel, *Introduction to Mathematical Statistics,* 3d ed., Wiley, New York, 1962; M. E. Munroe, *Theory of Probability,* McGraw-Hill, New York, 1951; and W. Feller, *An Introduction to Probability Theory and Its Applications,* 2d ed., Wiley, New York, 1957.

havior of natural language will remain unexplained.[2] We shall not attempt here to indicate all available techniques, common pitfalls, and likely directions for new research, but merely to provide a reasonable starting point.

This discussion will be limited in several respects. First, emphasis will be placed on the written mode of natural language rather than the spoken mode. In part, this is because the former is better understood by statisticians. Second, the use of general-purpose digital computers, rather than analog computers, will be stressed. This is only partially due to the fact that there are more general-purpose digital computers in existence and that their use is more widespread.

In fact, it is no accident that these two limitations are imposed simultaneously, for they are related. It is simply that the inherent discrete or digital nature of written language (i.e., the letters, morphemes, syllables, words, phrases, clauses, sentences, etc., of graphic data) requires that digital computers be used for analysis and synthesis. Hopefully, future advances in computer technology and linguistics will permit significant application of analog computers to phonemic data. In this connection it should be remembered that care must be taken to distinguish between a computer and a computer program. For example, consider the question: Can a computer be made to translate one natural language into another? This is really not the proper question. The physical components such as memory units, logical units, arithmetic units, input and output buffers, etc., can be made of sufficient capacity, speed, and sophistication to permit this. However, the computer is not the crux of the matter. A computer program must be created to perform the translation once the necessary machine capability is given. The writing of flowcharts, routines, and programs is the critical intellectual hurdle for the mathematician and linguist. In this sense, the program does the translating, not the computer.

Statistical and Linguistic Methods Since this paper presents a statistician's view, we will find it convenient to group statistical methods into

[2] See G. Herdan, *Language as Choice and Chance,* P. Noordhoff Ltd., Groningen, Holland, 1956; *Type-Token Mathematics,* Mouton and Co., 's-Gravenhage, 1960; R. Jakobson (ed.), "Structure of Language and Its Mathematical Aspect," *Proceedings of Symposia in Applied Mathematics,* vol. XII, American Mathematical Society, Providence, Rhode Island, 1960; B. Mandlebrot, "Simple Games of Strategy Occurring in Communication through Natural Languages," *Transaction of the IRE Professional Group on Information Theory,* no. 3, pp. 124–137, 1954; A. G. Parker-Rhodes, "The Use of Statistics in Language Research," *Mechanical Translation,* vol. 5, no. 2, pp. 67–72, 1958; J. Ville, *Eighteenth International Congress of Philosophy of Science,* Paris (1949), published in *Actualités Sci. et Ind.,* 1145, pp 101–114, Hermann, Paris, 1957; and J. Whatmough, "Mathematical Linguistics," *Proceedings of the Eighth International Congress of Linguists,* Oslo (1957), Oslo University Press, Oslo, 1958.

two main classes: theoretical and empirical. By *theoretical* methods we will mean all those methods that remain essentially tied to the posing of new theories or the refinement of old ones. In turn, we may describe theories either as *macro-theories,* which treat phenomena in the large (e.g., Zipf's law), or as *micro-theories,* which consider more local phenomena (e.g., use of the English article *an*). By *empirical* methods we will mean those based on, or employing, actual observations of raw data.

On the other hand, we may describe linguistic research methods as either analytic or synthetic. Here, *analysis* will mean that natural-language text is examined and decomposed into its component parts (e.g., to permit the formulation of linguistic models of grammar, models of the stochastic formation of words, etc.). *Synthesis* will refer to the construction of computer systems that automatically process natural-language text (e.g., automatic-translation programs, automatic-indexing programs, etc.).

Linguistic Models For the purpose of this paper, a *linguistic model* is an abstract representation of a natural-language phenomenon. A model is usually a simplification, hopefully an insight, but always an approximation. The same phenomenon can be represented by more than one model, depending on which aspects of the phenomenon the model is intended to stress. The level of abstraction can vary from a simple representation in descriptive sentences (e.g., rules of grammar) to a mathematical or near-mathematical representation using symbols in a formal axiomatic system (e.g., transformation theory).[3] But whatever the level of abstraction, all models have at least one of two roles: explicative or predictive. Explicative models set out to explain or provide an understanding of the phenomenon (e.g., information theory).[4] Predictive models, whether based on deduction or induction, have the goal of predicting future behavior in the form of either new phenomena or new combinations of old ones (e.g., Zipf's law).

Some models of language are *deterministic;* that is, no considerations of chance are involved. The defining statements of deterministic models are statements of fact. On the other hand, many linguistic models are *stochastic* or probabilistic; that is, the events are described in terms of their probability of occurrence or their more complex statistical behavior.

Later on we will describe an example of a stochastic model that is based on the theory of information developed by Shannon, where the fundamental notions are taken directly from probability theory. In terms of this model, if one considers a string of words as being generated by

[3] *Cf.* N. Chomsky, *Syntactic Structures,* Mouton and Co., 's-Gravenhage, 1957. See also Stockwell, "The Transformational Model of Generative or Predictive Grammar," earlier in this volume.

[4] *Cf.* C. Shannon, "The Mathematical Theory of Communication," *Bell System Technical Journal,* vol. 27, pp. 379 and 623, 1949.

letters emanating from a source according to given probabilistic laws, then one can predict certain features of its statistical behavior. One of the interesting results is that the English language has a property called "50 per cent redundancy," which we shall discuss later.

Language-data Processing As a complement to a linguistic model, a *language-data process* is a system or program that processes natural-language text by means of a computer so as to produce as output either another natural-language text or a coded representation of it. Thus, language-data processing is a matter of transforming a natural language N_1 into either a natural language N_2 or an artificial language A.[5] For example, *automatic translation* is the transformation or mapping, denoted by $N_1 \rightarrow N_2$, of the source language N_1 into the target language N_2. *Automatic abstracting* is the transformation $N \rightarrow N$, since we are mapping natural-language text into itself where the image is a subset, called the abstract, of the original text. *Automatic indexing* is the transformation $N \rightarrow A$, since we map a natural language N into an artificial language A which may or may not consist of "words" of N.

Other examples of language-data processing are: *automatic editing,* where natural-language text is either edited for redundancy or put in canonical form; *automatic correlation,* where two strings of text are examined for association or trends; *automatic verification,* where natural-language text is compared with machine-stored text for consistency; and *automatic deduction,* where natural-language text is processed for logical implications that are derivable by deductive logic.

Interrelations of Models and Processes Statistics can aid in the analysis of a corpus of natural-language text by means of a computer program so as to produce the ingredients necessary for the formulation of a linguistic model such as those of Zipf, Shannon, Markov, and Carnap. Also, statistics can aid in the synthesis, from natural-language text by means of a computer program, of language-data processes such as automatic translation, indexing, abstracting, correlation, editing, verification, and deduction. These interrelations of models and processes are shown in the figure.

THEORY OF PROBABILITY AND STATISTICS

Let us now turn to the branches of mathematics called probability and statistics. It would be unwise to launch into a discussion of statistical approaches to linguistic models and language-data processing without reviewing the basic notions and notations of probability and statistics.[6]

[5] *Cf.* H. P. Edmundson, "Linguistic Analysis in Machine Translation Research," in M. Boaz (ed.), *Modern Trends in Documentation,* Pergamon Press, New York, 1959.

[6] See references cited in fn. 1.

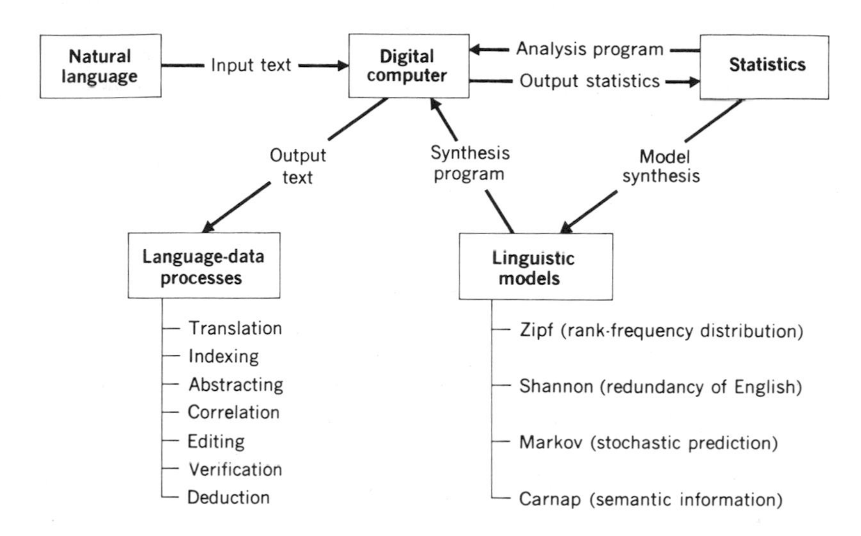

The two fundamental notions in statistics are *population* and *sample.* The meaning of these notions is commonsensically clear, but in linguistic research it is important to remember that in almost every instance we encounter only a sample of the population. For statistically oriented linguists the dichotomy is *parole* for population and *corpus* for sample, rather than de Saussure's linguistically oriented dichotomy of *langue* versus *parole*. Language undergoes continual change, and in our lifetime we see only samples of it. In statistics, we study properties of the sample in order to draw inferences about the population.[7] Statisticians are concerned with problems that arise because of a lack of knowledge about the population, so they examine samples in order to make inferences and decisions. Inference theory or decision theory is the general setting of statistics today; probability theory as its foundation will be considered first.

Probability Theory Probability, and hence statistics, deals with repetitive events where an *event* A is the outcome of an experiment or trial. The set of all logically possible outcomes is called the *event space* S. It is important to remember that probability is defined only for events (i.e., subsets A of the set S), and that it is meaningless to talk about probabilities unless there is a well-defined set of events. In the classical relative-frequency theory of probability,[8] the *probability* of an event A in a space S of events is the limit of the relative frequency of occurrence

[7] See I. J. Good, *Probability and the Weighing of Evidence,* Griffin and Co. Ltd., London, 1950.

[8] See Munroe and Feller, *op. cit.,* fn. 1.

$$P(A) = \lim_{n\to\infty} \frac{m}{n}$$

where m is the number of occurrences of A in n trials. For technical reasons this theory is inadequate to treat some important event spaces S, so the modern axiomatic theory of Kolmogorov is used instead. In this theory the probability of an event satisfies the following axioms:

Axiom 1 $P(A) \geq 0$
Axiom 2 $P(S) = 1$
Axiom 3 $P(A \text{ or } B) = P(A) + P(B)$ if A and B cannot occur jointly

In addition to the absolute probability $P(A)$, we require another type of probability called *conditional probability*. The above definition of absolute probability is used to define the conditional probability $P(A|B)$ that A occurs given that B has occurred by setting

$$P(A|B) = \frac{P(A \text{ and } B)}{P(B)} \qquad \text{if } P(B) \neq 0$$

The most important single notion in probability theory is that of independent events. Two events A and B are said to be (probabilistically or stochastically) *independent,* provided

$$P(A \text{ and } B) = P(A)\,P(B)$$

Similarly, three events A, B, and C are said to be *mutually independent,* provided

$$P(A \text{ and } B) = P(A)\,P(B)$$
$$P(A \text{ and } C) = P(A)\,P(C)$$
$$P(B \text{ and } C) = P(B)\,P(C)$$
$$P(A \text{ and } B \text{ and } C) = P(A)\,P(B)\,P(C)$$

and so forth for any number of events.

One of the basic theorems is Bayes' theorem: If the event B is due to exactly one of the n "causes" $A_1, \ldots, A_n$, then the conditional probability that the cause was A_i given that B has occurred is

$$P(A_i|B) = \frac{P(A_i)\,P(B|A_i)}{\sum_{j=1}^{n} P(A_j)\,P(B|A_j)} \qquad \text{for } i = 1, \ldots, n$$

This theorem is useful in determining the "posterior" probabilities $P(A_i|B)$ when the "prior" probabilities $P(A_i)$ are either known or assumed.

Distribution Theory Distribution theory is the most fundamental subject in statistics and is customarily the one studied first.[9] If we consider

[9]See Hoel, *op. cit.,* fn. 1.

an event space S of events A, then any function defined on S is called a *random variable* (or *stochastic variable*) and is customarily denoted by a capital letter, say X. It is customary to denote the value that a random variable can assume by the lower case of the capital letter that denotes the random variable, e.g., X assumes values x. Thus, the random variable X is simply a way of describing the distribution of the total probability mass or weight of 1 over the points or sets of points x of S. A random variable is said to be *discrete* if it can assume only discrete values x (e.g., x is the length or the number of words); a random variable is said to be *continuous* if it can assume an entire continuous interval of values x (e.g., x is the amplitude or the pitch of speech). The *probability mass function* of a discrete random variable X is given by the function

$$f(x) = P(X = x)$$

The *probability density function* of a continuous random variable X is given by the derivative

$$f(x) = \frac{d}{dx} P(X \leq x)$$

Interestingly, every constant c can be thought of as a special random variable X whose entire probability mass of 1 is concentrated at the point c—that is,

$$P(X = c) = 1$$

Every random variable X has a *distribution* representable by its graph $y = f(x)$. A distribution is called *discrete* or *continuous*, depending on whether its random variable is discrete or continuous. For a discrete distribution the graph is a steplike function and for a continuous distribution the graph is a smooth curve. In general the distribution for a population is a function of several population *parameters* $\theta_1, \ldots, \theta_k$ so that $f(x)$ should be written $f(x; \theta_1, \ldots, \theta_k)$. By specifying the parameters we specify a particular curve of a family of curves.

Several examples of distributions will now be considered. Three important discrete distributions are the uniform, the binomial, and the Poisson. The *uniform* distribution has a probability mass function

$$f(x; n) = \frac{1}{n} \qquad x = 1, \ldots, n$$

with one parameter n where n is a positive integer. The *binomial* distribution has a probability mass function

$$f(x; n, p) = \binom{n}{x} p^x (1 - p)^{n-x} \qquad x = 0, \ldots, n$$

with two parameters n and p where n is a positive integer and $0 \leq p \leq 1$. The *Poisson* distribution has a probability mass function

$$f(x; a) = \frac{e^{-a}a^x}{x!} \qquad x = 0, 1, \ldots$$

with one parameter a where $a \geq 0$. Two important continuous distributions are the rectangular and the normal. The *rectangular* distribution has a probability density function

$$f(x; a,b) = \frac{1}{b - a} \qquad a \leq x \leq b$$

with two parameters a and b where $a<b$. The *normal* distribution has a probability density function

$$f(x; a,b) = \frac{1}{b\sqrt{2\pi}} e^{-(x-a)^2/2b^2}$$

with two parameters a and b where $-\infty < a < \infty$ and $b > 0$.

It is often convenient to replace the curve description by one or more descriptive numbers called *moments*. The first moment is called the theoretical *expectation* or *population mean* $\mu = E(X)$ which is defined by the sum

$$E(X) = \sum_{x=1}^{\infty} x f(x)$$

when X is discrete and by the integral

$$E(X) = \int_{-\infty}^{\infty} x f(x)\, dx$$

when X is continuous. The exception $E(X)$ is a measure of the central tendency or center of mass of the distribution of X. The second moment about the mean is called the theoretical or *population variance* $\sigma^2 = V(X)$ which is defined by the sum

$$V(X) = \sum_{x=1}^{\infty} (x - \mu)^2 f(x)$$

when X is discrete and by the integral

$$V(X) = \int_{-\infty}^{\infty} (x - \mu)^2 f(x)\, dx$$

when X is continuous. The square root of the variance is called the *standard deviation* and is a measure of the dispersion or spread of the distribution of X. It is often useful to describe a distribution by its expectation and variance, even though these two moments may not completely characterize the distribution of the random variable. The moments are always functions of the population parameters. For example, in the binomial distribution the expectation $\mu = np$ and the variance $\sigma^2 = np(1-p)$, while in the normal distribution the expectation $\mu = a$ and the variance $\sigma^2 = b^2$.

When one deals with two random variables X and Y, the question of their statistical dependence arises. X and Y are said to be statistically *independent*, provided their joint density function $h(x,y)$ equals the product of their individual density functions $f(x)$ and $g(y)$ – that is,

$$h(x,y) = f(x)\, g(y)$$

for all x and y. X and Y are said to be statistically *uncorrelated*, provided the expectation of their product equals the product of their expectations–i.e., $E(XY) = E(X)\,E(Y)$. The relation of these two properties is given by the theorem: If X and Y are independent, then they are uncorrelated, but not necessarily conversely. A measure of the degree of correlation is given by the theoretical *correlation coefficient*

$$\rho(X,Y) = \frac{E(XY) - E(X)\,E(Y)}{[V(X)\ \ V(Y)]^{1/2}}$$

whose numerator is called the *covariance* $C(X,Y)$ of X and Y.

Now we will turn our attention from the population to the sample. A *random sample* is one in which the n observations or trials are mutually independent in the sense previously defined. In practice, whether a sample is random or not depends on the method used to obtain it. Any function of the n observations in a random sample is called a *statistic*. Thus, a statistic is a random variable, and so, by definition, must have a distribution function. The determination of the distribution of statistics is a never-ending quest for statisticians. Corresponding to the two theoretical quantities–the expectation and variance of the population–we have their random-sample analogs, the *sample mean* $m = (1/n) \sum_{i=1}^{n} x_i$ and the *sample variance* $s^2 = (1/n) \sum_{i=1}^{n} (x_i - m)^2$ which are statistics, since they are function of the n observations in the random sample. If we let $\overline{X}$ denote the random variable corresponding to the sample mean, then it can be shown that

$$E(\overline{X}) = E(X) \qquad \text{and} \qquad V(\overline{X}) = \frac{V(X)}{n}$$

That is, the sample mean $\overline{X}$ has the same expectation, but only one-nth the variance, as does X.

Inference Theory (Parameter Estimation) One of the two principal branches of inference theory is called parameter estimation. By a *parameter* of the population we mean a quantity which partially characterizes its distribution–for example, the theoretical moments. In general we do not know their values and are therefore confronted with the problem of estimating them. We do so by taking a sample, devising statistics whose values are computed from the sample, and using these statistics as *estimators* of the unknown parameters. To estimate the unknown parameter θ in a population whose distribution is given by $f(x; \theta)$, we must first choose an estimator $\hat{\theta}$ of θ. Of course, the estimator $\hat{\theta}$ is a statistic since it is a function of the observed sample values $x_1, \ldots, x_n$ of the random variable X. There are two methods of estimating parameters: point estimation and interval estimation. In *point estimation* we decide that the probability is one that θ equals the estimate $\hat{\theta}$. In *interval estimation* we decide that the probability is p (where $0 < p < 1$) that θ lies somewhere between a lower estimate $\hat{\theta}_1$ and an upper estimate $\hat{\theta}_2$. Naturally, the higher the desired confidence level p is, the longer must be the length $\hat{\theta}_2 - \hat{\theta}_1$ of the confidence interval $(\hat{\theta}_1,\hat{\theta}_2)$ of estimation. This longer interval is the price we pay for the higher confidence.

Thus, by either point or interval estimation we can estimate the unknown theoretical parameters of a population. Some of the parameters most commonly estimated in statistics are the theoretical mean, variance, standard deviation, median, percentage, probability, and range.

Inference Theory (Hypothesis Testing) The second principal branch of inference theory is called hypothesis testing. A *statistical hypothesis* H is an assumption about the distribution of a random variable. It often takes the form of a statement about the values of the parameters $\theta_1, \ldots, \theta_k$ of the population, e.g., H: $\theta_1 = 5$. A *test* of a hypothesis is a decision method for accepting either hypothesis H or an alternative hypothesis $\overline{H}$. For example, let θ be a location parameter, so that $f(x; \theta)$ denotes that the distribution of the random variable X is centered over the point θ, and let the hypothesis and its alternative hypothesis be

$$H: f(x; \theta) = f(x; \theta_1) \qquad \text{versus} \qquad \overline{H}: f(x; \theta) = f(x; \theta_2)$$

In deciding from a sample whether to accept H or $\overline{H}$ we can make two types of errors: we can (1) reject a true hypothesis H or (2) accept a false hypothesis H. We denote the probability of the *type 1* error by $P(\overline{H}|H)$ —in other words, the conditional probability of rejecting H (i.e., accepting $\overline{H}$) when H is true. Similarly, we denote the probability of the *type 2* error by $P(H|\overline{H})$. Since for technical reasons we cannot simultaneously minimize both types of error given a fixed sample size, statisticians have elected to minimize the probability $P(H|\overline{H})$ of the type 2 error while holding the probability $P(\overline{H}|H)$ of the type 1 error fixed at some preselected *significance level,* say $p = .05$ or $p = .01$. To reduce simultaneously the probabilities of both types of error, we must increase the sample size, but this, unfortunately, is often not feasible or desirable. The estimator $\hat{\theta}$ of parameter θ is a function of the n observations

$x_1, \ldots, x_n$ in the sample—i.e., $\hat{\theta} = w(x_1, \ldots, x_n)$. The set of all possible values of the parameter is called the *parameter* space, which consists of two regions called the *acceptance region A* and the *rejection region R* for hypothesis H. If the statistic $\hat{\theta} = w(x_1, \ldots, x_n)$ falls in A, then H is accepted at the preselected significance level; if $\hat{\theta}$ falls in R, then H is rejected at that level of significance.

The preceding discussion concerns only the fixed-sample-size, or nonsequential, method. If we employ a sequential method of testing we can often reach a decision with one-half the sample size required by a nonsequential method. Secondly, we have discussed only the parametric case of inference in which the exact functional form of the distribution is either known or assumed. Space does not permit the discussion of the interesting and powerful *nonparametric,* or *distribution-free,* method of inference which avoids the popular, but often unwarranted, assumption that the population is normally distributed.

Thus either by parametric or nonparametric testing we can test hypotheses about the nature of an unknown population. Some of the hypotheses most commonly tested in statistics are goodness of fit, independence, randomness, homogeneity, equality of means, and equality of variances.

Stochastic Processes A *stochastic process* is a probabilistic model of a physical process whose evolution is time-dependent. More precisely, a stochastic process is a family of random variables that are functions of time. If its random variables are defined for discrete points in time $n = 0, 1, 2, \ldots$, then the stochastic process $\{X_n\}$ is called *discrete;* if its random variables are defined for continuous time $t \geq 0$, then the stochastic process $\{X(t)\}$ is called *continuous.* For our purposes the stochastic processes called finite Markov chains are important.[10] A *finite Markov chain* is a sequence of random variables $\{X_n\}$, where X_n can assume only a finite number of values called *states* $i = 1, \ldots, s$ and the next state i_{n+1} depends probabilistically only on the present state i_n—that is,

$$P(X_{n+1} = i_{n+1} | X_1 = i_1 \wedge \cdots \wedge X_n = i_n) = P(X_{n+1} = i_{n+1} | X_n = i_n)$$

The system is said to be in state i at time n if $X_n = i$. A Markov chain is completely determined by two probabilistic quantities: a vector of initial probabilities and a matrix of transition probabilities. The initial probability vector $p^{(0)}$ describes the initial probability distribution of the system at time $n = 0$

$$p^{(0)} = (p_1^{(0)}, \ldots, p_s^{(0)})$$

[10] See Feller, *op. cit.,* fn. 1.

where $p_i^{(0)} = P(X_0 = i)$. The transition probability matrix P describes the one-step transition probabilities from state to state

$$P = (p_{ik})$$

where $p_{ik} = P(X_{n+1} = k | X_n = i)$. Roughly speaking, the initial vector starts the process and the transition matrix keeps it stepping. Hence, a Markov chain is a stochastic process with a slight amnesia present, in the sense that the probability that state k occurs next, given that state i occurs now, is stochastically independent of what states occurred before. A Markov chain is thus the first possible generalization away from a completely independent sequence of trials.

Information Theory The theory of information created by Shannon[11] concerns the amount of information communicated by a source that generates messages. This theory does not treat the meaning or semantic content of a single message, but is concerned with the statistical rarity of possible messages. The transmission of information may be initiated by either a phonetic (voice) or a graphic (written) *source*. The *transmitted message* or signal is carried through a *channel* whose output is the *received message*. The statistical difference between the transmitted signal and the received signal is used to define the informational *capacity* of the channel. Loss of communicated information is said to be due to *noise* in the channel.

Every source that generates messages composed from an *alphabet* of n discrete symbols can be represented by a discrete random variable X defined over the symbols $i = 1, \ldots, n$, with $p_i = P(X = i)$. The simplest possible alphabet consists of just two symbols, say the binary digits 0 and 1, and its messages are called *binary sequences*. This provides the basic unit of information called the *bit* (a contraction of the words *binary digit*), which is defined as the amount of information contained in the choice of one out of two equiprobable symbols (e.g., 0 or 1, *yes* or *no*, etc.). Every message whose alphabet has n symbols may be *coded* into such a binary sequence. Three bits are required for the selection of a symbol from among eight equally likely symbols because $2^3 = 8$ or $\log_2 8 = 3$. In general, each symbol of an n-symbol alphabet contains $\log_2 n$ bits, since that is the number of binary digits required to transmit each sym-

[11]See Shannon, *op. cit.*, fn. 4; see also C. Shannon and W. Weaver, *The Mathematical Theory of Communication,* University of Illinois Press, Urbana, 1949; R. Fano, *Transmission of Information,* Wiley, New York, 1961; F. Reza, *An Introduction to Information Theory,* McGraw-Hill, New York, 1961; D. A. Bell, "The 'Internal Information' of English Words," in W. Jackson (ed.), *Communication Theory,* Butterworths, London, 1953; and D. A. Bell and Alan S. C. Ross, "Negative Entropy of Welsh Words," in C. Cherry (ed), *Information Theory,* Third London Symposium, Butterworths, London, 1956.

bol. For example, a decimal digit equals $\log_2 10 = 3.32$ bits, a Roman letter equals $\log_2 26 = 4.68$ bits, and a Cyrillic letter equals $\log_2 32 = 5.00$ bits.

For a discrete source, Shannon defines a measure of uncertainty

$$H(X) = H(p_1, \ldots, p_n)$$

measured in bits per symbol, called the *entropy* of source X, by requiring that $H(X)$ satisfy three axioms:

Axiom 1 Uncertainty of a source is a smoothly changing function of its probabilities.

Axiom 2 Uncertainty of a source with equiprobable symbols increases with the number of such symbols.

Axiom 3 Uncertainty of a source is the same no matter how the symbols are chosen—whether a symbol is chosen directly according to its absolute probability or whether the symbols are grouped and a symbol is chosen first according to the probability of its group and second according to its conditional probability within the group.

A precise formulation of these axioms for the entropy of a source is

Axiom 1 $H(p_1, \ldots, p_n)$ is continuous in each p_i.

Axiom 2 $H(1/n, \ldots, 1/n)$ is an increasing function of n.

Axiom 3 $H(p_1, \ldots, p_n) = H(p_1, 1 - p_1)$

$$+ (1 - p_1) H\left(\frac{p_2}{1 - p_1}, \ldots, \frac{p_n}{1 - p_1}\right) \qquad \text{for } p_1 < 1$$

It is then possible to prove the uniqueness theorem: the only function satisfying Axioms 1, 2, and 3 is

$$H(p_1, \ldots, p_n) = -\sum_{i=1}^{n} p_i \log_2 p_i \qquad \text{bits per symbol}$$

The minus sign in the above expression makes $H(X) \geq 0$, since logarithms of the fractions p_i are negative. For example, when $n = 2$,

$$H(p, 1 - p) = -p \log_2 p - (1 - p) \log_2 (1 - p) \qquad \text{bits per symbol}$$

Here we notice that the minimum entropy or uncertainty of 0 bits per symbol occurs when either $p = 0$ or $p = 1$, and that the maximum uncertainty of 1 bit per symbol occurs when $p = 1/2$. Thus, in accord with our intuition, minimum uncertainty occurs when one symbol is certain, and maximum uncertainty occurs when the two symbols are equiprobable.

For a general n it can be shown that the minimum value of $H(p_1, \ldots, p_n)$ is 0 bits per symbol and occurs when exactly one symbol is certain; and that the maximum value of $H(p_1, \ldots, p_n)$ is $\log_2 n$ bits per symbol and occurs when $p_1 = \cdots = p_n = 1/n$ — that is,

$$\min H(p_1, \ldots, p_n) = H(1, 0, \ldots, 0) = 0 \qquad \text{bits per symbol}$$

$$\max H(p_1, \ldots, p_n) = H\left(\frac{1}{n}, \ldots, \frac{1}{n}\right) = \log_2 n \qquad \text{bits per symbol}$$

Because of this, the ratio $H(X)/\log_2 n$ is called the *relative entropy* and the difference

$$1 - \frac{H(X)}{\log_2 n} = \frac{\log_2 n - H(X)}{\log_2 n}$$

is called the *redundancy*.[12] The redundancy thus gives the factor by which the average lengths of messages are increased due to intersymbol statistical behavior beyond the theoretical minimum length necessary to transmit the desired message.

UNWARRANTED STATISTICAL ASSUMPTIONS

Researchers sometimes make unwarranted statistical assumptions that severely prejudice their results, and closer examination by a mathematical statistician invalidates them. This happens frequently enough to deserve comment here. The following statistical assumptions are often taken for granted, when they should be tested before they are used.

Assumption Regarding the Population The researcher often assumes that he knows the distribution function of the population when, in fact, he does not. The most common assumption is that the population has a normal distribution. This assumption is made either in the total absence of information or because the researcher wishes that the population obeyed the normal law. Other variations of this assumption are that the binomial distribution can be approximated by the Poisson distribution or by the normal distribution without verifying whether the proper conditions are met. Another popular assumption, in the absence of reasons to the contrary, is that the population has a uniform distribution–i.e., that all events are equally likely. This latter case often leads to the misuse of the theorem of Bayes when the researcher incorrectly, or without grounds, assumes knowledge of the "prior" probabilities. The hypothesis that the population has a certain distribution should first be tested.

Assumption Regarding Independence and Randomness With insufficient grounds it is often assumed that the observations or trials are sta-

[12] See C. Cherry (ed.), *Information Theory,* Third London Symposium, Butterworths, London, 1956; L. Brillouin, *Science and Information Theory,* Academic Press, New York, 1956; B. Mandelbrot, "Structure formelle des textes et communication," *Word,* vol. 10, pp. 1–27, 1954; and C. F. Hockett, "An Approach to the Quantification of Semantic Noise," *Phil. Sci.,* vol. 19, pp. 257–260, 1952.

tistically independent. The definition of a random sample centers around the condition that the observations are stochastically independent. In practice, whether a sample is a random sample or not depends on the means used to obtain it. Hence, the researcher should not attempt to create a random sample by mere guessing. Psychological traits make it very likely that so-called "random numbers" in a string are in fact highly correlated or show patterns of repetition or favoritism. The proper way to avoid this situation is to consult a table of random numbers, for example, the RAND Corporation's table "A Million Random Digits with 100,000 Normal Deviates." These tables were generated by means of an electronic computer, and the results passed several tests of randomness.

Assumption Regarding the Sample Size The researcher is often confronted with the problem of whether or not the sample size n is sufficiently large. It is unwise to arbitrarily state that $n = 5$ is small or that $n = 50$ is large for all problems. However, the effect of increasing the sample size on the reliability of sampling can be made clear. In support of our intuition it can be shown mathematically that statistical precision increases as the sample size increases. For example, the variance of the sample mean X is equal to one-nth of the variance of X for all random samples—i.e., $V(X) = V(X)/n$. Another way of putting this is that the standard deviation of the sample mean varies inversely with the square root of the sample size—i.e., $\sigma_{\bar{x}} = \sigma_x / \sqrt{n}$

Assumption Regarding the Statistic The professional statistician is often faced with the task of telling the researcher that the wrong statistic or statistical formula is being used. For example, some researchers, because of previous training, tend to prefer the correlation coefficient when another statistic is more appropriate. The solution here is for the researcher to consult the statistician before the choice of a statistic or formula is made.

Assumption Regarding the Conclusions Although an experiment is properly designed, the proper statistic is used, and the calculations are correctly made, it often happens that unwarranted inferences or final conclusions are drawn. It is in this last step of translating the statistical results to subject-matter results that care must be exercised. In fact, the same care should be used here as was originally used in translating the subject-matter problem into a statistical problem.

Of course, ways to avoid the above pitfalls depend on the particular problem being considered. It is impossible to describe complete solutions in this short discussion. A mathematical statistician should be consulted before the problem is formulated, the experiment is designed, the data are collected and analyzed, and the final inferences are made.

APPLICATION OF PROBABILITY AND STATISTICS

The preceding section briefly reviewed the theory of probability and statistics. In applying the theory we must face the fact that, since natural language is dynamic, most of the populations considered are functions of time. However, in order that our samples be representative of the population we shall assume, when necessary, that our populations change sufficiently slowly with time to allow us to ignore this change. Also, whenever possible, our populations will be defined by specifying some definite quantitative attribute of language such as word length or speech frequency rather than an indefinite qualitative attribute such as word or sound.

We now come to the application of probabilistic and statistical techniques to our two major fields: linguistic models and language-data processing. Under linguistic models we will discuss the distribution of word rank and frequency, a theory of semantic information, the redundancy of English, and a stochastic model of language.[13] Under language-data processing we will discuss automatic indexing, abstracting, and translation.[14]

LINGUISTIC MODELS

Rank-frequency Distribution Let f_i denote the relative frequency of occurrence of a lexical unit i (e.g., letter, word, index term, etc.) in a total vocabulary of m distinct units, and let n denote the sample size. Then f_i is the number of occurrences of lexical unit i divided by n. Let r_i denote the *rank* of lexical unit i—i.e., the most frequent i has rank 1, the next most frequent has rank 2, and so on. Dewey, Estoup, Condon, and Zipf observed empirically for language in particular, and for a large class of socioeconomic phenomena in general, that for every element i (in

[13]See Mandelbrot, *op. cit.,* fn. 12; C. B. Williams, "A Note on the Statistical Analysis of Sentence Length as a Criterion of Literary Style," *Biometrika,* vol. 31, parts 3–4, 1940; G. U. Yule, *The Statistical Study of Literary Vocabulary,* London, 1944; W. Fucks, "On the Mathematical Analysis of Style," *Biometrika,* vol. 39, p. 122, 1952; M. Aborn and H. Rubenstein, "Word-class Distribution in Sentences of Fixed Length," *Language,* vol. 32, p. 674, 1956; and *Proceedings of the International Conference on Scientific Information,* vols. I and II, Washington, D.C., 1959.

[14]See Y. Bar-Hillel, *Some Theoretical Aspects of the Mechanization of Literature Searching,* Hebrew University, Technical Report No. 3, Jerusalem, 1960; and "The Present Status of Automatic Translation of Languages," in F. Alt (ed.), *Advances in Computers,* Academic Press, New York, 1960; D. R. Swanson, "Information Retrieval: State of the Art," *Proceedings of the Western Joint Computer Conference,* vol. 19, Los Angeles, 1961; L. Doyle, *Library Science in the Computer Age,* System Development Corporation, SP-141, 1959; and A. D. Booth et. al., *Mechanical Resolution of Linguistic Problems,* Butterworths, London, 1958.

language, word) the product of its relative frequency f_i and its rank r_i is approximately the same constant c.[15] Zipf empirically obtained the constant $c = 1/10$. Thus Zipf's law is the hyperbolic relation

$$f_i = \frac{1}{10r_i} \qquad i = 1, \ldots, m$$

or, by taking logarithms to the base 10, is the linear relation

$$\log_{10} f_i = -\log_{10} r_i - 1 \qquad i = 1, \ldots, m$$

Mandelbrot, Good, Good and Toulmin, and Simon[16] have investigated the basis for this law. Koutsoudas, Koutsoudas and Machol, Cherry, Herdan, and Miller and Newman[17] have presented discussions and examples of Zipf's law and its manifestation in different styles of writing. Joos[18] has suggested the modified law of which Zipf's law is a special case:

$$f_i = \frac{1}{10r_i^a} \qquad a \geq 1 \text{ and } i = 1, \ldots, m$$

Now, if m is the total number of words in the vocabulary so that

[15] *Cf.* G. Dewey, *Relative Frequency of English Speech Sounds,* Harvard University Press, 1923; J. B. Estoup, *Gammes Sténographiques,* Paris, 1916; E. U. Condon, "Statistics of Vocabulary," *Science,* vol. 67, p. 300, 1928; and G. K. Zipf, *Human Behavior and the Principle of Least Effort,* Addison-Wesley, Cambridge, Mass., 1949.

[16] See B. Mandelbrot, *Linguistic Statistique Macroscopique: Théorie Mathématique de la loi de Zipf,* Institut Henri Poincaré, Seminaire de Calcul de Probabilitiés, Paris, 1957; "An Informational Theory of the Structure of Language Based upon the Theory of the Statistical Matching of Messages and Coding," *Proceedings of a Symposium on Applications of Communication Theory,* Butterworths, London, 1953; I. J. Good, "The Population Frequencies of Species and the Estimation of Population Parameters," *Biometrika,* vol. 40, p. 237, 1953; "Distribution of Word Frequencies," *Nature,* vol. 179, p. 595, 1957; I. J. Good and G. H. Toulmin, "The Number of New Species and the Population Coverage when a Sample is Increased," *Biometrika,* vol. 43, pp. 45–63, 1956; and H. Simon, "On a Class of Skew Distribution Functions," *Biometrika,* vol. 42, parts 3–4, pp. 425–440, 1955.

[17] See A. Koutsoudas, "Mechanical Translation and Zipf's Law," *Language,* vol. 33, no. 4, pp. 545–552, 1957; A. Koutsoudas and R. Machol, *Frequency of Occurrence of Words: A Study of Zipf's Law with Application to Mechanical Translation,* University of Michigan, Engineering Research Institute, Publication 2144-147-T, 1957; C. Cherry, *On Human Communication,* Wiley, New York, 1957; G. Herdan, *op. cit.,* fn. 2; and G. A. Miller and E. B. Newman, "Tests of a Statistical Explanation of the Rank-Frequency Relation for Words Written in English," *American Journal of Psychology,* vol. 71, pp. 209–218, 1958.

[18] M. Joos, Review of Zipf's "The Psycho-biology of Language," *Language,* vol. 12, pp. 196–210, 1936.

$$\sum_{i=1}^{m} f_i = 1$$

then

$$1 = \sum_{i=1}^{m} f_i = \sum_{i=1}^{m} \frac{1}{10 r_i^a} = \frac{1}{10} \sum_{i=1}^{m} \frac{1}{r_i^a} = \frac{1}{10} (1 + \frac{1}{2^a} + \frac{1}{3^a} + \cdots + \frac{1}{m_a})$$

This implies that m and a are functionally related; in fact, we must conclude that if $a = 1.000$, then $m = 12{,}000$, and if $a = 1.106$, then $m = \infty$.

The above mathematical conclusions are not linguistically acceptable. However, if the researcher had not been interested in the empirical behavior of language, then he might never have proposed this law and model; the model was not created before the researcher went looking for phenomena which matched it. Although linguists claim to be interested in the differential properties of words rather than in common properties, there undoubtedly are other interesting global laws of linguistic behavior that remain to be empirically discovered.

Even with Zipf's law several statistical problems remain. Despite the fact that Zipf, Joos, and others have expressed the law in terms of the sample quantities f_i and r_i in a sample of size n, the theoretical model should be expressed in terms of the corresponding population variables p_i and ρ_i. Thus we should write the law as

$$p_i = \frac{1}{c \rho_i^a} \qquad i = 1, \ldots, m$$

where c and a are the parameters. One important problem is to estimate the parameters c and a. A second problem is to test the hypothesis H_1: $c = 1/10$ and the hypothesis H_2: $a = 1.0$. In both these problems we could use $f_i = \hat{p}_i$ as the estimator for p_i and $r_i = \hat{\rho}_i$ as the estimator for ρ_i.

Semantic Information Carnap and Bar-Hillel[19] consider an artificial language that consists of

n individuals $a_1, \ldots, a_n$
m properties $F_1(\ ), \ldots, F_m(\ )$
Five logical connectives
— (not), ∨ (or), ∧ (and), → (implies), ⟷ (equivalent)

where the properties do not overlap in meaning and no property says anything about the use or nonuse of any other property. A *basic sentence* is of the form $F_j(a_i)$ – i.e., *individual* a_i *has property* F_j. A *sentence* x in

[19] R. Carnap and Y. Bar-Hillel, "An Outline of a Theory of Semantic Information," *MIT Research Laboratory of Electronics Technical Report* 247, 1953.

this language is a meaningful (true or false) string of basic sentences joined by some combination of logical connectives. A *state description* s is a conjunction of nm basic sentences containing each of the n individuals with each of the m properties, or its negation, but not both. A sentence is called a *tautology* t if it is logically true, a *contradiction* f if it is logically false, and *factual* i if it is logically indeterminate.[20] The fundamental assumption is contained in the following:

Axiom The semantic information content of a sentence is an increasing function of the number of sentences implied by it.

The following definitions stem from notions in inductive logic and its statistical nature.

We assume that there exists a *logical probability* $M(x)$ of sentence x that satisfies the following axioms:

Axiom 1 $0 \leq M(s) \leq 1$.

Axiom 2 $\sum_{s} M(s) = 1$.

Axiom 3 If sentence x is contradictory, then $M(x) = 0$.

Axiom 4 If sentence x is factual, then $M(x) = \sum_{s} M(s)$ for all s implying x.

Axiom 5 $M(s)$ is invariant under permutation of the individuals in s.

Axiom 6 $M(s)$ is invariant under permutation of the properties in s.

Axiom 7 $M(s)$ is invariant under replacement of a property by its negation in s.

Axiom 8 If x and y have no property in common, then
$M(x \text{ and } y) = M(x)\,M(y)$

Axiom 9 $M(x)$ is independent of the number of individuals not in x.

Carnap and Bar-Hillel define the semantic *content* of sentence x to be

$$C(x) = 1 - M(x)$$

and the semantic *information* in sentence x to be

$$I(x) = -\log_2 M(x)$$

The following elementary theorems are typical:

If $x \rightarrow y$, then $C(x) \geq C(y)$

$C(\overline{x}) = 1 - C(x)$

[20] See R. Carnap, *The Logical Syntax of Language*, Kegan Paul, Trench, Trubner and Co., Ltd., London, 1937; *Introduction to Semantics*, Harvard University Press, Cambridge, Mass., 1946; and *Logical Foundations of Probability*, University of Chicago Press, Chicago, 1950; and Y. Bar-Hillel, "A Quasi-arithmetical Notation for Syntactic Descriptions," *Language*, vol. 29, pp. 47–58, 1953.

$C(x \wedge y) \leq C(x) + C(y)$
If $x \rightarrow y$, then $I(x) \geq I(y)$
$I(x \wedge y) \geq I(x) \geq I(x \vee y)$

$$I(x) = \log_2 \frac{1}{1 - C(x)}$$

It is important to note that the theory of semantic information proposed by Carnap and Bar-Hillel[21] is quite different from the theory of information formulated by Shannon.[22] Also, its consequences have yet to be applied to natural language.

Redundancy of English Shannon[23] considered that the English alphabet consists of twenty-seven symbols—the twenty-six letters and one symbol for the space between words. English text can be generated by strings of k symbols subject to their laws of stochastic behavior. Let X_k denote the random variable corresponding to the string of k symbols. That is, the random variable X_0 assumes 27 values with equal probability, the random variable X_1 assumes 27 values with probabilities given by single-symbol frequencies, the random variable X_2 assumes 27^2 values with probabilities given by the frequencies of pairs of symbols, and so on.

By statistical count it has been found[24,25] that redundancies behave as follows:

X_k	*Probabilities*	*Entropy* $H(X_k)$	*Redundancy* $1 - H(X_k)/H(X_0)$
X_0	$1/27$	4.75 bits/symbol	.00
X_1	p_i	4.2	.12
X_2	p_{ij}	3.6	.24
X_3	p_{ijk}	3.1	.35
. . .	. . .	. . .	. . .
X_8	$p_{i_1 \cdots i_8}$	2.4	.50

Since the maximum uncertainty or entropy is $H(X_0) = \log_2 27 = 4.76$ bits per symbol for twenty-seven equiprobable symbols, the redundancies $1 - H(X_k)/\log_2 27$ increase as k increases, and for $k = 8$ the redundancy in X_k is $1 - 2.4/4.76$, or approximately 50 per cent. This result gives rise to the statement that "English is 50 per cent redundant," which means that half of what we write is determined by the structure of the English language while the remaining half is randomly determined. Actually, the

[21] *Op. cit.*, fn. 19.
[22] *Op. cit.*, fn. 4.
[23] *Ibid.*
[24] *Ibid.*
[25] See Brillouin, *op. cit.*, fn. 12.

limiting redundancy of English is greater than 50 per cent, since intersymbol influences extend beyond eight letters.

Stochastic Model of Language Markov[26] examined the first 20,000 letters in the first chapter and the first sixteen sonnets of the second chapter of Pushkin's novel in verse, *Eugene Onegin,* and from this developed a theory of chains of symbols. We will now consider a slightly more general stochastic model of language based on the resulting theory of Markov chains.[27] Suppose we have an alphabet of s symbols or states—the symbols could be letters, letters plus a word spacer, entire words, phrases, or parts of speech. First, a set of initial probabilities $p_i^{(0)}$ is needed to start the stochastic process of text generation. Let $p_1^{(0)}$ be the probability that the text begins with symbol 1, $p_2^{(0)}$ be the probability that the text begins with symbol 2, and so on. Second, we need a set of transition probabilities p_{ik} to continue the stochastic process once it is started according to the initial probabilities $p_i^{(0)}$. Let p_{ik} be the conditional probability that the kth symbol occurs next, given that the ith symbol has just occurred. Since both i and k can assume s values, the matrix P of transition probabilities has s rows, s columns, and s^2 elements p_{ik} where p_{ik} is the element in the ith row and kth column of P. For example, if $s = 27$, then P has 729 elements. Now imagine that a segment of natural-language text is generated by a random process that behaves according to these laws. Given the transition probabilities, we can compute the conditional probability that in n steps we move from symbol i to symbol k. For example, the probability $p_{ik}^{(2)}$ that in two steps (or two symbols) we move from symbol i to symbol k is nothing more than the probability of going in one step from i to j and then in a second step from j to k, summed over all possible intervening symbols j—that is,

$$p_{ik}^{(2)} = \sum_{j=1}^{s} p_{ij}p_{jk}$$

Similarly the probability $p_{ik}^{(3)}$ of going from i to k in three steps is

$$p_{ik}^{(3)} = \sum_{j=1}^{s} p_{ij}p_{jk}^{(2)}$$

and so on. Given the initial probabilities and the transition probabilities,

[26] A. A. Markov, "An Example of a Statistical Investigation of the Text of 'Eugen Onegin' Illustrating the Connection of Trials in a Chain" (in Russian), *Bulletin de l'Académie Imperiale des Sciences de St. Pétersbourg,* St. Petersburg, 1913.

[27] See Feller, *op. cit.,* fn. 1; and B. Mandelbrot, "On the Theory of Word Frequencies and on Related Markovian Models of Discourse," in *Structure of Language and Its Mathematical Aspects, Proceedings of Symposia in Applied Mathematics,* vol. XII, American Mathematical Society, Providence, R.I., 1960.

we can compute the absolute probability $p_k^{(n)}$ that the nth future symbol is symbol k—i.e., that in n steps we obtain symbol k. This probability is nothing more than the probability of starting initially with some symbol i and then moving in n steps from i to k, summed over all possible i—that is,

$$p_k^{(n)} = \sum_{j=1}^{s} p_i^{(0)} p_{ik}^{(n)}$$

For large values of s (i.e., large matrices) these computations can be readily performed on a digital computer.

In practice, however, we deal only with samples, and hence the population probabilities $p_i^{(0)}$ and p_{ik} are unknown. Thus it is necessary to analyze by machine a large volume of homogeneous text and to compute the sample frequencies $f_i^{(0)}$ and f_{ik} which will serve as estimates of $p_i^{(0)}$ and p_{ik}, respectively. If the sample size n is sufficiently large, these estimates will be close enough. If these computations are carried out and the frequencies used to predict for a new corpus, then a comparison of the actual results with the predictions will provide a test of the appropriateness of the stochastic model. In any case, the model provides considerable insight into the statistical behavior of language, even though, as Chomsky[28] points out, a finite-state model will not generate "all and only the grammatical sentences" of English.

LANGUAGE-DATA PROCESSING

Automatic Indexing and Information Retrieval We will consider first the process of indexing. The conventional method of indexing is simply a way of making a *yes* or *no* decision. If one is given a document D and an index term I, he finds that I either applies to D or it does not apply. Thus the deterministic notion of the *relevance* $r(D,I)$ of document D to index term I can be quantized as

$$r(D,I) = \begin{matrix} 1 & \text{if } I \text{ applies to } D \\ 0 & \text{if } I \text{ does not apply to } D \end{matrix}$$

This act of quantizing qualitative concepts is usually, although not necessarily, beneficial.

Deterministic indexing has been refined by the method of probabilistic indexing developed by Maron, Kuhns, and Ray[29] which replaced the completely deterministic *yes/no* decision of relevance by a probability weight lying in the interval 0 to 1. This permits finer shading of decision

[28] *Op. cit.*, fn. 3.

[29] M. E. Maron and J. L. Kuhns, "On Relevance, Probabilistic Indexing, and Information Retrieval," *Journal of the Association for Computing Machinery*, vol. 7, no. 3, 1960; and M. E. Maron et al., "Probabilistic Indexing," *Ramo Wooldridge Data Systems Project Office Technical Memorandum No.* 3, 1959.

(see Maron, "A Logician's View of Language-data Processing," earlier in this volume).

Probabilistic indexing is a statistical technique for literature indexing and searching in a mechanized library system. A concept of relevance is developed from probability theory which allows a computer, given an information request I_j, to make a statistical inference and to derive a relevance number $r(D_i,I_j)$ for each document D_i. This is done by defining the relevance number $r(D_i,I_j)$ to be the conditional probability $P(D_i|I_j)$ that the document D_i satisfies the user given that the request used index term I_j. A document D_1 is more relevant to index term I_j than in another document D_2, if the first relevance number is greater than the second one—that is, $r(D_1,I_j) > r(D_2,I_j)$. The result of a search is an ordered list of the documents that satisfy the request, ranked according to their relevance to the request.

In practice, $P(D_i|I_j)$ can be calculated from Bayes' theorem

$$P(D_i|I_j) = \frac{P(D_i)\,P(I_j|D_i)}{P(I_j)}$$

where $P(D_i)$ is the prior probability that D_i will satisfy the request, $P(I_j)$ is the prior probability of choosing index term I_j, and $P(I_j|D_i)$ is the conditional probability that the user will formulate a request by using index term I_j, given that he wants information contained in D_i. We estimate $P(D_i)$ from the number of uses of D_i divided by the total number of document uses. For any request I_j, $P(I_j)$ is a constant. We estimate $P(I_j|D_i)$ by using the subjective weight or degree to which the jth index term applies to the ith document, when properly scaled.[30]

Phyllis Baxendale[31] presented a method of automatically indexing a document which involved selecting the significant words and phrases and ordering them according to their post-selection frequencies. The index was then constructed from the n words or phrases with the highest frequencies, n being chosen so as to yield an index with the desired number of entries. Miss Baxendale suggested that n should equal from 0.5 per cent to 1.0 per cent of the number of words in the document. She experimented with three methods of selection: (1) selection of all words except pronouns, articles, conjunctions, conjunctive adverbs, copulas and auxiliary verbs, and quantitative adjectives; (2) selection of all words in only the first and last sentences of each paragraph; and (3) selection

[30] See M. E. Maron, "Automatic Indexing: An Experimental Inquiry," *Journal of the Association for Computing Machinery,* vol. 8, pp. 404–417, 1961; and H. E. Stiles, "The Association Factor in Information Retrieval," *Journal of The Association for Computing Machinery,* vol. 8, no. 2, pp. 271–279, 1961.

[31] P. Baxendale, "Machine-made Index for Technical Literature: An Experiment," *IBM Journal of Research and Development,* vol. II, no. 4, pp. 354–361, 1958.

of the first four words following each preposition unless a second preposition or a punctuation mark is encountered. Miss Baxendale's exhibited indexes are surprisingly similar—the same words, with approximately the same relative frequencies, tend to be chosen by each method—and the indexes consist of single words, even though she makes a strong case for using word groups.

Swanson[32] described a study of automatic indexing and test searching in order to offer an approach to the basic problem of library automation.[33] He presented and discussed a fundamental approach to automatic indexing and retrieval and reported the results of preliminary experiments on the searching of text, which he regards as equivalent to automatic indexing. A collection of 100 articles was chosen as an experimental library, and each article was studied for its possible relevance to each of fifty questions. Degrees of relevance were allowed. The results of a series of retrieval experiments were analyzed by a scheme which rewarded successful retrieval and punished irrelevant retrieval. Three methods of retrieval were employed: (1) conventional retrieval using subject-heading index but no machine procedures; (2) retrieval based on specification of words and phrases in disjunctive and conjunctive combinations but no retrieval aids; and (3) search requests formulated as in (2) but with a word and phrase list, similar to a thesaurus, and the index thereto as retrieval aids. The exact techniques and interesting comparative results are discussed later in this volume by Swanson in "The Formulation of the Retrieval Problem." Method (1) was shown to be uniformly worse than (2) or (3).[34]

Borko[35] described a method for developing an empirically based, computer-derived classification system. He studied 618 psychological abstracts, comprising approximately 50,000 words, of which nearly 6,800 were unique words. The text was coded in machine language, and the computer program arranged the words in order of frequency of occurrence. From the list of words which occurred at least twenty times, ex-

[32] D. R. Swanson, "Searching Natural Language Text by Computer," *Science*, vol. 132, no. 3434, pp. 1099–1104, 1960.

[33] See H. P. Luhn, "A Statistical Approach to Mechanized Encoding and Searching of Literary Information," *IBM Journal of Research and Development*, vol. I, no. 4, pp. 309–317, 1957; and "A New Method of Recording and Searching Information," *American Documentation*, vol. IV, no. 1, pp. 14–16, 1951; and Bar-Hillel, *op. cit.*, fn. 14.

[34] See C. Cleverdon, *Interim Report on the Test Programme of an Investigation into the Comparative Efficiency of Indexing Systems*, The College of Aeronautics, Cranfield, England, 1960.

[35] H. Borko, "The Construction of an Empirically Based Mathematically Derived Classification System," *Proceedings of the Spring Joint Computer Conference*, vol. 21, pp. 278–289, 1962.

cluding syntactical terms, he selected ninety words as index terms. These were arranged in a data matrix with index terms as rows and document numbers as columns. The elements of this data matrix denoted the number of times each term was used in each document. A 90-by-90 correlation matrix showing the relationship of each term to every other term was computed from the data matrix. The correlation matrix was factor-analyzed and the first ten eigenvectors were selected by him as factors. These were interpreted as the major categories of a classification system after rotation for meaning. These factors were shown to be compatible with, but not identical to, the classification system used by the American Psychological Association. The results tend to demonstrate the feasibility of an empirically derived classification system using factor analysis as the technique of language-data processing.

Another aspect of automatic indexing concerns the dual notions of index space (i.e., the set of all index terms) and document space (i.e., the set of all documents) . A point in the index space corresponds to a unique index term; a point in the document space corresponds to a unique document. Mathematically, the problem of classifying documents with respect to the set of index terms is the same as that of classifying index terms with respect to the set of documents. One problem can be called the dual of the other. The "distance" between two points in index space is a measure of the "closeness" of the corresponding index terms. Maron and Kuhns[36] have examined several statistical measures of closeness which involve either conditional probabilities or correlation coefficients. Tanimoto[37] defined a similarity coefficient of a pair of index terms with respect to a set of documents, which turns out to be the conditional probability of choosing at random a document that has both index terms, given that it has at least one of them. In an analogous way he defined the dual similarity coefficient of a pair of documents with respect to the set of index terms. Thus the elaboration of a request can be done rapidly by automatic grouping in index space.

Automatic Abstracting Some of the early work on automatic indexing led immediately to the process of automatic abstracting—how to condense many words of a document into a few significant words by machine. The first published work was by Luhn,[38] later followed by Edmundson and Wyllys[39] and others. Luhn's method uses the frequency of words in

[36] *Op. cit.*, fn. 29.

[37] T. Tanimoto, *An Elementary Mathematical Theory of Classification and Prediction,* International Business Machines Corporation Report, 1958.

[38] H. P. Luhn, "The Automatic Creation of Literature Abstracts," *IBM Journal of Research and Development,* vol. II, no. 2, pp. 159–165, 1959.

[39] H. P. Edmundson and R. E. Wyllys, "Automatic Abstracting and Indexing: Survey and Recommendations," *Communications of the Association for Computing Machinery,* vol. 4, no. 5, pp. 226–234, 1961.

the document. A word is called significant if its frequency f_i lies above a certain threshold but is not a common word, such as pronoun, preposition, or article. Each sentence of the text is assigned a score by squaring the number of significant words and dividing the result by the total number of words in the sentence. All sentences scoring above a certain threshold according to this mathematical rule are chosen as significant or key sentences. These sentences, listed in their natural order, comprise the automatic abstract. This abstract is really an extract since it is simply a selection of the author's sentences and not a creation of sentences by the machine program. Perhaps the process should be called *automatic extracting,* but the term *abstracting* is now generally accepted and understood by workers in the field; someday we shall have programs that produce a true automatic abstract.

As pointed out earlier, Luhn used the frequencies of the words in the document. Now, it is not clear that this is the best way to abstract. Edmundson and Wyllys[40] have studied the criterion of the frequency of words in a given document in relation to the frequency of those same words in a general reference corpus. Several functions have been proposed that bring into play not only the frequency f_i of the word i in the document, but also the frequency g_i of the word i in general text. The researcher can then specify what he means by this general reference class—for example, certain standard texts on chemistry or certain issues of a Russian publication. In any case, the significance of a word i is not just a function of f_i but also of g_i. Thus we have a concept of the significance of a word which is an extension of that of Luhn. There is an infinite number of functions of the two quantities f_i and g_i; which one should we choose? Four simple functions have been investigated: f_i/g_i; $f_i - g_i$; $f_i/(f_i + g_i)$; and $\log (f_i/g_i)$. The discriminatory and computability properties of these functions have been studied in order to eliminate a large class of unsuitable functions. The conclusions, although not final, seem to be that the ratio f_i/g_i and the difference $f_i - g_i$ are highly suitable.

Using the above statistical techniques, it is also possible to classify a document as to subject field. From general reference texts covering many subject fields the reference frequencies g_{ik} of word i in each subject category k are computed. These frequencies g_{ik} can be listed in a table or matrix with a row for each word i and a column for each subject category k. From the document the word frequencies f_i are then computed and listed in the same order as in the table. By matching the list with each column of the table, one can statistically determine the subject field of the document as the best match according to some suitable criterion of best fit. Tanimoto[41] has developed another method for handling the

[40] *Ibid.*
[41] *Op. cit.,* fn. 37.

problem of classification or taxonomy, and Bar-Hillel has some unpublished results.

Oswald[42] developed a method of automatic indexing and abstracting which differs from the techniques of Luhn and Baxendale in that it combines the notion of significance as a function of word frequency with the notion of significance as a function of word groupings, by employing *multiterms* (as defined below) as the basic unit for measuring the importance of a sentence. Words whose function is syntactic (i.e., articles, prepositions, conjunctions, etc.) along with qualifiers (for example, *good, very*) are discarded. The remaining words are frequency-counted. Next, juxtapositions involving a high-frequency word are recorded as multiterms. The recording of multiterms begins with those that contain the single word of highest frequency and continues until six successive words, in order of decreasing frequency, produce either no multiterms or no new multiterms. Sentences containing two or more multiterms are then listed as significant sentences. The automatic abstract is formed by the choice, beginning with the sentence having the largest number of multiterms, of enough significant sentences to meet one of two criteria: (1) a fixed number of sentences; or (2) enough sentences so that their total length approximates a given per cent of the text.

The reader should not get the notion that statistical methods alone are recommended. Particularly in automatic abstracting, we strongly recommend various measures of significance—statistical, positional, semantic, and pragmatic measures—perhaps by using weighted linear combinations. One can assign coefficients or weights according to whether or not a word occurs in the title, in the first or last paragraph, in the first or last sentence of a paragraph, in a sentence containing the words *conclusion* or *summary*, in a sentence with personal names or dates, and the like. Thus, it is possible to combine statistical and nonstatistical methods to get more powerful results.

Automatic Translation In automatic translation most of the methods are strictly nonprobabilistic. For example, problems of syntactic structure, segmentation, and polysemia are often handled by the purely deterministic mathematics of trees, graphs, lattices, and logic. However, we will point out certain problem areas where statistics plays a role.[43] First,

[42]See H. P. Edmundson et. al., *Automatic Indexing and Abstracting of the Contents of Documents,* Planning Research Corporation, R-126, 1959.

[43]See C. N. Mooers, "Zatocoding and Developments in Information Retrieval," *ASLIB Proceedings,* vol. 8, pp. 3–19, 1956; G. W. King and I. L. Wieselman, "Stochastic Methods of Mechanical Translation," *Mechanical Translation,* vol. 3, no. 2, pp. 38–39, 1956; V. H. Yngve, "Gap Analysis and Syntax," *Transactions IRE,* vol. IT-2, no. 3, pp. 106–112, 1956; and E. Delavenay, *An Introduction to Machine Translation,* Praeger, New York, 1960.

in the compilation of a machine dictionary we are interested in knowing how large a sample corpus to choose in order to have enough distinct words to translate new text with a given probability of coverage. Good and Toulmin[44] have shown that the probability of coverage is approximated by $1 - n_1/n$ where n_1 is the number of distinct words that occurred exactly once in a corpus of sample size n. As is theoretically expected, we find empirically that the percentage of coverage increases with dictionary size at first rapidly, then asymptotically, so that even a large increase in size produces little change in coverage.[45] Second, in dictionary compilation the listing of multiple equivalents for each source word can be done in any order, but in the early stages of a machine-translation project, it is best to list the multiple equivalents in decreasing frequency order if the program is limited to selecting only one equivalent. This technique requires frequency counts of target-language equivalents, but does not solve the problem of polysemia. However, some problems of polysemia can be reduced to simpler ones by empirical statistical investigations of language behavior.[46] For example, the translation of prepositions can be made statistically more accurate by programs that take into account the statistical preferences and exclusions induced by semantic and syntactic properties of the context of the preposition. Another example is the insertion of the English articles *a, an,* and *the* when the source language has no articles. Here, the statistical analysis of the target language—English—affords rules that increase the accuracy and idiomatic correctness.[47] In general, it will turn out that many of the rules of the ultimate machine grammar will be statistical rules, for, as Sapir said, "All grammars leak."[48] Another application of statistical techniques to automatic translation is evaluating the output of the process as to its correctness and readability. This problem also arises in automatic abstracting, but since more translation programs than abstracting programs are now in operation, the need has received more attention in automatic translation. There is no general

[44] *Op. cit.,* fn. 16.

[45] See H. Josselson, *The Russian Word Count,* Detroit, 1953; and M. Zarechnak and A. F. R. Brown, "Current Research at Georgetown University," in H. P. Edmundson (ed.), *Proceedings of the National Symposium on Machine Translation,* Prentice-Hall, Englewood Cliffs, N.J., 1961.

[46] See A. Kaplan, "An Experimental Study of Ambiguity and Context," *Mechanical Translation,* vol. 2, no. 2, pp. 39–46, 1955; and R. Gould, "Multiple Correspondence," *Mechanical Translation,* vol. 4, no. 1/2, pp. 14–27, 1957.

[47] See S. Glazer, *Article Requirements of Plural Nouns in Russian Chemistry Texts,* Georgetown University, Institute of Languages and Linguistics, Seminar Work Paper MT 42, 1957.

[48] E. Sapir, as cited in: C. F. Voegelin, "Casual and Noncasual Utterances within Unified Structure," in T. Sebeok (ed.), *Style in Language,* Technology Press–Wiley, New York and London, 1960, p. 65.

agreement on how best to evaluate translation output. One method is to perform a statistical analysis of the results of comparison tests of the machine output and human translator output. Another is to operate on the translated output with the inverse machine program to retranslate to the source language and then see how close one gets to the original text. However, there are some basic traps here, for it may be that such an inverse transformation is statistically error-correcting. One might have good retranslation, but the first translation might still be a poor one. General statistical criteria for evaluating the quality of automatic translation output still remain to be developed.[49]

We have surveyed the theory and application of statistics to the modeling and processing of natural language via a computer. It has been pointed out that modern computers thrive on a diet of statistics and that natural language abounds in statistics. But these two properties alone are insufficient. What is needed most are precise formulations of interesting linguistic hypotheses in order to test them, the adoption by linguists of clear inferential procedures of testing and estimating, and the establishment of statistical methods for handling the evidential value of linguistic phenomena.

Partial statistical solutions to some of the problems of linguistics and language-data processing have been discussed. In most cases these are nothing more than refinements of deterministic methods. For example, it is clear that probabilistic indexing is superior to deterministic indexing; however, in order to get the necessary probability weights and relevance numbers, one must first compile library-usage statistics. On the other hand, there appear to be no outstanding examples of complete solutions. The great question is whether this is because the field of language-data processing is underdeveloped, or whether it is due to the intrinsic difficulties of the problem area of natural language, or both.

[49]See Bar-Hillel, *op. cit.*, fn. 14; Delavenay, *op. cit.*, fn. 43; and Edmundson, *op. cit.*, fn. 45.

Machine translation

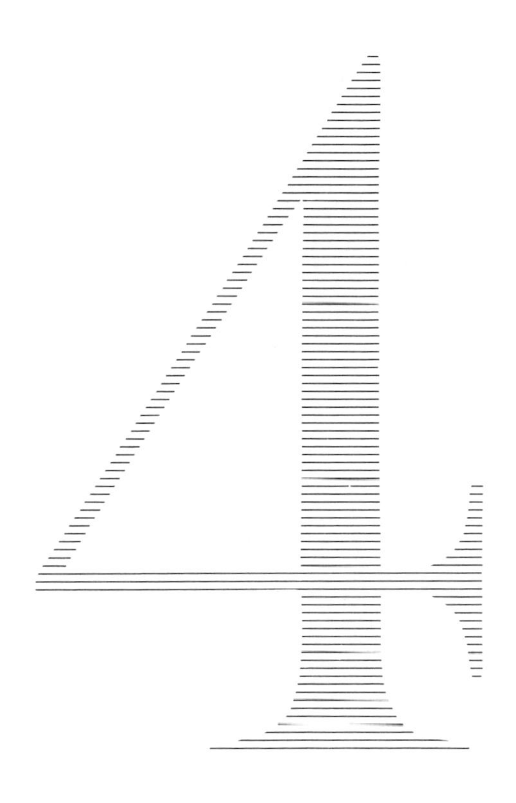

DAVID G. HAYS

Research procedures in machine translation

The symbolic nature of language is probably responsible for the widely held but erroneous view that linguistics is a branch of mathematics: a string of symbols "looks like" a mathematical formula. And, of course, a high school language textbook, with its rules, looks rather like a mathematical handbook. Mathematicians are forced to adhere to the rules of mathematical systems by the high cost of mistakes (i.e., of variations from the rules). Most speakers of most natural languages never learn the textbook rules, and those who do learn them discover soon enough that the cost of breaking many of the stated rules is negligible. In fact, whereas mathematical systems are defined by their axioms, their explicit and standard rules, natural languages are defined by the habits of their speakers, and the so-called rules are at best reports of those habits and at worst pedantry.[1] There is good reason for moderate pedantry in language teaching, as G. B. Shaw—lately with the collaboration of Lerner and Loewe—preached. But processing natural language on a computer calls for precise, accurate, voluminous knowledge of the linguistic behavior of the speakers or authors whose utterances or writings are to be processed. Here we shall consider acquisition of that knowledge.

TYPES AND SOURCES OF INFORMATION

Any language-data processing system has a purpose. A system for machine translation (MT) is expected to accept text in some natural language, perhaps Russian, and to produce text in another language, perhaps English. The output text should convey the same information as the input text; if it describes a chemical experiment, a chemist should be able to read the translation and reproduce the experiment with no more difficulty than if he had read the original report. Moreover, he should be able to

[1] See the discussion beginning with the words, "I am concerned with regularities; I am not concerned with rules," in Paul Ziff, *Semantic Analysis*, Cornell University Press, Ithaca, N.Y., 1960, pp. 34–38.

read the translation as easily as if it had been written by a person fluent in the output language—for example, Russian documents should be translated into versions that might have been written by Americans.[2] Other systems—for indexing, abstracting, automatic programming, sociological or historical research, legal documentation, and so forth—have other purposes, but here we shall concentrate on a detailed treatment of machine translation.

Knowing what a system must accomplish tells the designer—clearly or not—what information must be supplied it. An MT system[3] must include a list of source-language words with their target-language equivalents; when it becomes apparent that many words have alternative equivalents, and that choosing among them causes trouble for the reader (confusing him or at least slowing him down), the designer realizes that he must supply the system with information about equivalent choice—under what circumstances each equivalent is chosen.

Even if it were possible to translate every word accurately without reference to context, readers would be dissatisfied with the results. Individual words have meanings, but it is only by putting words together in sentences and paragraphs that authors can communicate useful ideas. In a source-language text, the relationships among the words in each sentence are indicated by natural devices belonging to the syntax of the input language. Translating word by word does not carry over the indicators of relationships, since natural languages share syntactic devices only to about the same extent that they share words; there are cognate words that can be recognized in French or German text by an American who knows no French or German, and there are cognate syntactic devices that make word-by-word "translations" partially understandable, but to rely on them would make reading the MT output like solving a word puzzle. Thus the designer must furnish his MT system with information about the syntactic structure of the input language and the output language and about the correspondence between them.

For sources of information the system designer will naturally turn first to published grammars and dictionaries. A grammar[4] lists categories (of words) and rules for combining categories; it purports to describe the syntax of its language. A dictionary lists words and specifies for each the

[2] For a broad discussion of the problems involved in evaluating MT output, see George A. Miller and J. G. Beebe-Center, "Some Psychological Methods for Evaluating the Quality of Translations," *Mechanical Translation*, vol. 3, no. 3, pp. 73–80, December, 1956.

[3] An early sketch of an MT system was presented by Victor H. Yngve, "A Framework for Syntactic Translation," *Mechanical Translation*, vol. 4, no. 3, pp. 59–65, December, 1957.

[4] For example, H. Poutsma, *A Grammar of Late Modern English*, 2d ed., P. Noordhoff, Groningen, 1928 (2 parts in 5 vols.).

categories to which it belongs; each entry also contains a discussion of the meaning of the word or a list of its equivalents in a second language. Taking grammars and dictionaries together, it should be possible to read and write grammatically correct sentences, translating each word accurately. Unfortunately, published grammars and dictionaries of the best sort are inadequate, even though they are vast compilations based on the prior original work of many linguists.

The largest dictionaries are intended to meet the needs of laymen, not of professional linguists; consequently, they omit reference to many categories that the layman can either recognize intuitively or disregard when he sees an unfamiliar word in text. The most detailed grammars are written for linguists who, recognizing that new words can be added to existing categories, make no attempt to list every word in every category. In general, until computational linguistics was conceived, no one needed a fully detailed account of any language for any purpose. Now that the need has arisen, new data must be collected and analyzed.

There are qualifications, of course. Fully detailed accounts of language have scientific value for linguistics, since they permit more exact tests of theory than gross statements about general tendencies could support. Furthermore, the major grammatical treatises dealing with Western languages—English, Russian, and others—contain many lists of words with special properties; these lists can be used to elaborate dictionaries by noting, in the dictionary entry for each word on the grammarian's list *X*, that the word has property *x*. But even a combination of information from multiple existing sources does not lead to a final, complete dictionary and there is still information to be gained from research.

The linguist has two sources of information beyond published studies. He can consult persons who speak the language, called *informants.* He can also study text, either written in the language or transcribed from conversations spoken in it. Of course, the published studies go back to exactly the same sources in the end. The two kinds of data sources can be used in tandem, with the informants serving as *editors* who comment on the text. Moreover, it is possible to obtain or create parallel texts in two languages, perhaps one known and one unknown, or one the input and the other the output of a proposed translation system.

The traditional methods of linguistics are based on the use of informants, or the alternate use of text and informants.[5] For non-Western languages, at least, it is fair to say that the success thus far achieved in scientific linguistics is the result of rich technical development and careful application of the informant method. Western languages have been studied by text methods and also with informants; often the linguist

[5] Zellig S. Harris, *Methods in Structural Linguistics,* University of Chicago Press, Chicago, 1951.

serves as his own informant when he is studying his own native language. The largest, most detailed grammars now in existence are the text-based grammars of Western languages, and it seems inevitable that text must supersede the informant when the details are to be filled in, simply because no one knows every particular of his language. Certainly no one knows any modern language, well developed as a medium for scientific and scholarly communication, in all its specialized ramifications. The informant learns his language by formal training and, more importantly, by constant exposure to its use. He cannot repeat to the linguist what he has never seen or heard. A sufficiently diverse set of informants would serve for any language, but the practical difficulties are obvious.

Moreover, data collected by textual research have a certain validity that data obtained from informants can never possess. An MT system, or any other automatic language-data processing (ALDP) system, will be called on to process segments of text from a definable stream. Predictions about the nature of that stream can be made, by the ordinary logic of statistical inference, from samples of it. Predictions can also be made from the responses of informants, but then the logic of inference must take into account the informant as a device that gathers information, summarizes, forgets, distorts, and reports.[6] The linguist should wonder whether he could not design a procedure that would process the same material as the informant more accurately and with less distortion.

The question of procedures for linguistic research always founders in discussion of the informant's intuition. The informant is more effective than a computing machine as a device for linguistic data reduction, according to this argument, because he understands the text to which he is exposed. The argument seems to come down to two points. First, the informant has a rough-and-ready grammar for his own language, which he uses as a framework on which to hang whatever new grammatical details come to him in reading or listening to new material. Second, he uses semantic analysis of text in deciding what its grammatical structure must be. As we shall see, the first point does not differentiate between computers and informants, since the linguist establishes some sort of grammatical framework at the very beginning of his research and commits it to machine memory; the framework may come from specific knowledge of the language to be studied or from a theory of linguistic universals, but it is essential. The second point is more significant: Can the gram-

[6] The methodological and technical problems raised by the use of informants are enormous. In psychological and sociological research, a sizable literature has grown up. See, for example, Robert L. Kahn and Charles F. Cannell, *The Dynamics of Interviewing,* Wiley, New York, 1957; Herbert Hyman, *Survey Design and Analysis,* The Free Press, Glencoe, Ill., 1955; Warren S. Torgerson, *Theory and Methods of Scaling,* Wiley, New York, 1958.

matical structure of a language be determined without reference to its semantic structure? If this question receives a positive reply, as it does from some but not all linguists,[7] then *should* grammar and semantics be kept apart? We cannot even begin to answer this question until we have looked into the nature of grammar, in following sections. In any case, research procedures based on text can be formulated with whatever admixture of informant intuition is considered appropriate.

The invention of techniques using text alone, with no help of any kind from informants, is one of the most exciting problems in linguistics today, and stimulation of work along this line may prove to be the most important contribution of the computer to the science of language.[8] The problem is to give an adequate characterization of the object of grammatical research without reference either to the intuitions of the informant or investigator or to the infinite *corpus* (body of text) that would resolve all questions if it could be written and studied.[9] (Grammatical statements often have the form *Item X can—or cannot—be used in context Y*. Such a statement would have an obvious empirical interpretation with reference to an infinitely long text in which everything occurred that could occur.)

Edited text can be used with less inventiveness; it is therefore a more practical material for the investigator who wants immediate results in the form of at least approximate knowledge about the speech habits of authors using a certain natural language. Given a text, editor informants can be asked to translate it, to paraphrase it, to describe the grammatical relations within each of its sentences, and so on.[10] The editor certainly uses his ideas about grammar, his semantic understanding of the text, and all his "intuition," in this process. The linguist's task is to generalize and formalize the informant's intuitive analyses of single sentences into a description

[7]Noam Chomsky, "Semantic Considerations in Grammar," *Georgetown University Monograph Series in Languages and Linguistics*, no. 8, pp. 141–154, Washington, D.C., 1955.

[8]Two papers on this subject have recently been published: Paul L. Garvin, "Automatic Linguistic Analysis: A. Heuristic Problem," and Sydney M. Lamb, "On the Mechanization of Syntactic Analysis," in 1961 *International Conference on Machine Translation of Languages and Applied Language Analysis*, vol. 2 pp. 655—686, H. M. Stationery Office, London, 1962. See also O. S. Kulagina, "A Method of Defining Grammatical Concepts on the Basis of Set Theory," *Problemy Kibernetiki*, no. 1, pp. 203—214, 1958.

[9]A point raised by I. I. Revzin, "On the Notion of a 'Set of Marked Sentences' in the Set-theoretic Concept of O. S. Kulagina," in N. D. Andreyev (ed.), *Abstracts of the Conference on Mathematical Linguistics, Leningrad, 1959*. Translation 893-D, U. S. Joint Publications Research Service, Washington, D.C., 1959.

[10]The latest edition of the guide used in this work at RAND is Kenneth E. Harper et al., *Studies in Machine Translation—8: Manual for Postediting Russian Text*, RM-2068, The RAND Corporation, Santa Monica, Calif., 1960.

of the language as a whole, testing along the way for consistency, completeness, and simplicity.[11]

This discussion, therefore, is largely devoted to research methods based on text. Informant-centered methods are well described in the current literature, and text-based methods have definite advantages.

Text-based methods also have disadvantages that must not be forgotten. A large amount of text has to be processed before the investigator collects an adequate number of occurrences of any but the few commonest words or constructions. The cyclic method, to be described below, avoids this difficulty so far as possible by using a computer for much of the processing work. Another problem is the influence of the general environment on the content of any text. Caesar never wrote about television, yet no linguist would believe that the rules of Latin grammar prevented him. If there are no "octagonal whales" in our text, is it because of grammatical rules or not? The answer can only be that the distinction between grammatical rules and rules of other kinds is somewhat arbitrary, and will often be decided in terms of formal criteria without help from intuition. Only a dogmatist invariably knows a grammatical regularity when he sees one.

GRAMMAR

Grammar is a branch of linguistics. In a coherent treatment of the science or of a language, the study of grammar follows discussion of phonetics and phonemics—dealing with the sound system by which language is communicated orally—and of graphetics and graphemics—dealing with the writing system. Grammar itself has two main branches, morphology and syntax. Beyond syntax lies semantics, which will be considered later.

Morphology has to do with the analysis of words and *forms* of words. In some but not all languages the word forms that occur in text can be subdivided into repetitive fragments; that is, relatively few fragments combine and recombine in many ways to yield a large vocabulary of forms. In an MT system it is economical to avoid storing repetitive data if they can be reconstructed by a simple program from a smaller base; hence storage of fragments instead of full forms is usually advocated by system designers.[12]

More than economy is involved, however, since morphological analysis lays the foundation for syntax. Typically, the forms of a language can be segmented into prefixes, stems, and suffixes. For example, *inoperative* = *in* + *operate* + *ive*. A single form can consist of no prefixes or one or more prefixes, one or more stems, and no suffixes or one or more suffixes.

[11]Louis Hjelmslev, *Prolegomena to a Theory of Language* (Francis J. Whitfield, tr.), Univ. of Wisconsin Press, Madison, Wis., 1961, pp. 16–18.

[12]L. R. Micklesen, "Russian-English MT," in Erwin Reifler (ed.), *Linguistic and Engineering Studies in Automatic Language Translation of Scientific Russian into English,* Univ. of Washington Press, Seattle, Wash., 1958, p. 5.

It seems to be a universal feature of natural languages that if forms can be segmented, some of the segments are involved in syntactic rules. Thus *operate* is a verb, but the *-ive* suffix converts it into an adjective; *boy* is a singular noun, *boy* + *s* = *boys,* a plural noun. In Latin, Russian, and other languages, noun forms can be segmented into stems and case-number endings; the case endings are involved in syntactic agreement with verbs, prepositions, etc.

The morphological classes in a language are classes of prefixes, stems, and suffixes. The classification is established by noting that some stems occur with certain prefixes and suffixes attached, but not with others. A noun stem, morphologically, is a stem that occurs with suffixes belonging to a definite set—the noun suffixes of the language. A verb stem is one that takes verb suffixes, an adjective stem one that takes adjective suffixes, and so forth. Prefixes are sometimes peculiar to nouns, verbs, adjectives, etc., and sometimes are attached to stems in categories that cut across morphological parts of speech.

A form, consisting of certain definite segments, can be assigned to a morphological *form class* according to the class memberships of its components. This classification of the forms in a language is the eventual contribution of morphology to syntax; any procedure for syntactic research can begin with form classes rather than with individual forms.

Syntax has to do with the analysis of sentences and the relations that obtain among the forms that occur in them. The structure of a sentence can be described in several ways; the theory of *dependency,* as used here, is familiar to anyone who has studied grammar in school. Tesnière elaborated the concept,[13] Lecerf contributed to the theory,[14] and the present author and his colleagues are using it in studies of Russian.[15] According to dependency theory, a partial ordering can be established over the occurrences in a sentence. One occurrence is independent; all the others depend on it, directly or indirectly. Except for the independent occurrence, every occurrence has exactly one *governor,* on which it depends directly. The diagram of relations among occurrences in a sentence is a tree, an example of which is given in Figure 1.

[13]Lucien Tesnière, *Eléments de Syntaxe Structurale,* Klincksieck, Paris, 1959.

[14]Y. Lecerf, "Programme des Conflits, Modèle des Conflits," *La Traduction Automatique,* vol. 1, no. 4, pp. 11–20, October, 1960, and vol. 1, no. 5, pp. 17–36, December, 1960.

[15]Kenneth E. Harper and David G. Hays, "The Use of Machines in the Construction of a Grammar and Computer Program for Structural Analysis," *Information Processing,* UNESCO, Paris, 1960, pp. 188–194. David G. Hays, "Grouping and Dependency Theories," in H. P. Edmundson (ed.), *Proceedings of the National Symposium on Machine Translation,* Prentice-Hall, Englewood Cliffs, N.J., 1961, pp. 258–266. Haim Gaifman, *Dependency Systems and Phrase Structure Systems,* P-2315, The RAND Corporation, Santa Monica, Calif., 1961.

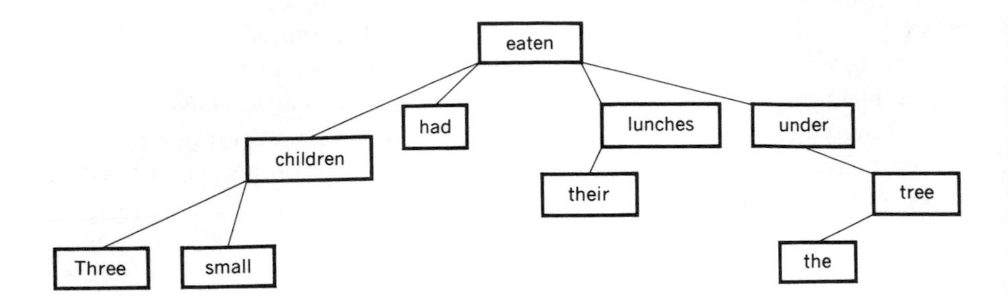

FIGURE 1 *Dependency structure.*

The syntactic structure of a sentence also includes a typification of each dependency link. Each dependent serves some definite syntactic *function* for its governor; one governor can have several dependents, all serving distinct functions, but it can have only one dependent serving any single function. (Of course, a given function can be served by several conjoined occurrences or by two or more occurrences in apposition.)

A sentence printed on a page is a linear array of letters, marks of punctuation, and spaces; morphological analysis converts it into another linear array, this one consisting of occurrences of segments grouped into forms and punctuated. If a sentence has a syntactic structure, it must be deducible from this array. The *indicators* that are available in natural language, the grammatical devices mentioned earlier as requiring translation along with the "words" in a text, include inflection, function words, occurrence order, and punctuation (in written language) or intonation (in spoken language). The use of these indicators is controlled by syntactic rules.

Inflection is used to show that a word that can serve several alternative functions in the language is in fact serving one in particular in this occurrence. For example, in Russian, a noun is inflected to show case: nominative when it functions as subject of a verb, accusative when serving as object, etc. Inflection is also used to show concord; a Russian adjective agrees with the noun it modifies in number, gender, and case, although one would not say that it has different functions corresponding to the different noun genders.

Function words are used in many languages; they have little or no *meaning,* in the ordinary sense, but serve only as indicators of syntactic structure. Prepositions, for example, differentiate functions more precisely than the case system can do; Russian has half a dozen cases and about fifty prepositions.

If each sentence contained no more than one word capable of governing any given function word or inflectional category, occurrence order would be almost irrelevant; an accusative noun in Russian, for example, might be recognized in any position as the direct object of the verb in the same sentence but for the fact that accusative nouns can serve other functions and other potential governors can occur along with a verb governing the accusative. (There is also the problem that some noun forms are ambiguous; they may be accusative or some other case.) Some prepositions, for example, govern the accusative, and a noun, a preposition, a verb, a comparative adjective or adverb, etc., can govern a genitive noun. Occurrence order therefore has to indicate which of several potential governors is actually served by a given occurrence. Occurrence order even differentiates functions; in English, the subject of a verb ordinarily comes ahead of it, whereas the object ordinarily follows, and the two are not morphologically distinguished except when one agrees with the verb in number and the other does not.

Punctuation serves sometimes to enforce a connection (as in hyphenated combinations), sometimes as a barrier to connection, sometimes to set off a semiparenthetic portion of the sentence. Intonation, historically the ancestor of punctuation, serves somewhat the same indicative role in spoken language.

One further kind of indication is given by word-class membership. The inflected forms of a word often share properties that help to indicate sentence structure. For example, words that govern objects (a syntactic function) can be taken as a class, and words that govern, as objects, accusative nouns are a subclass.

The *syntactic type* of a complete form is given by listing the functions that it can serve for all possible governors, the functions that possible dependents can serve for it, and the properties involved in agreement with potential governors or dependents. This information takes into account word-class membership and inflectional category; each function word in a language is likely to have a syntactic type peculiar to itself. Represented in a glossary by a grammar-code symbol, the syntactic type of a form is its whole contribution to the indication of the structure of any sentence in which it occurs.[16]

We can now see what the grammatical part of a machine-translation system must do: Using the indicators of a natural language—syntactic types, occurrence order, and punctuation, in conjunction with syntactic rules—the system must determine the structure of each input sentence,

[16]See, for example, K. E. Harper, D. G. Hays, and D. V. Mohr, *Studies in Machine Translation–6: Manual for Coding Russian Grammar,* RM-2066-1, The RAND Corporation, Santa Monica, Calif., 1958 (rev. 1960). A. S. Kozak et al., *Studies in Machine Translation–12: A Glossary of Russian Physics,* RM-2655, The RAND Corporation, Santa Monica, Calif., 1961.

i.e., the dependency links and their functional types. Then, given the structure of a sentence, the system must find devices in the output language with which to indicate that structure. On the input side, there may be ambiguities; sentence-structure determination can end with more than one possible interpretation of a given sentence. Semantic analysis, as we shall see, can reduce this ambiguity in many or most cases. On the output side the system should be designed to avoid introducing new ambiguities, although it seems likely that that goal can never be fully accomplished.[17]

SEMANTICS

Sounds or letter sequences indicate what forms occur in a text. Grammatical devices indicate what syntactic relationships obtain among the form occurrences. And the words and syntactic relationships in a text indicate its meaning. The concept of syntactic structure can be formalized, perhaps as outlined in the preceding section, and the grammatical devices of a language inventoried. When we turn from syntactic theory to semantic, we face a blank wall; no adequate formulation of semantic structure is available today. Nevertheless, we are already able to survey at least some of the problems with which a semantic theory must cope and to offer at least some specific characteristics that a semantic theory must possess.

The segmentation of forms into prefixes, stems, and suffixes does not imply that those segments are the units to be translated. As we have already seen, some segments are used in the input text to indicate syntactic relationships, and it is those relationships that have to be translated, by means of appropriate indicators in the output language, not the segments themselves. Other individual segments do in fact have to be translated, but it is sometimes most convenient to translate combinations of segments within one form and occasionally combinations that include segments of several forms. The choice of units is connected with the determination of meanings.

Much evidence goes to show that the words of natural languages are ambiguous—i.e., have multiple meanings.

In translation, as from Russian into English, French, German, etc., a given Russian word may have many different equivalents in each output language, and its English equivalents may not translate unambigu-

[17]This is only a brief statement of grammatical theory; for a more complete treatment see Charles F. Hockett, *A Course in Modern Linguistics,* Macmillan, New York, 1958.

ously into French even if the correlation with a Russian word is known.[18]

Monolingual dictionaries give multiple definitions for individual words, and, as Kaplan has shown, native speakers given context can "resolve the ambiguities" by assigning dictionary definitions to form occurrences.[19] Here it is only the fact of interinformant reliability that is convincing; no one informant could convince us that a real difference exists between two dictionary definitions of the same word, but if several informants, consulted independently, agree that occurrences *A, B, C,* . . . , take the first definition, whereas occurrences *X, Y, Z,* . . . , take the second, the difference clearly exists for speakers of the language. In conducting a test of this type it is necessary, of course, to remember that informants can be ignorant of distinctions that other users of their language make with regularity and precision. On the other hand, dictionaries are not infallible either, and they undoubtedly contain distinctions that are not known to speakers of the language, at the same time missing distinctions that are widely known.

A third line of evidence suggested by Harris[20] is that words with the same meaning should occur in the same range of contexts (have the same distribution, in the linguistic sense). It follows that a word with two meanings should occur in two distinct, separable ranges, i.e., its distribution should have distinguishable parts corresponding to the two meanings. All known suggestions for the resolution of ambiguity in ALDP systems, as well as all suggestions conceivable in computing systems limited to textual input, are based on this notion. Our point for the moment is simply that if a word occurs in two distinct ranges of contexts, and grammatical theory does not explain its distributional peculiarity, then semantic theory must be adduced.

The evidence that establishes multiple meaning as a linguistic phenomenon does not provide for determining exactly how many meanings each word has and how the boundaries are to be drawn. Informants may agree that a certain word has two meanings, yet not agree on its meaning in certain contexts, or a large group of informants may agree that it has two, while a subgroup divides one meaning into two, making three altogether. Translation into one language may require two equivalents for a certain word, into another three, and it may be argued that

[18]I. A. Mel'chuk, "Machine Translation and Linguistics," in O. S. Akhamanova et al., *Exact Methods in Linguistic Research,* Moscow University Press, Moscow, 1961. Translation: Univ. of Calif. Press, Berkeley, 1963.

[19]Abraham Kaplan, "An Experimental Study of Ambiguity," *Mechanical Translation,* vol. 2, no. 2, pp. 39–46, November, 1955.

[20]Zellig S. Harris, "Distributional Structure," *Word,* vol. 10, pp. 146–162, 1954.

some of the equivalents differ only stylistically or syntactically. Distributional evidence likewise ranges from strikingly clear to suggestively vague. In point of fact, a search for precision by any of these methods is likely to be thwarted, since all of them are indirect.

The three lines of evidence so far mentioned are all linguistic, whereas semantics must deal with the relations between language and reality, or, if reality is elusive, cognitive and cultural elements. Reality, as far as we now know, is infinitely complex, and languages, like science and all of culture, are finite. On a smaller scale, it would be nonsense to claim that the English word *hat* has as many meanings as there are, have been, or will be hats (headgear) in the world. All those hats are simply different referents for a single meaning of the word. No more does *bird* have as many meanings as there are species or varieties of Aves; one meaning covers them all. If a badminton bird is something else, it is because the culture has an organization independent of the language, and egg-laying birds are culturally differentiated from feathered hemispheres at a very deep level. It is *not* primarily a linguistic fact that the properties characteristic of birds (robins, canaries, etc.) and the properties characteristic of (badminton) birds are practically nonoverlapping. This fact pertains to the culture, to the cognitive systems of persons bearing the culture. Reality influences culture, and culture influences language; better said, the nonlinguistic part of culture influences the linguistic. Hence linguistic evidence, though indirect, can be used in the study of meaning.[21]

Each meaning of a word, then, is a cultural unit corresponding to a segment of reality that the culture regards as relatively homogeneous. A formal theory of meaning will have to go further, relating meanings to one another and giving an exact theoretical account of "relative homogeneity." One possible method is to list properties that the culture employs in forming concepts of reality; then a segment is relatively homogeneous if it can be distinguished from other segments by many properties but only subdivided by a few. Or it may be necessary to recognize that some properties are more significant to a culture than others and to decide homogeneity on the basis of the significance of the properties that isolate a segment as against the significance of those that cut it into subsegments. As yet we can say no more than this about the formal analysis of ambiguity.

Another semantic problem that we must consider is the calculation of the meaning of a sentence from the meanings of its constituent words or word segments. Syntax is needed in language to reveal semantic connections among the parts of sentences. In most sentences, for example, interchanging the subject and object of a verb alters the meaning of the

[21]The author is indebted to Duane G. Metzger and A. Kimball Romney for the point of view adopted here.

whole in striking fashion; when the propaganda organization of a dictatorship announces that "Nation A has committed acts of aggression against nation B," interchange of A and B in such an announcement would be treasonable. Semantic relations are not identical with syntactic relations, however, and the same problems of identifying distinct meanings and resolving ambiguities arise with relations that we have already considered for words. We can begin with syntactic functions and attempt to determine how many different semantic relations can be indicated by each function. As before, we can use textual methods in research, but we must remember that these methods are indirect; the meaning of a syntactic function is a kind of relation that is identified by the culture and isolated from other kinds of relations.

With a theory of semantics in view, we can return to the problem of isolating translatable units in language. For some—but not necessarily all—of the segments that he isolates in a language by morphological methods, the linguist can determine one or more independent meanings. He certainly excludes those segments that serve only to indicate syntactic relations, since he must deal with them separately. He next considers word forms made up of combinations of segments, always excluding segments of purely grammatical (syntactic) significance. If the meaning of a word form can be calculated from the meanings of the component segments by a standard rule—i.e., a rule that holds for many forms in the language—then the segments are translatable units. If not, the form itself must be taken as a unit for translation.[22] Thus there are meaningful morphological relationships in language as well as meaningful syntactic relationships; each permits determination of the meaning of a combination from the meanings of the parts. Again, the linguist must examine combinations of forms in the language, testing whether the meaning of the combination can be calculated from the meanings of the forms and the syntactic functions that tie them together. When a combination appears with meaning that cannot be calculated in this fashion by a general rule, the combination must be treated as an *idiom*, or translation unit larger than a single form. The general rules correspond to semantic relations one to one; a single rule may not suffice for all occurrences of a single syntactic function and therefore would show multiple meaning: the syntactic function can indicate more than one semantic relation, each associated with a rule.

Consider now the requirements of the semantic part of a machine-translation system. Taking sentences with known syntactic structures as input, the system identifies the translatable units and determines both the meaning of each unit and the semantic relations that obtain among the units. Then, given a representation of the meaning of each input

[22]The author is indebted to Martin J. Kay for discussions of this point.

sentence, the system must find words and semantic relations in the output language that express the same meaning. The output-syntax system operates on the results to produce sentences in which the meaning is indicated as clearly as possible. There may be ambiguities, of course, and two or more possible meanings may be discovered for a single sentence. Until semantic theory and research have progressed and additional systems are elaborated to go beyond semantics, the MT program can only offer alternative output sentences or a single sentence with the same ambiguity as that of the input.

SENTENCE-STRUCTURE DETERMINATION

In the input section of an MT system (or, apparently, any other ALDP system), a necessary step is determination of the syntactic structure of each input sentence. Computer programs for this purpose, called *parsing* or sentence-structure-determination (SSD) programs, can be written in many ways.[23] Different theories of syntax call for different programs, but a theory of syntax does not automatically suggest a definite method for SSD. The designer and programmer must attempt to satisfy several criteria. A good SSD program should always discover the correct structure of a sentence; at the same time, it should not propose more than the unavoidable minimum of incorrect structures. The minimum is fixed by the grammar of the language, but in practice good programming is needed, in addition to good linguistics, to approach the minimum. Second, the SSD program should operate economically; all other things being equal, a faster program is better than a slow one that wastes computing time. Finally, the SSD program should be economical to teach, modify, or adapt to a new language, even if these requirements can only be satisfied by a program that is not as fast as possible; fortunately, simplicity and speed go together to some extent. The need to teach programs is obvious. Modification is needed as empirical knowledge and formal theory advance; no formalism can be called final and complete. Adaptation to new languages is certainly to be expected, and this requirement means that a good SSD program is designed around "universal" features of language.

[23]For examples, see Ida Rhodes, *A New Approach to the Mechanical Translation of Russian,* Report No. 6295, National Bureau of Standards, Washington, D.C., 1959; papers by A. G. Oettinger, M. E. Sherry, M. Zarechnak, and P. Garvin in Edmunson (ed.), *op. cit.,* fn. 15; papers by I. Sakai, A. F. Parker-Rhodes, M. Corbe and R. Tabory, and F. L. Alt and I. Rhodes in 1961 *International Conference on Machine Translation of Languages and Applied Language Analysis, op. cit.,* fn. 8; D. G. Hays and T. W. Zeihe, *Studies in Machine Translation—10: Russian Sentence-structure Determination,* RM-2538, The RAND Corporation, 1960; and Lecerf, *op. cit.,* fn. 14.

The syntactic indicators that we have noted (agreement rules involving inflection, stem classes, and function words; occurrence order; and punctuation or intonation) can be taken, roughly, as linguistic universals. Not all languages use all these devices, and certainly not to the same degree or in the same fashion, but the list is exhaustive, and each device is used in many languages. These devices have different logical characteristics that entail different treatment in a program.

Every language seems to have some degree of grammatical classification, and it has been suggested that every language must have at least two classes. But the classification schemes of natural languages vary enormously, and the agreement rules vary correspondingly. Hence tabulation of grammatical classes is a new task for each new language, and whatever program is used for SSD must be able to accept new agreement systems. One scheme that will most probably work for any language is to use a table of pairs (or perhaps triples, etc.) of syntactic classes in testing agreement. A grammar-code symbol is assigned to each class in the language. The table of *dependency types* is entered with a pair of grammar-code symbols; if their agreement indicates syntactic connection, they are listed with an indication of which member of the pair is governor and what function the dependent serves.

More sophisticated, simpler, and faster schemes have been proposed.[24] For example, each form can be assigned to a part-of-speech class according to the syntactic functions that it can govern and those that it can serve as dependent. Part-of-speech pairs such that one member of each pair can serve a certain function for the other are listed in a small table. Then a set of additional tables is used to determine whether two forms agree in those respects that are significant for the possible function. This technique is advantageous for forms that have many grammatical properties most of which do not relate to any particular function; this condition is satisfied for many languages, perhaps for all.

Occurrence order can be factored into *direction* and *separation*. Direction is similar to grammatical classification; its indicative function is specific to the grammatical classes involved and therefore varies from one natural language to another. This aspect of occurrence order can be effectively handled by tabulating it with grammatical classes in the table of dependency types.

Separation is the subject of a putative universal. In terms of de-

[24]A. F. Parker-Rhodes, "A New Model of Syntactic Description," *Proceedings of the International Conference on Machine Translation of Languages and Applied Language Analysis,* op. cit., fn. 8, vol. 1, pp. 26–60. See also RamoWooldridge reports, *Machine Translation Studies of Semantic Techniques,* 1960 and 1961; the grammar-coding scheme reported there is due to Paul Garvin.

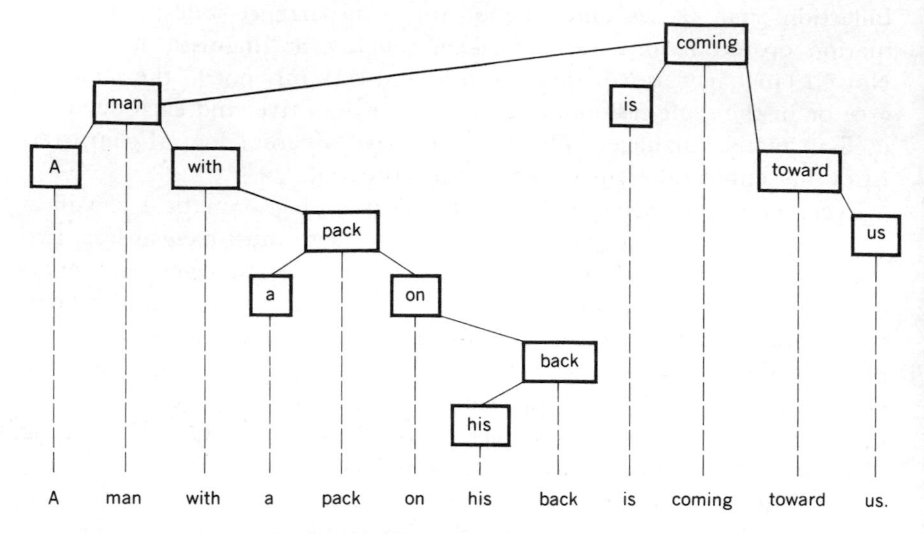

FIGURE 2 *A sentence with projective dependency structure.*

pendency theory, Lecerf calls this feature of language *projectivity*.[25] According to this rule two connected occurrences are separated only by occurrences that depend on them, directly or indirectly. In Figure 2, a sentence is displayed with its dependency structure; governors are placed higher than their dependents, and occurrence order is followed from left to right. Dropping a projection line downward from each node in the tree to the occurrence below it, we see that no two dependency connections intersect and that no connection line intersects a projection line; hence the name projectivity.

The practical significance of this observation in SSD, whether attempted by a computer program or by a human listener, is that it reduces the labor involved in the process. A program can be written on the basis of the projectivity rule alone, without reference to grammatical classes and agreements, that identifies pairs of occurrences as connectable or not; if one occurrence is separated from another only by occurrences that depend on one or the other, the first is said to precede the second. Agreement need be tested only for precedence pairs, and not for all pairs in the sentence. Without regard to projectivity or rules of agreement,

[25]Lecerf, *op. cit.*, fn. 14, is based on a Euratom report published at a conference in February, 1960; the SSD program given by Harper and Hays, *op. cit.*, fn. 15. relies on projectivity, but mentions the property without naming or analyzing it. Lecerf and the present author met and learned of each other's work only late in 1960.

5×10^{24} distinct tree diagrams can be drawn for a sentence of twenty form occurrences; the rule of projectivity reduces this number to 4×10^{13}.[26] The program that tests for precedence can be written just once and applied to any language characterized by projectivity.

It would be possible, but uneconomical, to list all the projective trees with a certain number of nodes and then, using agreement rules, test each of them against a particular sentence. Since the number of trees is in fact too large, an iterative plan is required instead. In its simplest version, this plan lists the precedence pairs in a sentence of which nothing is known; each of these pairs consists of two occurrences lying side by side. Then agreements are tested and some connections made which lead to establishment of precedence between new pairs of occurrences; new agreements can be tested, new connections made, and so forth.

The general organization of an SSD program determines whether it yields all grammatically possible structures for a given sentence or only one. If it were possible to guarantee that the one would always be correct, it would be economical to choose a plan of the latter type, but there are at least temporary advantages in finding all possible structures. One plan is to form all possible subtrees of two nodes, then all those of three nodes, etc., until finally all possible trees have been formed containing nodes for all the occurrences in the sentence.[27] Economy demands that no subtree be formed by two or more paths; this demand can be satisfied by accepting two restrictions. First, no new dependent is added to any node in a subtree other than the unique independent node. Second, the order in which dependents are attached to any governor is fixed; for example, after any dependent is added that precedes the governor, no further following dependents are attached.[28] (Since projectivity precedence requires nearer dependents to be attached earlier than those more distant, this rule makes the order of attachment unique.) Disregarding agreement rules, a sentence of three occurrences can have seven distinct projective tree structures (see Figure 3). Following the above sequencing rules those seven structures can be obtained with connections made in the order shown in the figure; without the sequencing rules, three structures would be obtained in two ways each (those labeled with an asterisk). As the number of occurrences in a sentence increases, the saving increases disproportionately.

Without projectivity, a search for all possible structures would be time consuming indeed. It is well known that nonprojective sentences

[26]Y. Lecerf, "Analyse Automatique," in *Enseignement Préparatoire aux Techniques de la Documentation Automatique,* Euratom, Brussels, 1960, pp. 179–245.

[27]This point was communicated to the author by John Cocke of IBM Research.

[28]This suggestion comes from Lecerf.

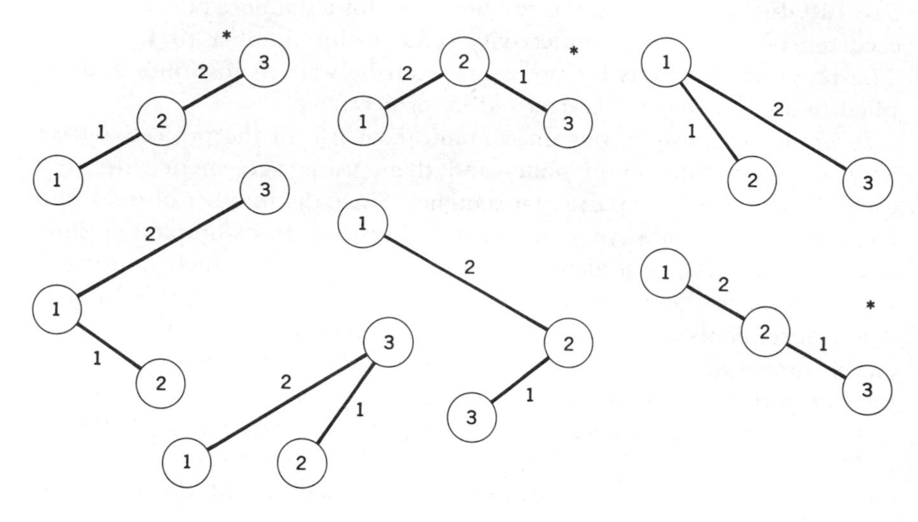

FIGURE 3 *The seven possible projective structures for a three-occurrence sentence.* **See text for alternative.*

occur frequently in some languages, and occasionally even in languages that are largely projective, such as English and Russian. A survey of nonprojective structures appears necessary as a possible means of discovering regularities that can be used in SSD.[29] The present computational cost of assuming that every sentence is nonprojective would be too high, and the approximation—in many languages—is too good, to permit outright rejection of the concept.

SEMANTIC RECOGNITION

When the syntactic structure of a sentence has been determined, and the minimal units with independent meaning have been identified, the meaning of each occurrence in the sentence and the nature of the semantic connections among them have to be determined. Work in this field does not yet enable us to describe procedures of proven effectiveness, but some suggested methods can be reported.

It may be possible to assign meanings to semantic agreement classes.[30] In that case, a table could be used much as a table of dependency types is used in SSD. An entry would consist of a pair of semantic-class symbols and

[29]Lydia Hirschberg of the Free University of Brussels is engaged in such a study.

[30]See, for example, Kenneth E. Harper, "Procedures for the Determination of Distributional Classes" in 1961 *International Conference on Machine Translation of Languages and Applied Language Analysis, op. cit.,* fn 8, vol. 2, pp. 687-700.

an indication of a syntactic function. The question would then be, *Can an item of this class serve that function for an item of the other class? If so, what is the semantic relation between the two?* For example, *Can the name of a person serve as the (syntactic) subject of a verb of communication?* The answer would be, *Yes; the person is actor.* The classes in this example, are, of course, not necessarily those that would appear from empirical research.

Following this plan leads to success if one and only one meaning of each occurrence in a sentence agrees with the meanings of neighboring occurrences and if each syntactic connection is resolved to a unique semantic relation. If the sentence has more than one possible syntactic structure, semantic disagreements may rule out some or all of them. The semantic classes and agreement rules therefore have to be designed to determine a unique meaning for each word occurrence and each syntactic relation in every sentence, to eliminate all but one possible structure for each sentence, and to assign to every (intuitively acceptable) sentence a semantic description that can be translated or otherwise manipulated to the satisfaction of whatever external criteria are applied. As yet there is no evidence that any semantic agreement system can approach this design standard.

Another proposal is to organize the vocabulary of *meanings* hierarchically; formally, the organization would be a lattice.[31] Choosing any set of meanings arbitrarily, we find that there is some set of meanings in the hierarchy that includes all of them; in fact, there may be many sets with that property, one having a smaller count of meanings than any of the others. The occurrences in a sentence have meanings that can be found in this hierarchical system, but each occurrence can have one or more meanings. In a three-occurrence sentence, for example, let the first occurrence have two meanings: 1*a* and 1*b*. Let the second have two meanings also—2*a* and 2*b*—but let the third occurrence be unambiguous—call its meaning "3." We must choose one meaning for each occurrence; we can choose: 1*a*, 2*a*, 3; 1*a*, 2*b*, 3; 1*b*, 2*a*, 3; or 1*b*, 2*b*, 3. Trying each set of meanings in turn, we learn the size of the smallest class in the hierarchy that includes all meanings in the set; e.g., how large is the smallest set that includes 1*a*, 2*a*, and 3? We thus obtain four quantities, one associated with each set of equivalent choices for the sentence, and we take the set of equivalents associated with the smallest of those quantities, since semantic *homogeneity* is to be expected in an ordinary text. Ties are possible, however, which lead to semantic ambiguities.

[31]Margaret Masterman, "Potentialities of a Mechanical Thesaurus," *Mechanical Translation,* vol. 3, no. 2, p. 36, November, 1956. See also her paper in *Proceedings of the International Conference on Machine Translation and Applied Linguistic Analysis, op. cit.,* fn. 8, vol. 2, pp. 437–474.

The difficulty with this model is that syntax cannot be combined with it in any obvious way. In fact, the proper solution to semantic problems could be a combination of the two methods that we have described—the first takes advantage of local context, the second uses broad context. The ambiguities not eliminated by one might then be resolved by the other.

THE CYCLIC METHOD

Linguistic research, if it is to be based on text at all, must be based on a very large corpus, since many rare words and constructions must be discovered and described. The advent of the automatic digital computer makes a very large amount of text-based linguistic research economically feasible for the first time. However, if informant editors are to be used in the system, care must be taken to keep their task under control. The cyclic method makes as much use of computers as possible: Each cycle is based on a fresh batch of text and consists of automatic application of what is known about the language followed by editorial review and reduction of the new data to a form that can be used in the next cycle.[32]

Glossary expansion furnishes a simple illustration of the cyclic approach. A glossary is, for the moment, an alphabetic list of all the forms that have occurred in text. A form is a distinct sequence of alphabetic characters that occurs preceded and followed by spaces or marks of punctuation. When a fresh batch of text has been prepared, it is segmented into form occurrences, and each form occurrence is matched, by spelling, against the known forms of the language—that is, against the old glossary based on previous batches of text. The unmatched items constitute new information about the language; they are alphabetized and merged with the old glossary. Thus a cycle ends, and a new one can be initiated with the preparation of a fresh batch of text.

If the glossary contains segments—prefixes, stems, and suffixes—rather than forms, each form occurrence must be identified as a sequence of known segments that are described in the glossary as capable of cooccurring in a form or as partially, perhaps entirely, unknown. A new form might consist, for example, of known prefix, unknown stem, and known suffix. If the prefix and suffix can cooccur around a stem, the morphological type of the stem may be deducible. The glossary-development program can list, for an informant editor, the new stems and their possible morphological types. The editor, who also needs a list of the full forms in which the new stems occur, must decide whether the segmentation is valid; if it is not, he corrects the segmentation and code assignments. His

[32]This method was adopted at RAND in 1957; see H. P. Edmundson and D. G. Hays, "Research Methodology for Machine Translation," *Mechanical Translation,* vol. 5, no. 1, pp. 8–15, July, 1958.

notes are returned to the computer and the new material is added to the glossary in preparation for the start of another cycle.

To find new idioms, the editor must read the text in full. Each batch of text is machine translated; each sentence is translated by whatever approximation to the MT system is available at the time. Some occurrences are translated by sophisticated techniques, some are translated in idiomatic combinations, and others are simply given whatever equivalents are in the glossary. The text and its "translation" are printed out in parallel columns, matched item by item. The editor reads the printout, looking for all kinds of errors. In particular, he looks for new idiomatic combinations—sequences of form occurrences that are mistranslated individually but can be given an accurate translation as a group. He writes in the translation that he wants, marking the extent of the idiomatic sequence. His notes are keypunched and entered into the computer along with the original text and its machine translation.

An analytic program selects all occurrence sequences marked as new idioms and sorts them, alphabetically or otherwise. If the same form sequence has occurred several times, and the same idiomatic equivalent used each time, the occurrences can be summarized. A summary list of new idioms is prepared, inspected by linguists, and returned to the computer for another operation.

The final step automatically merges the new idioms with the old, creating a new idiom list, and adds to the glossary of forms or form segments whatever indicia are required for idiom recognition.

The addition of new idioms is a complete, albeit simple, illustration of the cyclic method as practiced at RAND and elsewhere. In each cycle, text is prepared for computer input, submitted to machine translation, and postedited. Analytic routines reduce the postediting data in accordance with linguistic requirements, and linguists inspect the result. The new information is finally merged automatically with old information of the same type. This sequence is characteristic of the method; it gives the computer a major share of the work but also permits both informants and linguists to apply their intuition. Cutting out a single task, such as the search for new idioms, is also characteristic. Economy dictates that the editor read each corpus as few times as possible, but analytic operations have to be isolated for theoretical reasons. Moreover, the whole MT system—comprising a sequence of processes applied to text one after another, each using the results of those already completed—suggests separation of the research cycle into subcycles. Glossary expansion can be completed before idiom lookup is performed; sentence-structure determination can be postedited before its output is submitted to semantic recognition procedures. Stepwise postediting of this variety saves editorial labor by preventing carrying over mistakes from step to step. On the other hand, the technique would leave, at each step, ambiguities that could be eliminated at the next, and it requires the informant editors to read each text more than once. The stepwise editing plan has not been tried out as yet, but the cyclic method with posteditors has been in use for some time.

TRANSLATION OF WORDS: SEMANTICS

Standardization of Equivalents Let us next turn to a more general view of the problem of pairing meaningful units in the input and output languages. Suppose that we must begin with a new pair of languages, for which the only available information is that contained in published dictionaries. We are to proceed by the cyclic method, processing text in successive batches. At first the relatively few most common words in the language will dominate our lists of new forms; many forms found in the first batch of text will occur frequently both in that batch and in succeeding batches. Other words in the first batch, and most new words in later batches, will be rare. The basic plan for assigning equivalents can therefore reasonably change as the number of batches processed increases.

The first batch is prepared, and an alphabetic list of the forms that it contains is made. It is convenient to collect forms into groups, when the input language is highly inflected, since the translational equivalents of different inflected forms of the same word will usually be identical (except for what we will regard as grammatic variations). Now each form or word in the text-based list can be looked up in a published bilingual dictionary and the equivalents listed for it copied into machine storage. The list of forms, each accompanied by one or more equivalents, is an initial glossary.

The next step is to list the first batch of text, with its machine translation in parallel. But of course the translation is merely a statement—for each form occurrence—of the equivalents shown for that form in the initial glossary. Now the editor informant, who should be well acquainted with the subject matter of the text, selects an equivalent for each occurrence in the first batch. He can mark one of the listed equivalents, write in a new one, or identify an idiom. His marks are keypunched and correlated with the machine-stored text and translation.

The number of times that the editor selected each equivalent for each form in the first batch is easily determined by an automatic process. Then the equivalents of each form, including those inserted in advance and those added during editing, can be ordered automatically by frequency of choice. Although separate records must be kept for each *form*, the ordering should be done for each *word*; i.e., the equivalents of all forms of a word should be kept in the same order. Now the typical glossary entry consists of a form and an *ordered* set of equivalents, together with a code symbol if the form was used idiomatically.

Treatment of the second, third, etc., batches of text proceeds in the same fashion, with two modifications. Beginning with the second batch, the editor is instructed to use the first equivalent listed with each occurrence whenever it is substantively accurate. When the second and subsequent equivalents of a word are never used by editors working under this instruction, the linguist can be sure that the alternatives differ only stylistically in the stream of text that he is processing. On the other hand, if one (or more) of the alternatives is still used, its meaning is substantively distinct from the meaning of the most frequent equivalent, and the linguist can look for contextual indicators of the difference.

The second change in procedure is omission of the first step—the insertion of tentative equivalents found in a published dictionary. This change is justified when the average number of occurrences of each new form is small enough; generally, the reasonable level is an average of two occurrences in a batch of text. There are several reasons for this modification. For one thing, the new words are hard to find; some are in the dictionaries, some are not. For another, the proportions of cognates and proper names increase. And for another, the equivalents obtained grow less and less reliable. Altogether then, it seems best to add equivalents only during editing, once a good glossary has been developed.

Input-language Inflection and Choice of Equivalents Most words, or form groups, have uniform translations, but not all. Some Russian verbs have one English equivalent in their nonreflexive occurrences, another (not passive of the first, which would be considered the same equivalent, modified grammatically) in reflexive occurrences. Some nouns have one equivalent in the singular, the same equivalent or another in the plural. These exceptions to the general rule must be discoverd and taken into account. The procedure is simple and straightforward. A file of equivalent-choice data, tallied by form and grouped by word, is required. With each form, the file must include a grammatic description. The procedure is applied to each word that satisfies three tests: (1) at least two forms have occurred; (2) at least two nonidiomatic equivalents have been chosen; and (3) enough occurrences of the word have been processed for reliable conclusions to be drawn.

The procedure is to sort the forms of a word into grammatic categories and for each equivalent test whether it occurs equally often in each category—that is, in proportion to the total number of occurrences of the word in each category. A statistical test for nonproportionality should be applied; although the satisfaction of its underlying assumptions is by no means clear, the chi-square test is perhaps appropriate.

The exceptional words can be listed and the findings installed in the glossary so that when new text is processed only applicable equivalents will be printed with each form occurrence.

Equivalent Selection by Contextual Criteria Perhaps the majority of substantive equivalent-selection problems can be resolved by reference to grammatically related occurrences in context. A verb, for example, may take one equivalent or another depending on its subject, its object, or a modifier. An adjective is most likely to be influenced by properties of the noun it modifies, since adjectives usually occur without dependents. In any event, establishment of rules for the determination of equivalents must include analysis of context.

It appears that analysis of related occurrences should be organized by kind of relation—i.e., by grammatic function. The procedure would be applied to each word with two or more equivalents, both applicable to at least some forms, when sufficient occurrences had been processed to permit anticipation of reliable results. All occurrences of the multiple-equivalent form are collected; the required file of information includes *what* words were related to the given word, and with what function, as well as the choice of equivalent that was made.

The analysis then takes one function at a time; since every occurrence has a governor, let us start with that. A particular word can serve different functions for its governor in different occurrences: A certain noun can occur in one place as subject of a verb, in another as object of a preposition, etc. If the multiple-equivalent word that we are studying has only one equivalent in each kind of relation that it enters as dependent, the analysis is complete; the problem shifts, as it were, from semantics to grammar. If there is any kind of relation in which the word has two equivalents, the analysis continues by examining each *word* that governs the multiple-equivalent word. If a certain word as governor always—in the processed text—implies a certain translation for its multiple-equivalent dependent, that fact is recorded; if the same can be said of every governor, the evidence suggests that choice of equivalent depends on type of governor. If not, a summary statistic can be computed—that is, the percentage of occurrences for which the correct equivalent can be selected by inspection of the governor.

The summary statistic is computed in the following manner. Let $E_1, E_2, \ldots, E_n$ be the equivalents of a word, and $C_1, C_2, \ldots, C_n$ be criterion classes. Considering only one class of related words (e.g., governors), assign each related word to class C_i if E_i is chosen more frequently than any E_j, $j \neq i$ when the related word is present. (In case of ties, assign at random.) Then, assuming that E_i is chosen when a word in class C_i is present, the summary statistic is just the number of correct choices divided by the number of occurrences of the multiple-equivalent word. This fraction, which we can call p, is at least as large as the ratio of choices of E_1, the most frequent equivalent, to occurrences of the word under study; and p is no larger than unity, which would indicate complete accuracy. In fact, since the number of errors with each distinct related word is limited to $(n - 1)/n$ times the number of occurrences of that word, the expected value of p must increase with the number of distinct words related in the given way. The sampling distribution of p, under the hypothesis that the classification of related words is irrelevant, still has to be calculated, and from it, parameters for normalizing p could be deduced.

Continuing our analysis of a multiple-equivalent word, we would examine words in each possible grammatic relation to it, calculating p, or a normalized variant p^*, for each relation. The relation for which p^* had highest value would deserve the attention of a linguist, since a few errors that might prevent p^* from reaching unity could be due to careless editing. If no value of p^* was high enough to be useful, the automatic analysis would have to continue by combining criteria. Harper, for example, working with a less formal method of analysis, used both governors and objects of prepositions to determine the equivalents required.[33] There is no certainty, of course, that the governors and dependents of an occurrence determine its translation, but it seems plausible that they will often do so.

When the criterion classes can be discovered, their members have to be marked in the glossary. A generalized semantic-recognition program can use these marks to select meanings, and thus equivalents, for occurrences of the words to which the method is applicable.

So far it has been assumed that criterial classes are defined independently with respect to each multiple-meaning word. That plan would eventually call for the storage of a vast amount of information. However, it is desirable to reduce the requirements, or at least to be assured that redundant information is not stored. Furthermore, the criterial classes can reasonably be interpreted as semantic classes only if they are relatively few in number and if word meanings fall into classes that allow use of the same criteria with all members of any given class. The question is therefore whether criterial classes formed in different ways are identical. With finite text no two classes are likely to have exactly the same members, but a degree of overlap exceeding random expectations would be evidence of relatedness. Two classes, criterial for selection of the meanings of two different words, are the same class if every word belonging to one also belongs to the other; no matter how large the corpus, there is always some chance that a sentence will occur in which a member of one class gives an incorrect result when treated as a member of the other class. This possibility must be eliminated before a sound model for stasistical inference can be formulated. If "exceptions" are allowed, an alternative formulation is to coalesce two classes whenever the cost of storing

[33]Kenneth E. Harper, *Machine Translation of Russian Prepositions,* Paper P-1941, The RAND Corporation, Santa Monica, Calif., 1960.

and manipulating one list with known exceptions is less than the cost of storing two lists with no exceptions. To make this alternative attractive, an intuitively acceptable estimation of the relative costs must be made.

SYNTACTIC RESEARCH

Problems of morphology come up in the study of non-Western languages and even in work with Russian or English when it becomes necessary to cover all details with a uniform scheme, but problems of syntax are much more significant in current work on well-known natural languages. In this section we shall assume the existence of a complete and unchangeable morphological description of the subject language; working on that assumption, we consider several plans for syntactic research.

After a sentence-structure-determination program has found all possible structures for a sentence, an editor informant examines them and chooses the correct one if it is listed. Errors in grammatical classification or tabulation of dependency types, as well as failures of the syntactic theory, can cause the SSD program to miss the correct structure; in that case, the editor must add the structure he desires to those listed. His notes, covering both connections and functions, are keypunched and collated with the stored output from SSD in preparation for analysis.

The sentences for which the editor wrote structures not found by the SSD program must be processed first, since they reveal major gaps in the system. The first step is to test for projectivity. The program examines each connection in a sentence and determines whether every occurrence between the members of the connected pair derives from one or the other of them. If not, it marks the connection as nonprojective; such a connection needs further study by a linguist.

In the SSD program considered above, the establishment of connections in a sentence is in a fixed order, which we can call the *recognition order*. The primary sequencing variable is the size of the subtree that results from a connection. Two subtrees are assembled only by connecting the independent element of one with the independent element of the other; dependents of a given node must be attached first on one side and then on the other. For several reasons, it is necessary to alter grammar-code symbols as connections are made; the alterations follow instructions in the table of dependency types. Thus at the time any connection is made, the grammar-code symbols of the occurrences to be connected are the result of all prior connections in which they have participated. When the correct structure of a sentence is not found by the SSD program and if the structure is projective, it must contain a connection that is impossible according to the existing system. To ascertain the cause, the SSD operation has to be repeated.

A controlled SSD program can be used for this purpose. The control is based on knowledge of the correct connections in the sentence; these connections are taken in recognition order and tested in turn against the table of dependency types. Alterations in grammar-code symbols are made as they were originally. When the "impossible" connection is reached, the SSD program has constructed a list of all grammar-code symbols assigned to each of the two connected members as a result of the alterations keyed by prior connections. Considering all possible pairs of these symbols, the program determines whether some alteration is responsible for the failure to find a suitable entry in the table of dependency types. In other words, if the impossible connection could have been made but for the alteration of a grammar-code symbol at the time of a prior connection, the alteration can be blamed for the failure to produce a correct structure for the sentence, and the relevant information must be printed out for a linguist to examine. The linguist can decide whether to change the alteration instructions, change an entry in the dependency table so that the latter connection can be made in spite of the alteration, etc.

If no alteration is responsible for the failure, the difficulty is in the grammar-code symbols, in the dependency table, or in lack of an alteration that should have been made. What is possible at this stage depends somewhat on the organization of the table.

In the simplest case, the table is a list of pairs of full grammar-code symbols. The symbols belonging to any pair of occurrences that have to be connected can be added to the table, but a screening process must eventually be carried out to avoid recognition of an excessive number of false structures for sentences in the future text. The screening program can be exemplified in Russian. In this language there is a morphological category of nouns; noun forms are morphologically subclassified by case. When enough connections between noun governor and noun dependent have been recogized in text, the screening program can detect that the case of the dependent is relevant to the function it serves, whereas the case of the governor is not. To reach this conclusion, the program must consider all morphological categories, testing for morphological diversity within each functional type; finding that every noun dependent serving a given function for a noun governor is in a certain case, the program can conclude that the case of the dependent is relevant. On the other hand, the program finds that a noun governor in any case can take a dependent noun with a given function; hence the case of the governor is irrelevant. The screening program also builds word classes. In a statistical sense, the nouns that can serve a given function when they occur in a given case are lexically diverse—many different nouns are found as dependents with any given function. Governing nouns, by contrast, are lexically restricted; the number of different nouns that govern the instrumental case, for example, is much smaller than the number expected by chance if every noun is capable of governing instrumental nouns. The statistical evidence proves the existence of a syntactic class; membership in the class is proved only by occurrence in the defining context—in the example, a noun is added to the class when it occurs as governor of an instrumental noun serving a particular function.

Once syntactic word classes are established, the organization of the dependency table can profitably be elaborated. Each grammar-code symbol will be cut into three parts: the morphological part of speech, other morphological properties, and syntactic word-class memberships. When two occurrences are said to be connected and the dependency table cannot connect them, the parts of the grammar-code symbols can be tested in turn. Continuing the previous example, let us suppose that both occurrences are nouns. First, parts of speech are consulted. Second, given the function named by the editor, the relevant morphological properties are sought in the table. If two occurrences of the given morphological types cannot be connected, an entry must be added to the table (but see below). If the morphological requirements are satisfied but a connection still cannot be established, syntactic word-class memberships must be involved in the agreement. If the class memberships of both occurrences are relevant and one belongs to a single relevant class, the grammar-code symbol of the other can be changed in the glossary; the same is true if only one occurrence in the pair must belong to a special category. On the other hand, if both occurrences must belong to particular classes and neither belongs to a relevant class, the glossary entries can be changed only if the classes are unique; otherwise, the pair must be set aside for further analysis. For example, suppose that the connection is possible if the governor belongs to class *A* and the dependent to class *B*, or if the governor belongs to class *C* and the dependent to class *D*. It follows that the governor belongs to one of two classes, *A* or *C*, and the dependent to class *B* or *D*, but the information provided by one occurrence is inadequate to make a definite assignment. Other occurrences can make the choice unique if the linguist assumes that the minimum number of assignments per form is desirable, or he can make the decision for each pair.

The possibility of altering grammar-code symbols during SSD raises further problems that must be recognized in the research procedure. The purpose of alteration, roughly speaking, is to prevent connections that are impossible in a certain context. First, a certain word may be restricted to a given class of governors when it is accompanied by one or more dependents of particular types; for example, the object of a preposition sometimes restricts the range of governors that the prepositional phrase can serve, and a genitive singular noun can serve as the subject of a plural verb only if it is accompanied by a cardinal number. Second, the various dependents of a single governor may impose restrictions on one another; most verbs can take a direct object in the genitive case only if they are modified by a negative particle, and a verb cannot take two direct objects. When an entry is added to the table of dependency types, as described above, or a grammar-code symbol is changed in the glossary, the possibility of altering a symbol during SSD is not considered. A screening process can be used thereafter.

In deciding whether alteration of a grammar-code symbol is desirable, negative evidence is needed. The evidence is that a connection between two occurrences is allowed by the dependency table but not by posteditors. The false connection can be eliminated in several ways: by semantic procedures, by subclassification of grammatical categories, or by recognition of contextual restrictions. Only the last leads to alteration of grammar-code symbols. If two grammatical categories are connected by the dependency table, sometimes correctly and sometimes not, a test for contextual restriction should be performed on the pair. As indicated above, there are two cases.

The restriction can involve a chain of three connected occurrences. If the data show that an occurrence of type *A* governs one of type *B* only when the latter governs an occurrence of type *C*, then type *B* should be altered to type *B′* when type *C* is attached, and a dependency-table entry linking types *A* and *B′* should replace the *AB* entry. Type *C* can be a morphological category, a syntactic word class already established on the basis of other evidence, or a new category established ad hoc, provided that the existence of a class can be shown by the usual statistical evidence of lexical limitation—the number of different words in the class must be less than the number expected by chance.

The restriction can also involve a governor and two of its dependents. If the data show that an occurrence of type *A* governs one of type *B* only when it also governs one of type *C*, then *A* should be altered to *A′* when the first of the two dependents is added. Suppose that the *AB* connection is always earlier than the *AC* connection in recognition order; then *A* becomes *A′* when *B* is attached, and *A′C* replaces *AC* in the dependency table. Type C must satisfy the requirements stated in the preceding paragraph.

The programs described above lead to the establishment of many independent syntactic word classes. Economy demands that the number of distinct classes in the grammar be reduced as much as possible, and it has been suggested that a category is grammatical only if it appears in a number of different rules.[34] The methods and statistical problems of class comparison have been discussed in the section on semantics; the same methods can be applied to syntactic classes, and the statistical problems have to be solved.

One answer to the question of what distinguishes syntactic classes from semantic seems more acceptable than the others. Starting with the notions of morphological classification, function words, occurrence order, and punctuation, the research procedures that have been described here pro-

[34]Edward Klima, personal communication.

duce certain categories of words. All the word classes that can be defined by rules involving them *and* the initial syntactic indicators are taken as syntactic classes; any class that can be defined by rules involving it and a syntactic class is also a syntactic class. The rules are those that differentiate between structures acceptable to editors and structures that editors reject. It is an empirical question whether a program capable of determining a single acceptable structure for almost every sentence in a large corpus—and more structures than one for almost all of the remainder—can be based entirely on syntactic classes, morphological classes, function words, occurrence order, and punctuation. If the answer is affirmative, then semantics (by this analysis) is not required for sentence-structure determination; but if the answer is negative, semantics is required for the elimination of *syntactic* ambiguity.

The possibility of writing a grammar for a language by purely automatic methods, using unedited text as data and an analytic program based on linguistic universals, is currently being raised.[35] Although it is still too early to say what results can be obtained with such methods, an important theoretical difference between methods with and without informant editors should be noted at once and remembered as research progresses.

We have seen three levels, or strata,[36] in language: the level of the writing system, the level of the grammar, and the level of semantics. It is apparently characteristic of editor informants—of all users of language—that they deal with all its levels simultaneously and, for the most part, unconsciously. When an informant is asked whether two sound sequences are "same" or "different," he evidently answers according to the grammatical-level patterns that they indicate; as sounds, the sequences can be quite distinct, yet if they stand for the same string of inflected forms, they are "same" to the informant.[37] Two sentences with different composition at the grammatical level are "same" if they are semantically identical, that is, if they indicate the same semantic content; but consciousness reaches the grammatical level, and it is more difficult to apply the test. The point is that informants use their higher-level understanding of a sentence whenever they are asked to comment on it.

An automatic system for grammatical analysis is usually conceived as working its way upward from level to level. First morphological analysis is carried out in accordance with morphological criteria (and lower-level criteria as well; similarity of sound or spelling is used in deciding whether

[35]See references cited in fn. 8.

[36]Sydney M. Lamb, "The Strata of Linguistic Structure," presented at a meeting of the Linguistic Society of America, Hartford, Conn., December, 1960. (His strata are not identical with these.) *Cf.* also the three sets of levels in Garvin, "The Definitional Model of Language," earlier in this volume.

[37]See Chomsky, *op. cit.,* fn. 7.

two forms are forms of the same word). Next syntactic analysis is carried out, using morphological and syntactic criteria. Then semantic analysis, using semantic and syntactic criteria, is performed. How far the sequence of levels continues is still an open question, but the proposed automatic analysis programs pass from level to level in one direction only.

If informants and automatic analysis programs operate in exactly opposite directions, are they not certain to yield vastly different results? Perhaps not, for two reasons. A minor point is that informants use criteria at all levels simultaneously; they are not unidirectional. A major point is that language seems universally to have correlated structures on its various levels. The grammatical structure obtained by grammatical criteria corresponds closely with the grammatical structure obtained by semantic criteria. Were this untrue of any language, it would be unspeakably complicated, too complicated for the human organism to learn quickly and use fluently—and if it were learned nevertheless, it would in time be altered for the convenience of its users. Although formal tests of level-to-level structural similarity have never been conducted on a grand scale, the weight of years of linguistic research favors the hypothesis.

Similarity does not imply identity. The syntactically most elegant morphology of a language is not likely to be achieved by following morphological criteria exclusively. The ultimate program for automatic research in linguistics is therefore likely to go forward, then back: A fairly good morphological analysis, based on morphological criteria, paves the way for syntactic analysis; once completed, the syntactic analysis furnishes criteria for adjustment of the morphology. The syntax obtained by using syntactic criteria likewise furnishes the basis for semantic analysis, but the semantic structure, when known, permits refinement of the syntax.[38]

Linguistic methodology is being developed very rapidly; the sound work of recent decades is being tested and enriched by linguists concerned with computers. The criticism sometimes voiced,[39] that computational methods lead to ad hoc schemes unthinkingly propounded and not to understanding of the true structure of language, can be refuted if not silenced by attention to some general principles. First, the temptation to overgeneralize must be denied. The modest samples currently available for computational research permit no general statements about languages, and it may be some years before adequate samples can be obtained and analyzed. Second, the search for linguistic universals must continue. Those that are well supported by evidence and relevant to the research

[38]David G. Hays, "Linguistic Methodology and the Theory of Strata," presented at a meeting of the Philological Association of the Pacific Coast, Santa Barbara, Calif., November, 1961.

[39]Dean S. Worth, "Linear Contexts, Linguistics, and Machine Translation," *Word,* vol. 15, no. 1, pp. 183–191, April, 1959. Noted with agreement and expanded by Mel'chuk, *op. cit.,* fn. 18.

now being conducted with computer aid are (1) natural languages can be closely approximated by simple formal models; (2) the appropriate models have recursive features; (3) the appropriate models are multilevel; (4) the appropriate models include simple postulates about occurrence order (at least with respect to separation); (5) the appropriate models include classification of recurrent units (e.g., word classes); (6) the classifications are multidimensional; and (7) simplicity and economy are significant criteria in classification as in the structural design of the model. Third, results obtained by various methods of research should not propose to refute results obtained by other methods until a more complete, integrated theory of linguistic research is written.

KENNETH E. HARPER

Dictionary problems in machine translation

The machine-translation process is customarily divided into four stages: input, analysis of input-language units (normally, the sentence unit), synthesis of the output-language unit, and output. The problems connected with the first and last stages are primarily technological, whereas the two middle stages are the province of the linguist. The problems of analysis and synthesis must be solved in terms of morphology, syntax, lexicography, and semantics. Although technology can certainly contribute to a more accurate formulation of these linguistic problems and to more specific answers to them, it is safe to say that an adequate linguistic theory is still the prerequisite for successful translation.

The role of the MT dictionary in the central translation process has frequently been misunderstood. This misunderstanding has to do with the content and function of the dictionary. A view still prevalent is that the dictionary is a word list, however obtained, and that its exclusive function is the identification of items in the input text. It is only in recent years that a broader concept of the MT dictionary has evolved. The thesis of this discussion is that this broader concept must be more generally accepted if MT research is to advance beyond its presently primitive state.

The chief reasons for the original view of the MT dictionary are reliance on tradition and a misunderstanding of the role of technology. Traditionally, dictionaries have been word lists; as inventories of the words in a language, they contain more or less complete information about the sound, meaning, and grammatical properties of the items recorded. The science has its own name: lexicography. Grammar and semantics are separate fields of study. On this traditional foundation, the early MT researchers proceeded to build word lists by, and for, machines.

There was some disagreement on the manner of selecting entries for the dictionary, and the MT linguist frequently insisted that the dictionary contain more information of a grammatical nature than is customary in published word lists. Usually, however, this excess of grammar was viewed as a necessary evil, admissible as an aid in the fulfilling of the primary function of the dictionary—text lookup with a stem dictionary. Beyond this, the MT linguist has customarily been content to go along with the traditional division of labor; if he studies syntactic structure, he thinks of resolving such problems by means of separate routines that operate on the discrete items in the dictionary. The lexicon and the grammar are as distinct as they have always been, and new knowledge obtained in one area is not seen as important for the other.

Students of MT have in general clung to the conventional division of grammar and lexicography, without recognizing that technology has provided a means of fusing the two. To put it differently, technology has at best been applied unimaginatively. The trend might be defended if existing dictionaries and grammars were adequate to the tasks posed by MT. They are, in fact, woefully inadequate, as an intelligent analysis of the failures of machine translation will reveal. It should be noted that when failures are encountered in test translations, the tendency of MT workers has been simply to improve the technology; when the translation difficulty is "resolved" by the expedient of placing the problem and its solution in storage, the "technical improvement" essentially amounts to an increase in the size of the store. The utter impracticality of such "solutions" can be readily demonstrated. The whole situation has evolved, somewhat naturally, out of the linguist's overestimation of the powers of the technologist and the technologist's overestimation of the achievements of lexicography and linguistics.

The following discussion of the chief problems in building and operating MT dictionaries is not a critical survey of past work; the literature reveals that much of this work is tentative and exploratory. The purpose of the discussion is to point out the areas in which progress has been made and those in which work has lagged. Throughout, the orientation is linguistic.

PHYSICAL CHARACTERISTICS OF MT DICTIONARIES

As text enters the MT system, the text items are compared with the items in storage. The two obvious requirements of the machine store are a large capacity and rapid access, although what is meant by "large" and "rapid" is still indefinite. It is clear, however, that the dictionary-lookup process should result in the identification of all but a very small fraction of the items in a given text, at a rate that is at least equal to the translation process itself.

These minimum requirements apparently rule out certain types of stores that are otherwise promising, such as punched cards, magnetic drums, and discs. The advantages of punched cards include unlimited capacity, variable length of record, and relative ease of modification; the decisive disadvantage, as with magnetic discs, is slow and cumbersome handling. The chief drawback to the magnetic drum is limited capacity. Other types of stores, including magnetic tape and the photoscopic store, avoid these difficulties but introduce new problems. Magnetic tape, which provides an unlimited store, has been used as an instrument for text lookup in at least three ways: (1) an alphabetized text tape is compared with an alphabetized dictionary tape; (2) assuming core storage as the locus of input text, a text occurrence is transformed into a memory address, the same transformation rule is applied to dictionary items, and the assignment of a text occurrence to the same address in memory as a dictionary item constitutes a match; and (3) a character-by-character table lookup is performed for the input occurrence, assuming that a considerable portion of the dictionary is present in core storage. The chief drawbacks to the tape dictionary are serial access and the necessity of writing a new tape when modification of individual records is required. The latter difficulty is most apparent in the case of the photoscopic store, which otherwise answers quite well the initial requirements of size and speed. See "Programming for Natural Language" by L. C. Ray, earlier in this volume.

It is not yet clear that a special-purpose device will be required for an MT dictionary. A number of factors are involved; it would make a difference, for example, whether the store is used for the sole purpose of the MT dictionary, or whether it is to be shared with nonlinguistic users. At any rate, it is obvious that the thinking of most MT researchers has been dominated by the theoretical requirements of capacity and speed. It is also obvious now, if not always so, that this cart-before-the-horse approach is the result of a naïve faith in the efficacy of the dictionary as a word list, and of pressures to get MT on a "production" basis. The further requirements of an MT dictionary discussed below have been either ignored or attended to in a piecemeal fashion.

CONTENTS OF THE DICTIONARY

A bilingual MT dictionary consists of a series of "records" encoded in the machine language of the storage unit. These records bear only a general resemblance to the entries in ordinary dictionaries, and their ordering may be quite different. The main elements in a record are representations of the input-language lexical item, its correspondent (s) in the output language, and attached codes relating to grammatic and semantic properties of one or both of the lexical items. For purposes of discussion, we shall treat these elements separately, despite the fact that this separation may not always be preserved in practice.

REPRESENTATION OF THE INPUT-LANGUAGE LEXICAL ITEM

In ordinary dictionaries, a "record" is headed by a canonical form of a given word, i.e., by a form arbitrarily chosen as the "name" of the word.

This convention is rarely observed in MT dictionaries, since the input-language item must be recognized in terms of graphemes (letters, spaces, and punctuation). Lexical items have generally been represented in one of two ways: by listing members of the paradigm for inflected words (the form dictionary), or by listing a segment of inflected words (the stem dictionary). A variation employed in the photoscopic store is the listing of certain word combinations as main entries. For example, *once in a while* may be listed as a single entry, because the combination may be considered as a lexical unit, or because it is idiomatic or difficult to translate. A more common practice is to list the four elements separately in the dictionary; the combination and its translation are stored in a separate table, to which reference is made by codes attached to the separate lexical items.

The question of form versus stem dictionaries is still unsettled. The form dictionary has certain advantages in MT research. Operation and maintenance are relatively simple; as text is processed, phenomena such as form frequency and frequency of equivalent (corresponding output-language word or words) can be conveniently studied. The chief disadvantage is, of course, the size of store required. In a highly inflected language such as Russian, the required storage is some fifteen times greater than for a stem dictionary with the same number of lexical items. In English, the ratio is approximately three to one. This discrepancy has influenced a number of MT researchers toward a stem dictionary.

There are really two types of stem dictionaries: the *stem-affix* type, in which *affix* signifies only inflectional endings; and the *root* type, which provides for the storage of roots, inflectional endings, derivational suffixes, and prefixes. The latter type obviously represents a saving in storage over the former and has as an advantage the potential capability of recognizing and translating lexical items in text that are not contained in the dictionary. It would not be practicable, for example, to list in storage all the English nouns and verbs to which the prefix *re-* can be added. A number of such words have never appeared in published dictionaries, and indeed have never appeared in print. Normally, if the root is stored, even neologisms of this type can be identified in text and translated.

The saving in storage in all types of stem dictionaries is, of course, accompanied by a far greater complexity of operation than is characteristic of the form dictionary. The degree of complexity is proportionate to the degree of segmentation. The main problems are occasioned by multiple stems, stem homographs,[1] and the use of morphological codes that will permit the correct juxtaposition of stem and affix and the correct reference to the output lexical item. The bookkeeping problem is enormous, and generalized solutions are hard to find. Although sub-

[1] Homographs are different words that are spelled alike, such as *lead*.

stantial efforts have been made, it has not yet been demonstrated that the inherent problems can be solved through the application of non-linguistic techniques. It can well be argued that large-scale stem dictionaries depend on a much greater knowledge of lexicology, grammar, and semantics than we now possess. To put it differently, a strategic, rather than a tactical, assault on the problem may be required; the efficacy of the tactical assault, in any case, has not been proved.

One other aspect of the input-language item should be mentioned: its source. Two general selection procedures have been used: (1) only those items appearing in processed text are stored; and (2) the items are taken from published dictionaries. A combination of the two methods has also been used. The text-based dictionary has the advantage of greater precision: its items are endowed with reality (they have really appeared in given texts), and their frequency, forms, and translation in these texts is known. It can be argued that only a text-based dictionary can provide a true idioglossary;[2] certainly it is an excellent instrument for automatic language-data processing. Its disadvantage is incompleteness, short of the processing of a very large body of text. Experience at one MT study center has shown that after the first few hundred pages of text were glossarized (in the general field of physics), one new word was encountered for every sixty running words of new text. This proportion is likely to decrease very slowly.

MT dictionaries compiled from existing dictionaries (and supplemented by text processing) are larger and provide more complete "coverage" for new text. They are also imprecise. Some of the entries will always be superfluous, since they will never be encountered in text ("never" is used here in a relative sense). Similarly, many items contained in the dictionary are of dubious value until also found in text: the information attached to the item will be incomplete and/or inaccurate for purposes of syntactic analysis and translation.

GRAMMAR CODE

A minimum of morphological information is encoded in all MT dictionaries, indicating the part-of-speech and inflectional characteristics of each lexical item. As noted above, the amount of detail in these codes depends on the degree to which the lexical items are segmented. Codes specifying the syntactic properties of the items may also be included, either in combination with the morphological codes, or separately. The existence or detail of syntactic codes depends on the degree to which syntactic analysis is applied to the input sentence. If syntactic analysis is not attempted, these codes will clearly be unnecessary; if the aim is a complete structural description of the input sentence, detailed information about the

[2] An idioglossary is a dictionary of terms used in a single field of interest.

combinatorial properties of each item is highly desirable. There has been a trend in recent years toward more detailed syntactic analysis.

The main problem of the grammar code is one of content: What grammatic information should be coded for each item in the dictionary? Most MT research groups have assumed that since morphology is well described and the basic facts of syntax (government and agreement) are well known, the only problem was to imbed these facts in the grammar code. The involuntary consequence of this reliance on existing grammars has been a built-in intractability—grammar codes are difficult to modify. In some instances, this is due to the compactness of the code (the use of a single symbol to represent two or more grammatic properties). The obvious virtues of compactness (saving in storage space) are more than offset by the considerable complexities that arise when a multiple-purpose symbol must be changed. In other instances, the problem is simply one of economics: The physical characteristics of the store make alteration of any item expensive. At the root of all such difficulties is the original assumption that the contents of the grammar code could be fixed in advance.

It is by now widely recognized that as we process more and more texts, we learn a great deal more about grammar. Although automatic language-data processing has so far taught us little that is really new, it has enabled us to organize and codify the thousands of facts, particularly about syntax, that "everyone knows." Nor do we need to rely on text processing to obtain this necessary detail. The point is simply that there is an enormous advantage in a greatly enriched "grammar code" for every lexical item in the dictionary. A Russian grammar code, for example, should contain information about the nonexistence of a short form for a given adjective, or about the absence of an adjective-adverb pairing for a given word. This information should be stored in the dictionary, in the same way that part-of-speech codes are stored. The clear implication is that MT dictionaries of the future must have ample storage space for this information and must easily accept alteration. The grammar code of any entry will be altered from time to time, as new information is gathered; it can be said that an MT dictionary that does not possess the capability of easy modification is already obsolescent.

"SEMANTIC CODES"

The use of semantic codes has been proposed when an input-language occurrence or phrase is ambiguous in the output language. These codes, attached to the input-language items in the dictionary, are intended to apply to the residue of problems that cannot be solved with other techniques (e.g., the idioglossary). Many problems of ambiguity are connected with high-frequency general-language words, translatable only on the basis of specific word combinations (if at all). Decisions must be made in terms of context, which means, for the most part, on the basis of syntactic combinations. For example, the translation of a multiple-equivalent noun used as subject of the sentence will often depend on the kind of verb for which it is subject. The kind of verb will be indicated by the semantic code. The study of syntactic combinations for purposes of establishing semantic codes is only beginning. Again, considerable storage space in the dictionary will be required, and the dictionary must have the capability of easy modification as new evidence is acquired.

REPRESENTATION OF OUTPUT-LANGUAGE ITEM

The output-language item may be stored in MT dictionaries in one of two locations: as a part of the record that contains the input-language item or in a separate dictionary. In the latter instance, the lexical item is represented by a code which serves as the address of the item in the separate dictionary. In either instance, we have the same problem as with the input-language item: Shall the item be represented by full forms or by stems? For English output, where the inflectional problem is less severe, some groups have proposed a form dictionary. Others have stored an English canonical form with a code which will permit inflection of the item in accordance with the rules of English grammar and orthography. The problem is a minor one, and should be decided on the basis of appropriateness to the whole MT system. It may be difficult, for example, in a given context to decide whether to add the ending *-ed* or *-ing* to an English verb; the decision must take into account the input sentence and the requirements of English grammar. The implementation of this decision, however, is a simple matter. The techniques for carrying out such a decision are well known and widely applied.

The chief problem of the output-language item in a bilingual MT dictionary is again one of content: Which equivalents should be stored for the input lexical item? Experience has shown the danger of placing too much reliance on published dictionaries, even "technical" dictionaries, as a source for the output items. The problem may be illustrated by citing two entries from Callaham's *Russian-English Technical and Scientific Dictionary:*

Probeg m. run, mileage; race; *ispytanie -om* road test.

Prodolzh/at' v. continue, go on, go ahead, proceed; carry on, pursue, persist; resume; prolong, extend; elongate, lengthen, broaden; *-at'sya* v. continue, last, be prolonged, be extended.

In the translation of Russian physics texts at the RAND Corporation, the noun *probeg* occurred 157 times; the equivalents chosen were either *range* or *path*. The verb *prodolzhat'* occurred 16 times, always with the translation *continue*. In the case of *probeg,* it is clear that the published dictionary is not an idioglossary for physics (which, of course, it does not pretend to be). In the case of *prodolzhat'*, we have "too much" information: Although the wealth of synonyms and nuances may be helpful to the human translator, they will be useless to a machine-translation system unless a selection procedure is provided. The customary procedure in such instances is editing—i.e., the arbitrary selection, by the MT researcher, of a minimum number of English equivalents. The selection process may be more or less successful, depending on the experience, judgment, intuitive powers, and luck of the editor. In any event, his choices must be subjected to verification (text processing) before they can be declared valid, or before any remaining problem of ambiguity can be studied. There are good grounds for arguing that the assistance of the best editors in the world does more harm than good in building of MT dictionaries.

The sad truth is that very little progress has been made in this area of MT research in the past ten years, despite the fact that it is an easy and obvious place to begin. A survey of the literature indicates that little has been done in the building of idioglossaries since the early work of Oswald and Fletcher.[3] Although a substantial amount of text has been processed, no one has yet produced a good idioglossary, nor made a systematic study of the coverage provided by glossaries of different size and composition, for texts of a specified nature.

In summary, consider the following important points brought out in the preceding discussions.

1 A great deal of work has gone into the preparation of MT dictionaries. Reasons for the concentration of effort in this area include the following: *(a)* the fact that dictionaries are a prerequisite for text processing, whether for purposes of translation or research; *(b)* the assumption that existing dictionaries and grammars are adequate and suitable for MT dictionaries; *(c)* the belief that machine translation is essentially an engineering problem, solvable, at least in part, by the application of engineering techniques.

2 The chief developments in MT dictionaries have been in terms of the text-lookup function: Is the dictionary big enough and fast enough for the job?

3 The desirability of performing syntactic analysis on the input sentence is now generally accepted. Dictionaries that serve only the lookup function have limited usefulness in the area of language processing.

4 Present and future MT dictionaries must have the capability of easy and cheap modification. As more grammatic and semantic information is acquired (from whatever source) about the items in storage, it will be stored in the dictionary. In essence, the dictionary is a tool for research.

[3] *Cf.* V. A. Oswald, Jr., and R. H. Lawson, "An Idioglossary for Mechanical Translation," *Modern Language Forum,* vol. 38, nos. 3/4, pp. 1–11, 1953.

PAUL L. GARVIN

Syntax in machine translation

The general problem area of machine translation has been outlined and related to other fields of language-data processing in Garvin's "A Linguist's View of Language-data Processing." It has been discussed in some detail in the two immediately preceding sections by Hays and Harper. This discussion will deal more specifically with the question of syntax: both with the place of syntax in the over-all design of a machine-translation program, and with the detailed problems of syntactic resolution.

Machine translation is a process for translating text automatically from one language to another. This process is embodied in a program—that is, a set of instructions for a computer. With such a program, any large-scale computing machine can be transformed into a translating machine.

A genuine translation is more than just the replacement of individual foreign words by individual English words. It must transmit the essential information contained in the foreign text to an English reader who is unfamiliar with the language. The meaning of each sentence is more than the sum of the meanings of each word—it also depends on the structure of the sentence and the function of each word in that structure. To obtain a satisfactory translation, the program must therefore contain not only a dictionary lookup for finding individual word meanings, but also a translation algorithm for making correct translation choices and for detecting the elements of meanings implicit in the sentence. The core of such a translation algorithm is a *syntax routine.*

The major purpose of a syntax routine in machine translation is to recognize and appropriately record the boundaries and functions of the various components of the sentence. This syntactic information is essential for the efficient solution of the problem of word order for the output and is equally indispensable for the proper recognition of the determiners for multiple-meaning choices.

It is furthermore becoming increasingly apparent that it is the design of the syntax routine which governs the over-all layout of a good machine-translation program and lends it the unity without which it would remain a patchwork of individual subroutines and piecemeal instructions. The conception of syntax thus becomes important beyond the immediate objectives which the routine serves in the program.

A syntax routine for machine translation can be described from two viewpoints: (1) the underlying linguistic conception of syntax (the syntactic "model"); and (2) the logical technique employed in the design of a syntax program.

Two kinds of linguistic conceptualization underlie current work in machine translation: formal or quasi-formal models of language on the one hand, and more discursive conceptual frameworks on the other. The former are illustrated by the transformational model and the dependency model, as discussed earlier by Stockwell and D. G. Hays respectively. The latter are illustrated by the informational and definitional models, as presented by Sebeok and Garvin.

Formal models attempt to base a conceptualization of language upon a previously derived system. In machine translation, D. G. Hays and his coworkers have extensively applied an approach based on the dependency model referred to above. Discursive frameworks, on the other hand, can be developed by a formalization of common-sense criteria and the systematization of the experience of trained observers. In Russian-English machine translation, such common-sense approaches largely consist in a modification of traditional Russian grammar for data-processing purposes. Since the traditional grammar of Russian is, on the whole, not too far removed from linguistic reality (see "The Definitional Model of Language"), the various adaptations to machine translation undertaken by American research groups have proved quite adequate.

The conception of linguistic structure as presented here, in so far as it concerns syntax, is comparable to what has become known as the *immediate-constituent model,* but with some significant differences. Where the immediate-constituent approach takes the maximum unit—the sentence—as its point of departure and considers its step-by-step breakdown into components of an increasingly lower order of complexity, we can start out with the minimum unit—the morpheme in straight linguistic analysis, the typographical word in language-data processing—and consider its gradual fusion into units of increasingly higher orders of complexity, which we have termed *fused units.* A sentence is thus viewed not as a simple succession of linear components but as a compound chain of fused units of different orders of complexity variously encapsulated in each other. Syntactic analysis, including the automatic analysis which an MT syntax routine must perform, then has as its objective the delineation of this encapsulation of fused units by ascertaining their boundaries and functions.

For MT purposes, the most significant order of fused units are the major members—subjects, predicates, and objects—of clauses. The languages of the world differ significantly in the manner by which these clause members are formally marked. In a language such as Russian, for instance, the clause members are characterized primarily by a particular selection of grammatical endings, the functions of which must often be ascertained from the context. Only in case of unresolvable ambiguity of endings will conditions of word order and the semantic nature of particular words indicate the functions of the clause members. In languages such as English or French, on the other hand, word order is the primary means for identifying and characterizing the clause members.

A recognition routine for Russian syntax must therefore in some way search the span of the entire clause to identify appropriate endings, and from them ascertain the boundaries and functions of the major clause members. The corresponding command routine for translation into English or French must then have the capability for the rearrangement of entire clauses, in order to generate correct word order for the output language.

A recognition routine for English or French syntax, on the other hand, can draw on word order in the identification of the major clause members. This identification, however, presupposes that the grammatical function of each constituent word of the clause has been unambiguously ascertained. Since in English, for instance, a great many words have ambiguous part-of-speech membership (for example, *love* functioning as a verb, noun, or modifier, depending on the context), the identification of the clause members can not proceed until these ambiguities have been resolved. A command routine for translation into Russian must then generate correct grammatical endings and stem modifications where necessary, in order to render the functions of the major clause members which in English or French are marked by word order.

The following discussion will be limited to a detailed consideration of the problems arising in the machine translation of Russian into English. The fused-unit conception is particularly well suited to MT since the minimum units—for this purpose the typographical words—constitute the primarily given input units; the program then computes the fused units and their interrelations from the grammar codes (see below) of the words. The methodological basis used here for this computation is what we can call the *fulcrum approach* to syntax. Its basic features have been adopted and have been implemented to a considerable extent by the machine translation group at Thompson Ramo Wooldridge Inc. This approach is a suitable point of departure for the discussion, not only of our own work in syntactic resolution, but also of the work of other groups that use a common-sense grammatical framework as the basis for their approach to Russian-English MT.

The fulcrum approach consists in directing the primary syntactic searches toward those pivot words (fulcra) within the sentence, around which other words are centered. The fulcra contain the maximum amount of grammatical information, thereby allowing an optimization of further searches within the sentence. Not only is the sentence as a whole assumed to have a fulcrum, but the various constituents of a sentence in turn are assumed to have their fulcra.

Thus, the fulcrum of the Russian main clause is assumed to be its predicate. Once the predicate is known, it allows a reasonable prediction concerning possible subjects and objects. The number (and, when present, the gender) of the predicate will be in agreement with the subject and hence will predict the corresponding features of the latter. The predicate has certain inherent government characteristics: some verbs govern the accusative, other verbs govern the instrumental, etc. These government characteristics of the predicate allow prediction of the corresponding characteristics of the object(s). The converse does not apply.

The fulcrum of a nominal block (that is, a noun with modifiers and other dependents) is assumed to be the noun: It is that member of the block which determines the case and number forms of the other members, and not conversely.

The syntactic searches, whether based on an overt fulcrum approach or not, are made possible by including, with each word of the machine dictionary, a grammar code containing all the grammatical information inherent in the particular word. The grammar code is thus a representation of all the potential functions and relations of a word; the syntactic searches then serve to determine which of these inherent possibilities actually does apply for the particular sentence in which the word occurs.

The grammar code utilized by TRW is organized in terms of this potential function of the words, rather than simply their morphological shape, particularly for the indication of parts of speech in the grammar code. In traditional Russian grammar, parts of speech are largely determined on the basis of the nature of the stem and the grammatical endings. In our grammar code, priority is given to the capability of a word to constitute the predicate, subject or object, or other functional component of the sentence. Increasing emphasis on functional rather than morphological grammar coding is becoming apparent in the work of other groups as well.

Thus, words with the same functional capabilities are given the same code designation, even though in traditional Russian grammar they are not considered the same part of speech. For example, some Russian predicative adjectives function as predicates of sentences in much the same way as verbs (barring certain ambiguities to be discussed further below). They, together with verbs, are given the same grammar code digit for "predicativeness." Another example are certain modifying adjectives which share an important characteristic in common with participles—both may be accompanied by certain governed structures (for example, "analogous *to this*," "pertaining *to this*"). These are jointly coded as *governing modifiers*.

On the other hand, words which in traditional grammar are considered different forms of the same part of speech are treated separately in our grammar code if they have different functional potential. An example of this are infinitives, which are traditionally considered merely a form of the verb. Since, however, they differ significantly from finite verb forms (e.g., by not having a capability for taking a subject), our grammar code assigns to them a separate "infinitive" digit, while finite verb forms are coded for "predicativeness."

The actual syntax routines utilize the information contained in the grammar code for a series of searches intended to detect and record the interrelations of the words of each sentence and the function of the words within this net of relations. Two major methods for organizing these syntactic searches deserve mention. The first is a search pattern in which all syntactic information is immediately recorded from the grammar code as each word is encountered; the second consists of a sequence of passes at the sentence, in which each pass is designed to retrieve and record information about a particular set of word relations and functions, in order to identify fused units of a particular order and type. Further information is retrieved in later passes. A well-known and very ingenious example of the first-mentioned search pattern is the method devised by Mrs. Ida Rhodes of the National Bureau of Standards, and named *predictive analysis* by her followers in the machine-translation group at the Harvard Computation Laboratory. The TRW group, on the other hand, uses a pass method.

A question of logical flow, less related to linguistic considerations than the above, is the extent to which the syntactic algorithm is based on a table-lookup or a logical-tree principle. A table lookup, as the term indicates, consists in the storage of information in tables in memory, to be looked up when a particular subroutine calls for it. A logical tree, on the other hand, in this connection refers to a program design in which a small amount of information is looked up at a time, and the subroutines of the program branch extensively in terms of the answers obtained to the questions asked by the program.

The argument in favor of a table-lookup approach to syntactic programming is that the same small lookup routine can be used to call a variety of tables and, hence, yields a more flexible program; and that even large tables are easier to construct and revise than complex logical trees with many branches. Logical trees by contrast are favored because of their greater relative efficiency, and because of the concern that tables, even if well organized, become unwieldy once they increase beyond a certain size. The TRW syntax algorithm is largely designed as a logical tree and uses comparatively few tables.

The advantage of a pass method implemented by a logical-tree design is that instead of having to account, at each step of the left-to-right search, for each of the many possibilities contained in the tables, every pass is limited to a particular search. With the proper sequencing of passes, the syntactic retrieval problems presented by each sentence can be solved in the order of their magnitude, rather than in the accidental order of their appearance in the text.

In a program based on the pass method, each individual pass is laid out in terms of the information available when the pass is initiated and in terms of the objective that the pass is intended to accomplish. These two factors are closely related to each other, in that the output of a preceding pass becomes the input of the subsequent pass. The scope of each pass and the order of the various passes thus together present the most significant design problem of the program.

The various passes are concerned either with individual words and strings that function as single words (such as symbols and numerals), or with fused units that the program labels as *word packages,* in order to treat them as single entities. The former set of passes serves to ascertain the function of a particular word or string in order to assign to it the grammar code required for further syntactic processing in the passes designed for word packaging. The purpose of the latter is to identify the boundaries and functions of the word packages that constitute the components of the sentence. The word-packaging passes first identify the potential fulcrum of a given package and then use it as the initial point from which to search for the required boundary and function information to delimit and define the package.

The linguistic considerations affecting the design of a syntax program stem from the assumption that the various orders of units and their relations do not have the same degree of significance for the over-all structure of the sentence. An adequate analysis of the sentence must give priority to the identification of the major sentence components (subjects, predicates, objects), since the relations between these components are the focal point around which the remaining syntactic relations are centered.

Applying this to the organization of the passes, it means that the main syntax pass—that is, the pass designed to identify the boundaries and functions of the major clause members of the main clause—becomes the pivot of the program. The remaining passes can be laid out in terms of the input requirements and expected output of this central pass. Preceding it will be preliminary passes designed to assign grammar codes to words which are not in the dictionary (a missing-word routine) and to aberrant typographical matter such as symbols and formulae, as well as passes designed to compute from the grammar codes information needed as input to the main syntax pass. Following it will be terminal passes, the function of which is to fill the gaps in syntactic information remaining after the main syntax has accomplished its objective.

The present TRW syntax algorithm works in the following manner: To find a fulcrum, the program reads the word-class field of the grammar code of each word that the lookup has brought into the work space. This may be either an original grammar code as brought in from the dictionary, or a revised grammar code as assigned to a word or string by an earlier pass. If the word is of a class that may function as the fulcrum of a word package, this information serves as the signal for later calling the subroutine designed to identify the boundaries and possible function of the package in question.

Each pass of the program is concerned with either the assignment of an appropriate grammar code or with the identification of an appropriate word package. The word packages correspond more or less closely to the fused units of the Russian structure; the order of passes constitutes the sequence in which the search for the various fulcra and fused units is conducted, with the aim of the correct recognition of their encapsula on.

The syntax program consists of four series of passes:

Preliminary passes are designed to insure that all the words and strings of the sentence are provided with the appropriate unambiguous grammar codes.

The preliminary passes are required by the discrepancy between the information contained in the grammar code and the information necessary for the main syntax passes. The grammar code furnishes three sets of indications: word-class membership, agreement characteristics, and government characteristics. As is well known, for each dictionary entry some of this information will be unambiguous, some ambiguous, depending on the particular word forms involved.

Aside from accidental typographical homonyms (such as *est'* meaning *is* or *to eat*), grammatical ambiguities relate to word-class membership and agreement characteristics (where ambiguities as to government characteristics are found, they are dependent on another grammatical function, that of word-class membership).

While the main syntax passes may tolerate agreement ambiguities, they cannot admit word-class ambiguities in their input, since the fulcrum approach is based on the recognition of the fulcra by their word-class membership. One of the essential functions of the preliminary passes is thus the resolution of ambiguous word-class membership.

It is furthermore reasonable to expect that sentences will contain discontinuous fused units—that is, fused units interrupted by variously structured intervening elements. Unless such intervening structures are properly identified in prior passes, the program will not be able to skip over them in the search for elements functionally relevant to the objectives of the later syntactic passes.

Finally, since the internal structure and external functioning of units are relatively independent of each other (as discussed in "The Definitional Model of Language"), a number of constructions can be expected within each sentence which by their internal structure resemble potential major clause members, but do not have that external functioning.

An example of this are relative clauses: Their internal structure resembles that of a main clause, and they contain similarly structured clause members, but their external functioning is that of inclusion in nominal blocks as modifying elements. Constructions such as these have to be identified by appropriate prior passes, and their boundaries and functions recorded for inclusion in the main syntax.

Minor syntax passes are designed to identify and label the word packages which are candidates for inclusion in, or exclusion from, the major sentence portions upon which the next series of passes operates.

Major syntax passes are designed to identify and label the major portions of the sentence.

Terminal passes are designed to identify and label certain word packages not previously identified and labeled.

The following passes enter into each of the four series in the present TRW program:

The *preliminary passes* include a numeral-and-symbol pass and a set of homograph-resolution passes. The numeral-and-symbol pass serves to assign a grammar code to number-symbol strings in the sentence, the homograph-resolution passes serve to resolve various systematic word-class ambiguities (such as the well-known predicative adjectives ending in *-o*, which also function as adverbs).

The *minor syntax passes* include a nominal-blocking pass, a prepositional-blocking pass, an inserted-structure pass, and a governing-modifier pass.

The purpose of the nominal-blocking and prepositional-blocking passes is to identify and label nominal blocks and prepositional blocks respectively. A nominal block consists of a noun and its accompanying modifiers; a prepositional block consists of a preposition and the nominal block which it governs.

An inserted structure is one which is not grammatically related to the remainder of the sentence (comparable to English *as it were* in a sentence such as *this, as it were, can be considered an inserted structure*). The purpose of the inserted-structure routine is to identify and label these structures so that they can be skipped over by later syntactic searches.

The purpose of the governing-modifier pass is to identify and label governing-modifier packages. The word class of governing modifiers includes both attributive participles and those adjectives which can in turn govern certain dependent structures (see above).

A governing-modifier package is the word package which contains a governing modifier together with the structures that it governs. The fulcrum of this package is the governing modifier; the program reads its word-class code to call the appropriate routine, then reads the government code in order to search for an appropriate governed structure.

The *major syntax passes* include a clause-boundary-determination routine, a relative-package routine, and the main syntax routine.

The clause-boundary-determination routine serves to ascertain the boundaries between the several component clauses of a compound sentence, in order to process one clause at a time.

The relative-package routine identifies relative clauses by finding the relative pronouns introducing them. It then sets the clause boundary to allow the main syntax routine to process the components of the relative clause. Finally, the package as a whole is labeled for inclusion in the appropriate nominal block.

The main syntax routine serves to identify the major clause components—namely, subject, predicate, and object—and to ascertain their boundaries. The routine first searches for the fulcrum of the clause, the predicate, and then uses the information derived from the grammar code of the predicate to search for the subject and object.

Two *terminal* passes are included in the present program: (*a*) a predicate-packaging pass, serving to include adverbs and other dependent words together with the predicate in a predicate package; and (*b*) a genitive-blocking pass, serving to identify genitive nominal blocks and attach them to the preceding nouns which are likely to govern them. Both passes identify and label the packages, and set their boundaries.

A syntax program of the kind described above will produce a record of the syntactic structure of the sentences of the input text, as recognized by the program. This syntax record furnishes a significant part of the information required for the correct application of the command routines for word rearrangement and multiple-meaning choice. At the present developmental stage of machine translation, an important function of the syntax record is its use in checking out the operation of the syntax program. It allows the analyst to determine what routines have been applied and why, and to introduce required modifications on the basis of an examination of the translation output and the syntax record.

At Thompson Ramo Wooldridge Inc., the syntax record is stored on an information tape which can be printed out separately. It contains the grammar codes of each word (whether brought in from the dictionary or assigned by the program), as well as an indication of the word packages that have been identified and additional syntactic and semantic information.

The remaining information required by the command routines is semantic. It has to be retrieved by a semantic program linked to the syntax. The semantic program can deal with the meanings of the input words on the basis of an appropriate semantic code contained in the machine dictionary. The code will serve to call the routines needed for the resolution of semantic choices.

Semantic resolution presents a much more difficult problem area than syntax. Our knowledge of the inherent semantic system of a language is as yet sketchy and indefinite (see "A Linguist's View of Language-data Processing"). Consequently, the semantic codes used in present machine-translation programs are not as systematic as the grammar codes. The resolution routines are piecemeal, and what coordination there is in these routines is based on their link to the syntax program. An organizing principle for semantic information, comparable to the fulcrum approach to syntax, will have to be found before a more efficient and exhaustive approach to semantic resolution can be envisioned.

JULES MERSEL

Programming aspects of machine translation

During the years that have elapsed since high-speed digital computers first became generally available, knowledge about the art of programming has been acquired by many groups. The first part of this discussion is intended for those readers who have not had an initial exposure to programming.

Programming can be considered as being similar to writing instructions for a girl who is working with a desk calculator. The analogy becomes exact if you assume that such a computress has the virtues of being very quick, of never making mistakes, and following instructions perfectly—and that she has the glaring defect of being incapable of thinking.

If it were required that our computress solve a problem, a notebook of instructions could be prepared for her. She would be told to go to line 1, page 1 of that notebook. There she might find an instruction which reads *Add the number on line* 6, *page* 73, *to the number found on line* 19, *page* 12, *and place the result on line* 13, *page* 62. *After you have done that, go to line* 3, *page* 9, *to find out what to do next.* There she might find a similar instruction. The differences in the instructions would involve simply a change in line and page number and a change in the arithmetical operation to be performed. Only occasionally would she be called upon to make a decision. The decision would be as trivial as *Look at the number on line* 12, *page* 3, *and compare it with the number on line* 24, *page* 22. *If the first number is bigger, go to line* 16, *page* 36, *to find out what to do next. If the first number is not bigger, go to line* 9, *page* 7, *to find out what to do next.* Eventually she would find an instruction which said *Hand the notebook back to me; your task is finished.*

Programming for a computer is no more and no less than the writing of such a notebook. The instructions available to the programmer, though more extensive than just the arithmetical commands, are few and quite simple. The additional instructions consist of such things as writing onto magnetic tape, reading from magnetic tape, and performing certain simple Boolean operations. Unfortunately there are no such instructions as *be intelligent, do the right thing, jump to a conclusion,* or *find an adjective.*

As can be seen from the above analogy, digital computers do not think; they merely do the mechanical part of the white-collar work. In order for any problem to be solved on a computer, it must be well stated. Such instructions as *supply the appropriate preposition* (and this did appear on our original syntactic flowcharts) must be amplified so that the digital computer is told very specifically exactly what to look for, by what characteristic to recognize it, and then as a result of its search to decide exactly which preposition must be supplied and where it must be inserted.

Writing such a notebook is a time-consuming and tedious task. However, it would take less time to perform the desired operations manually than to program them. Digital computers are advantageous only when one is going to perform the same task over and over again. Then the speed of the computer makes its application economical. As an example one might give the problem of finding the sum of a million numbers. One wouldn't say, as one might in hand calculations, *add the first number to the second number, add the third number to the sum, add the fourth number to the sum,* until one finally said *add the one-millionth number to the sum.* Instead, one would do something logically more complex and fantastically shorter. The instructions would be:

Set the sum to equal 0.
Set i to equal 1.
Add the ith number to the sum.
Does i = 1 *million? If so, you are finished. If not, increase i by one and proceed through the third and fourth instructions.*

We now can begin to get a glimmer of how a computer can be useful. It wouldn't take the computer long to do such a computation, provided the programmer can find a short way of telling the machine explicitly how to do it.

In recent years compilers have been developed that simplify the task of writing programs. One such program, COMIT, was specifically written for language-data processing. However, even with compilers, the detailed spelling out of instructions is not avoided—it is merely raised to a less dreary level.

INPUT AND OUTPUT

Our computress analogy can be expanded to embrace the notion of input, output, and erasable storage. Let us assume that instead of giving our fictional computress just one notebook, we gave her four such books.

One of the books would be the same as the kind described above—it would contain the program and no numbers would be written into it by the computress.

Another notebook, which we can call the input, would contain all the numbers which change from problem to problem and which are used in this calculation by the computress.

A third notebook, the output, would originally be blank and would eventually contain just those numbers that the problem-giver eventually wanted to see. The fourth notebook, the erasable storage, would contain all the intermediate results and modified instructions that were needed to arrive at the output. In our computress–desk calculator analogy, this fourth notebook would be thrown away when the problem was solved; in computing machines, the erasable storage is part of the equipment, and is merely wiped clean so that new information can be written over it. The point to be remembered in machine translation, or for that matter in any other type of research, is that if the intermediate results will be needed for future use, they must be placed into the output. If they are left in erasable storage they will be erased, and the only way of retrieving them would be to go through the whole problem again and record from erasable storage before erasure takes place.

TYPES OF COMPUTER STORAGE

In computing machines, storage, or memory, can consist of three types: The first type is *random-access* storage. Random-access storage is typified by the speed with which one can write into or read from any storage location. This speed is based on the equal availability of all storage locations. The time required for such reads and writes varies from a fraction of a microsecond (1 μsec = 0.000001 second) for evaporative-film memory to 20 μsec for the slower magnetic-core memories.

A second type of memory is *serial* memory. Serial memories require positioning for either writing into or reading from them. A common type of serial memory is the magnetic drum. Reading or writing can be done only when the drum has turned to a certain position. Waiting for this to occur can take as much as 32 milliseconds (1 msec = 0.001 second). Though this is a far longer wait than would be required with even the slowest core storages, the drum has the compensating advantage of providing much more storage per dollar expended.

The third type of storage is exemplified by *magnetic tape*. Magnetic tapes can hold extremely large amounts of information. Unfortunately if the information is far from the reading head of the tape unit, minutes may elapse before the information becomes available. To a large extent, these long waits can be avoided by careful programming. Tapes have the advantage of being inexpensive: a reel of tape costs $50, machine time may cost $400 per hour. They also can be removed from the computer for later use: output can be written onto them, and later input can be read from them. This input-output use is one of the main advantages of magnetic tapes; the ability to save intermediate results is important economically.[1]

DICTIONARY SEARCH

The programming of any particular problem is affected almost as much by the characteristics of the available computer as by the nature of the problem itself.

In the following discussion we shall consider the programming techniques used by three different machine-translation groups to solve the problem of searching a Russian-English machine dictionary.

If we ignore the question of what a dictionary should contain, then the best-defined portion of the machine-translation process is the dictionary lookup. In concept, nothing could be simpler. Given a word from text, look it up in the dictionary. If we had an ideal machine with an infinite and instantaneous-access memory, we would merely take the Russian word, use it to find our item in the dictionary, and be through with the lookup. Unfortunately such a machine does not exist. The problem is complicated by the limited amount of fast storage available on computers today.

The random-access memories on present general-purpose computers do not have room for a complete bilingual dictionary with all the necessary information.

Though a dictionary can be ordered (the most common ordering being alphabetical), natural text comes in a completely unpredictable and random order. The problem therefore is that if only part of the dictionary is placed in storage, there would be no assurance that when the next text word is selected, the required portion of the dictionary would be easily available. The solutions to this problem reflect the interests and goals of various machine-translation groups.

One solution to the problem is that used by the group at Thompson Ramo Wooldridge Inc. This group uses a computer with good computational ability, a small but fast internal storage, and excellent magnetic tapes. The computer can transfer information to and from magnetic tapes while performing other computations.

The dictionary is stored in alphabetic order on magnetic tape. Four thousand words of text are transferred to internal storage. These text words are sorted into alphabetic order. The beginning of the dictionary is then brought into the internal memory. The alphabetically ordered text words are now compared with the dictionary items that are in fast storage.

This comparison does not simply follow the alphabetic order. Instead,

[1]Since the time this paper was given at the UCLA lecture series, disk-type memories have become an important type of storage medium associated with high-speed computers.

a binary search is performed. The text word is compared to the last word of the dictionary portion in fast storage. If it is alphabetically smaller, it is compared to the middle word of the dictionary; depending on this last comparison, the text word is then compared to the word one-quarter of the way through or three-quarters through the dictionary portion. Thus, the amount of dictionary to be compared is halved at each test. Consequently, looking at a table of 1,024 words requires at most ten comparisons rather than the average of 512 that would come from a straight search in alphabetic order.

As soon as it has been determined that a word of text is alphabetically beyond the part of the dictionary that is in memory, that part of the dictionary is replaced by dictionary items further down the alphabetic list. This is done simultaneously with dictionary lookup.

In order to allow that portion of the dictionary which is in memory to include as much of the whole dictionary as is possible, very few forms are carried for any one word. Thus there is a high likelihood of a text word not finding a representation in the dictionary.

When a text word is not in the dictionary, the word is analyzed morphologically; that is, an attempt is made to separate the stem of the word from its ending. This process of stem-ending analysis requires a good computer and an extensive program. It is aided by storing a list of possible endings in memory. Dictionary words surrounding the place where the text word should have been found are then split into stem and ending. If a dictionary word and a text word have the same stem, the endings are compared to see whether the ending of the text word will predict a grammar code compatible with the grammar code of the dictionary word. If this is the case, then the text word is given a revised grammar code derived from the grammar code of the dictionary word as adjusted on the basis of the ending of the text word. The English equivalents associated with the dictionary word are reinflected so that they represent the tense, number, or person corresponding to the form of the text word. The text words are thus replaced by the corresponding dictionary entries, revised wherever necessary by stem-ending analysis.

The lookup process is continued until all 4,000 text words have been examined. Then the beginning portion of the dictionary is brought back into internal storage and the next 4,000 words of text are looked up by the same method.

When the complete text has been examined, the dictionary items corresponding to the text words are restored to text order. The text is then examined in order to identify contiguous idioms.

The batching method just described utilizes the speed of the computer to enable it to supply missing forms in less time than would be required to spin a tape which contained all the forms. Another method, in use at the University of California (Berkeley), was programmed for a machine with good computational ability, but no ability to spin tapes during computation. Here an attempt is made to get a very large dictionary into memory. Since the memory itself is not very large, this is ingeniously achieved by dividing the dictionary items so that the Russian word is completely separated from the other parts of the dictionary entry. All of the Russian portion of the dictionary is brought into memory at one time. Space is conserved by eliminating the first two letters of each word and indicating in a table where each two-character list starts. Space is also saved by making the dictionary purely a stem dictionary. The Berkeley group estimates that it has the capability for storing 20,000 stems.[2]

As each text word comes in, its first two characters are examined to find the appropriate two-character list. Then the remainder of the word is looked at in successive locations of that portion of the dictionary. The dictionary items are not stored in alphabetic order but rather in order of length. When a dictionary item is found whose characters exactly match the beginning characters of the text word, a similar search is instituted to find out whether the remaining portion of this text word also has a dictionary stem equivalent or a dictionary ending equivalent. Thus, in this dictionary, the word *microorganisms* would be found in three searches: one for *micro,* one for *organism,* and one for *s.* After the word has been identified, the locations of the dictionary items pertaining to this word are stored in successive order. Since this redundant information can be stored in comparatively little space, the Berkeley system allows passing approximately 30,000 words of text through the dictionary before the storage space is filled up. When the examination of the Russian portion of the dictionary is completed, the next segment of the dictionary is transferred to internal storage. Here, no further search is involved. For each text word, the correct segment can be picked up right away and placed onto tape. This is continued until all segments of the dictionary have been brought into memory. This technique allows the Berkeley group to claim the fastest lookup of any of the dictionary search methods. Its drawbacks are that there is no guarantee that the Russian portion of the dictionary will not eventually grow too large for storage, and the dependence on the assumption that the correct translation of a word can be put together from the English equivalents of its separate parts.

Another type of dictionary lookup has been constructed at the RAND Corporation. Here again, there is an attempt to get the whole dictionary into the memory. The whole dictionary, however, does not consist of the

[2]Since the time this paper was given at the UCLA lecture series, Sydney Lamb, head of the Berkeley group, has made major modifications to his initial dictionary concept. These now allow his research group to state that its technique will allow for the handling of a far larger lexicon. Similar improvements have been made by other groups.

Russian lexicon but rather of the lexicon that is needed for the first portion of text. The size of this first portion is determined by the nature of the text itself. Two passes at the text are made. The purpose of the first pass is to determine how many text words can be handled by a dictionary which fills the available space in high-speed storage. Recognition is made of the fact that 4,000 words of dictionary may easily be sufficient to handle 100,000 words of text. Thus, after the first pass is made, the RAND program knows exactly what words from the dictionary need to be in high-speed storage. These dictionary items are brought in and the text is passed again. This double pass at the text eliminates the problem of re-sorting and thus considerable efficiency is effected.

Another solution to the problem has been attempted at IBM. Here, as befits a computer manufacturer, the solution has been to build an internal storage large enough to hold an extremely large memory. This storage is a photoscopic disk. It is a serial storage that is read by optical techniques rather than magnetic sensing. The storage cannot be written on during computation. Since the storage capacity of the disk is quite large and the period of rotation short, text is not sorted.

The capacity is large enough to allow storage of phrases. The lookup proceeds by phrases; single words are treated as "degenerate" one-word phrases. This storage of idioms has allowed for a fairly extensive but slow dictionary search.

In summary, we can see that though the problem of looking up items in the dictionary is conceptually easy, the configuration of hardware either requires the use of less than straightforward methods, or has inspired at least one group to build special hardware.

SYNTAX

Programming the syntax portion of machine translation differs from the dictionary portion in that words on an individual basis are not the primary concern, rather certain grammatical characteristics which a word may share with thousands of other words. The grammatical characteristics are recorded in the grammar code for the word. If the goal were the maximal conciseness of the grammar code, it could be compressed into just a few alphabetic characters. Indeed, the grammar code that the Ramo Wooldridge group first started working with (it was borrowed from the RAND Corporation) consisted of three alphanumeric characters. The decoding of these alphanumeric characters for use in the algorithm, though possible, is not convenient. TRW and Wayne State University, therefore, chose a binary representation which C. Briggs of Wayne[3] referred to as the vectorial representation of the word.

[3]Personal communication.

Figure 1 shows the grammar code for a modifier. It is called a *modifier* grammar code rather than an adjective grammar code because in our representation of the parts of speech (word classes) of Russian the modifier class includes not only adjectives, but also participles and possessive pronouns.

The grammar code consists of 108 binary digit positions, shown in the figure in 3 columns of 36 each. Each position contains either a one or a zero. It allows no other representation.

The first column of the grammar code has the same format for all parts of speech. Positions 1 through 9 indicate the word class of the word. Only one of these positions will contain a one; all the others will contain zeros. In our example, bit position 3 is occupied by a one. It is reserved for indicating modifiers.

In column 2, bit positions 11 through 36 are labeled the *agreement code*. They represent the possible genders, numbers, and cases that a given word may assume: M stands for masculine, F for feminine, N for neuter, P for plural, S for nominative, G for genitive, D for dative, A_i for accusative inanimate, A_a for accusative animate, I for instrumental, and L for prepositional. Unlike the word-class code, the agreement code and the government code of the third column do not have the constraint that only one position is allowed to contain a one. As many ones may be used as are needed to describe all possible features of gender, number, and case of a given word, or of the gender, number, and case of the words that this word might govern. Note that this requires many more ones in the government code than would be needed if we were merely to indicate by a single symbol the possible cases that a word could govern. Note also that the binary agreement code requires more storage than a more condensed representation such as the earlier one consisting of alphanumeric characters. The reason for this lack of compactness is the great convenience afforded by the binary codes in agreement and government checks.

This will become apparent after we take a brief digression into the area of Boolean logic. As indicated by Maron earlier in "A Logician's View of Language-data Processing," $A \wedge A = A$; $A \wedge B$ indicates the common portions of A and B. In the computer when doing a Boolean operation, $1 \wedge 1 = 1$, $1 \wedge 0 = 0$, $0 \wedge 1 = 0$, $0 \wedge 0 = 0$. In the grammar code, the presence of a one in a particular bit position indicates that the gender, number, case for which this bit position is reserved, applies to the word in question.

In a government check, the government code of the governing word is compared to the agreement code of the potential governed word. This comparison is done by a *logical-and* operation. The result of this operation is that those bit positions which in both grammar codes are filled by

	First word	Second word	Third word
1	Word class	Homograph	Skip*
2		Abnormal agreement	
3	1	1 **pyat'**, 0 **dva**	
4		Unmodifiable	Perfective
5		1 active, 0 passive	Requires inversion even withou
6		Governing modifier	Past governed struc
7		Adjective	Reflexive
8		Agreement code: 1st person	Government code: 1st person
9		2d person	2d person
10	Verb of motion governs prep. struct.	3d person	3d person
11		MS	MS
12	Governs specific prepositions	FS	FS
13		NS	NS
14		MG	MG
15		FG	FG
16		NG	NG
17		MD	MD
18		FD	FD
19		ND	ND
20		MA	MA_i
21		NA	NA
22		MA_a	MA_a
23		FA_a	FA
24		MI	MI
25		FI	FI
26		NI	NI
27		ML	ML
28		FL	FL
29		NL	NL
30		PS	PS
31		PG	PG
32		PD	PD
33		PA_i	PA_i
34		PA_a	PA_a
35		PI	PI
36	Governs **chem**	PL	PL

FIGURE 1

ones remain filled by ones in the sum. This indicates that there is a relation of government in this case. Conversely, if the result is a string of zeros without any ones, then there are no ones in corresponding bit positions, and hence the first word cannot govern the second word. In an agreement check, the agreement codes of two potentially agreeing words (such as a noun and preceding adjectives) are compared by a logical-and. Those bit positions which contain ones in both agreement codes result in ones in the sums. Bit positions that are not occupied by ones in both codes, but only in one of them, result in zeros in the sum. These additional ones indicate ambiguities in gender, number, and case; their zeroing in the logical sum indicates a resolution of the ambiguity. The logical-and operation requires only one computer instruction.

Each column of the grammar code shown in Figure 1 represents a separate *computer word*—that is, a fixed grouping of memory locations. Each computer word of the grammar code can be tested separately. Using the logical-and operation on the appropriate computer word, a Russian word can be tested to determine whether it is a modifier. A second test can be used to determine whether it is a *governing modifier*—that is, a modifier which can govern a dependent structure (e.g., the word *important,* as in *important-by-comparison results*).

The question may well be raised whether one and zero (standing for *yes* and *no*) are sufficient for the grammar code of a Russian word. In our own case, a ternary system may be needed, where "+ 1" indicates *yes,* "− 1" indicates *no,* and "0" indicates *I don't know.* Ida Rhodes of the National Bureau of Standards uses a quaternary representation for government where a "3" indicates that something is mandatory, a "2" that something is highly probable, a "1" that it is merely possible, and a "0" that it is impossible. Mrs. Rhodes goes even further and makes the code octal, which adds one more bit location. This extra bit location is used to indicate whether the condition must be fulfilled immediately or at any time within the clause.

As pointed out in Garvin's "Syntax in Machine Translation," the syntax-analysis method used in the Ramo Wooldridge machine-translation program is *multiple-pass.* The first pass consists of examining the whole sentence for numerals and symbols. Whenever a symbol or a numeral is detected, its neighborhood is examined in order to find the conditions for supplying a grammar code. The second pass again consists of an examination of the whole sentence, this time in order to isolate and resolve word-class homographs. Figure 2 shows one portion of the homograph-resolution flowchart. As the flowchart is entered, it has already been determined that the homograph has the potential part-of-speech functions of a predicate, an adverb, or a preposition. The start is at the circle labeled HR1. Each box on the flowchart represents a question and can be answered by either *yes* or *no*. The circles, with the exception of those marked PP2, represent jumps to other parts of the same flowchart. PP2 represents a jump back to another routine which searches the sentence for further homographs.

The next pass is devoted to the packaging of nominal blocks, which may consist of just a noun or a noun modified by one or more adjectives. The process of nominal blocking allows for the reduction of case, gender, and number ambiguities through a matching of the agreement codes, as discussed above.

After the nominal blocking is completed, the next pass is devoted to the creation of prepositional packages, consisting of prepositions together with the words they govern. Here the government code of the preposition allows an opportunity for reduction of ambiguities, comparable to that afforded by agreement checks. After this pass the adverbs of the sentence are searched for and inspected to see whether they can be included in the previously prepared nominal packages. Following the adverb pass, the routine goes searching for inserted structures—these are structures which are independent of the remainder of the sentence, and once identified, they can be skipped over and ignored in the major syntax, which is discussed further below. The search for inserted structures requires a fairly close examination of the commas and other punctuation of the sentence.

After the inserted-structure pass, a search is made of the sentence for governing modifiers, which include mainly participles. These are examined to see whether they are acting merely as adjectives or whether they govern other word groups in the sentence. If rearrangement of the English is called for, indication of this rearrangement is made.

After the governing-modifier pass, the routine once again goes hunting for commands in order to determine where major clause boundaries can be definitely established. The next and last search preceding the major syntax is the search for relative clauses, which are identified and labeled *relative packages*. Up to this point we have dealt with packages which can be skipped over in the search for the predicate, subject, and objects of the sentence, and we have reduced certain ambiguities by inspecting individual words and including them in blocks where possible.

The major syntax consists of a search of the main clause (skipping over inserted structures, governing modifier packages, and relative packages) in order to find first the predicate of the sentence. Once the predicate has been found, this gives us certain information about the nature of the subject (certainly a plural verb will not have a singular subject) and about the possible object or objects of this predicate. Then a search is made to the left of the predicate for the subject. If one is not found and if the predicate is not of the type allowing an implied subject, our earlier

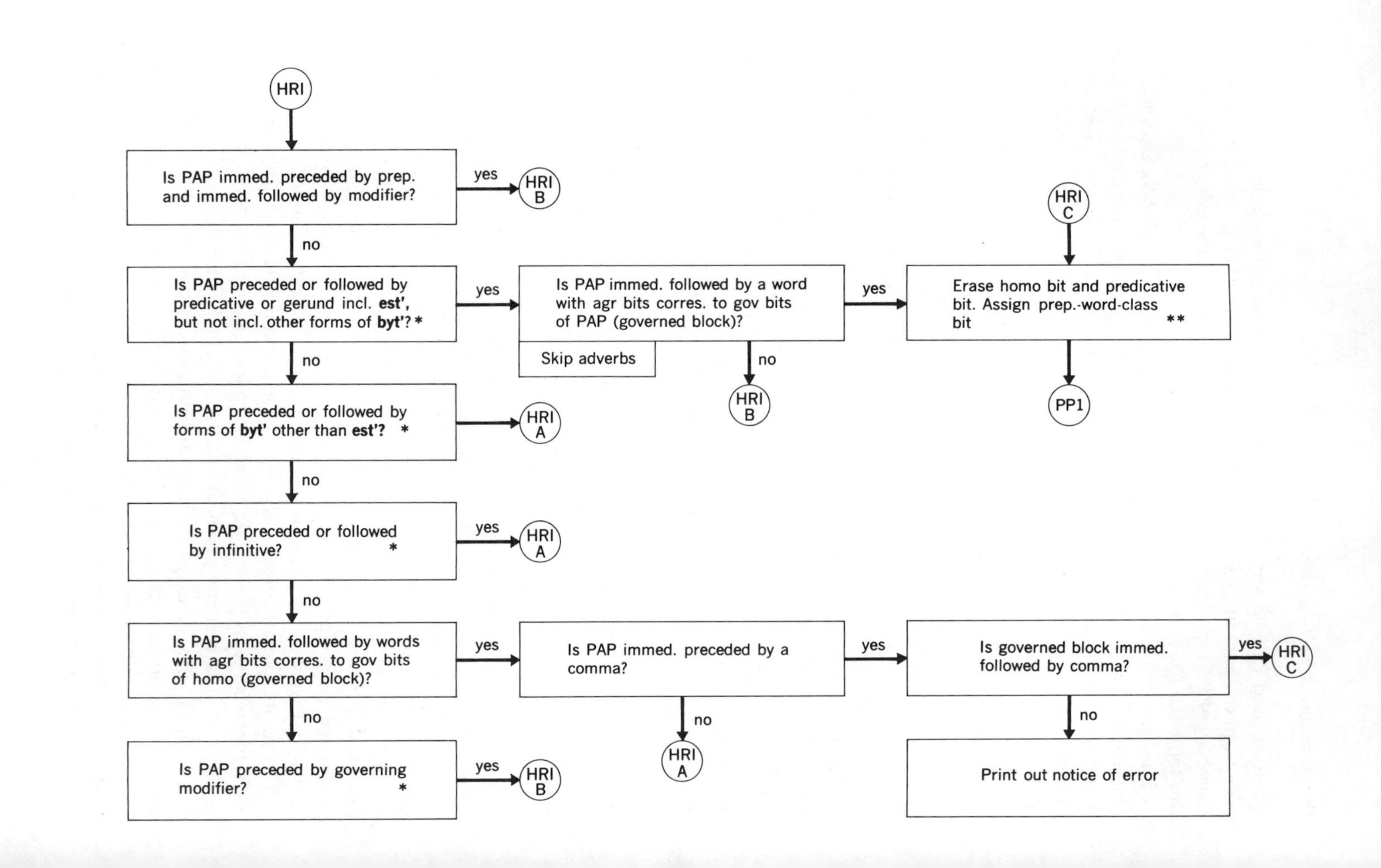
HRI
Is PAP immed. preceded by prep. and immed. followed by modifier?
yes
HRI B
no
Is PAP preceded or followed by predicative or gerund incl. est', but not incl. other forms of byt'? *
yes
Is PAP immed. followed by a word with agr bits corres. to gov bits of PAP (governed block)?
Skip adverbs
yes
no
HRI B
HRI C
Erase homo bit and predicative bit. Assign prep.-word-class bit **
PP1
no
Is PAP preceded or followed by forms of byt' other than est'? *
HRI A
no
Is PAP preceded or followed by infinitive? *
yes
HRI A
no
Is PAP immed. followed by words with agr bits corres. to gov bits of homo (governed block)?
yes
Is PAP immed. preceded by a comma?
yes
no
HRI A
Is governed block immed. followed by comma?
yes
HRI C
no
Print out notice of error
no
Is PAP preceded by governing modifier? *
yes
HRI B

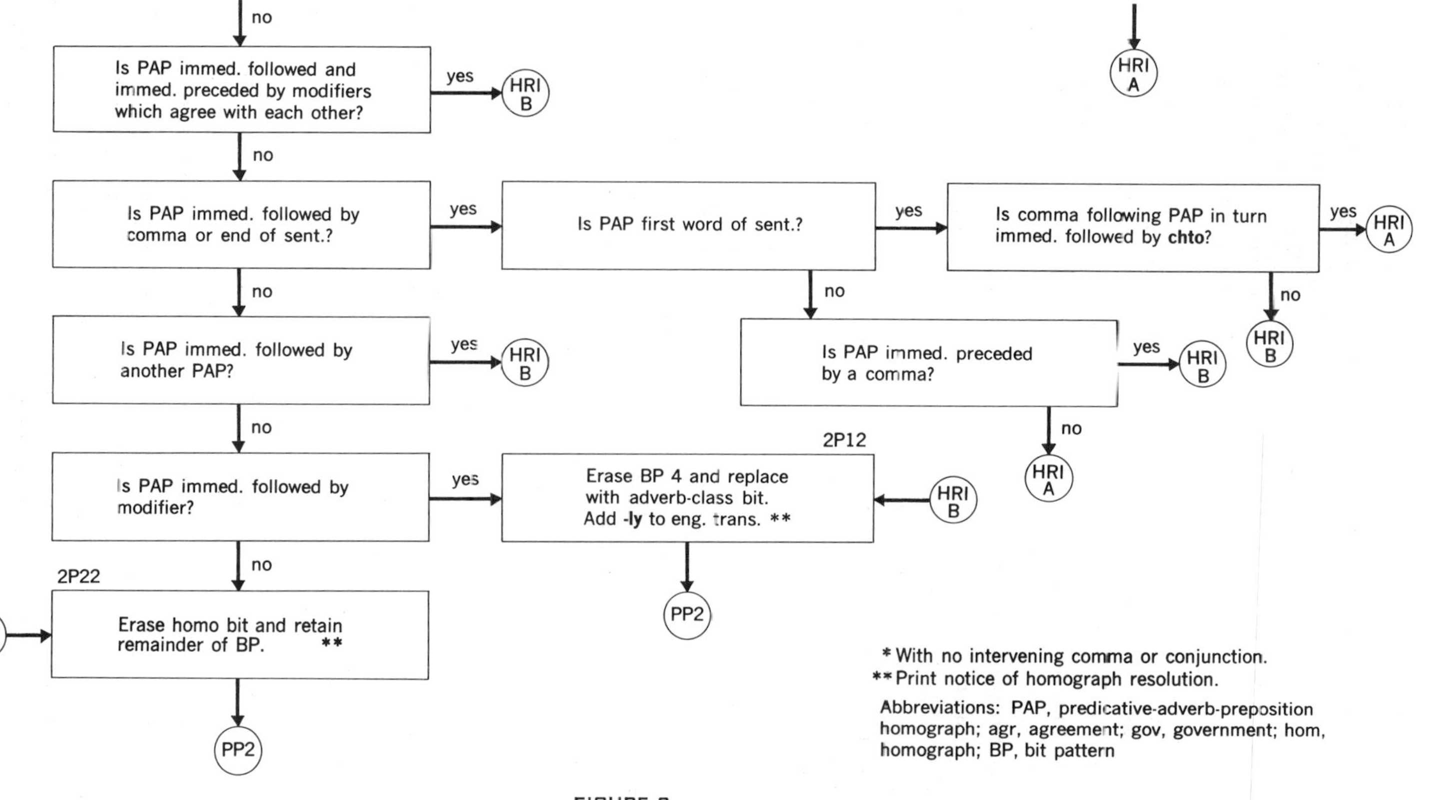
no
Is PAP immed. followed and immed. preceded by modifiers which agree with each other?
yes
HRI B
no
Is PAP immed. followed by comma or end of sent.?
yes
Is PAP first word of sent.?
yes
Is comma following PAP in turn immed. followed by **chto**?
yes
HRI A
no
HRI B
no
Is PAP immed. preceded by a comma?
yes
HRI B
no
HRI A
HRI A
no
Is PAP immed. followed by another PAP?
yes
HRI B
no
Is PAP immed. followed by modifier?
yes
2P12
Erase BP 4 and replace with adverb-class bit. Add **-ly** to eng. trans. **
HRI B
PP2
no
2P22
HRI A
Erase homo bit and retain remainder of BP. **
PP2
* With no intervening comma or conjunction.
** Print notice of homograph resolution.
Abbreviations: PAP, predicative-adverb-preposition homograph; agr, agreement; gov, government; hom, homograph; BP, bit pattern

FIGURE 2

program would print out *notice of syntactic difficulty,* indicated by the alphanumeric code number 41 in the vertical output (see below). We no longer do so; we now determine which part of the clause portion that follows the predicate should precede it. This can be done successfully in a surprisingly large number of cases. Code 41 now implies a certain type of sentence rearrangement.

If a subject has been found to the left of the predicate, a search is made for the possible objects which the government code of the predicate indicates. This search will often detect whether or not an English preposition should be inserted in the final translation. If any difficulties have been encountered in the major syntax, the computer exits to a cleanup pass where as much of the clause as can still be identified is analyzed.

The syntactic analysis of the clause is completed, but the syntactic information that has been gleaned must be thoroughly examined. The results of the syntactic analysis permit the resolution of certain translation problems by means of a word-combination routine. This routine examines verbs and their complements, after their connection has been established by the syntax routines, in order to determine their correct translations on the basis of their joint occurrence in a sentence. The word-combination routine ascertains the meaning of certain verbs on the basis of their complements, and even in those cases where the meaning of the verb cannot be determined, the translations of certain of the prepositions (implied or otherwise) are selected. After the word-combination routine, the rearrangement of the English in the sentence is performed. After the rearrangement, the correct English equivalent for certain Russian words is selected on the basis of the Russian case number and gender which by now may have been determined; the definite article is inserted in front of certain packages, and in front of those genitive, instrumental, and dative packages for which a preceding preposition has not yet been inserted, the appropriate insertions are now made; finally, ad hoc multiple-equivalent rules are applied.

In the multiple-pass method just described the sentence is examined many times, each time to hunt for specific items. Another method, less resembling that which would occur to a linguist, is the method of *predictive analysis* developed by Mrs. Ida Rhodes of the Bureau of Standards. In her method, the sentence might only be examined twice. The first examination, which she calls the *profile pass,* has as its purpose to label which clause each word in a sentence is in. She allows for, and treats, nested clauses. The search for clause indicators is primarily a search for commas, conjunctions, and certain specific words. After she has created this clause identification, which she calls the *profile* of the sentence, she then is ready for the second and possibly last pass. Here, her technique consists of examining each word in turn and asking whether it satisfies any predictions, and then asking what further predictions the presence of the word allows her to make. "Predictions" are assumptions of varying strength regarding the presence of certain grammatical conditions. If the assumption is borne out, the prediction is considered satisfied. She handles her words in the order of their appearance in the text, without backtracking to earlier words, but backtracking to earlier predictions. She enters each clause with two mandatory predictions that are contained in the program: A clause must have a subject and a clause must have a predicate. Hence, she can ask with the very first word of the clause, *Does it satisfy a prediction?* If a word satisfies a prediction, she crosses this prediction from her list. She examines her predictions in reverse order, that is, the last prediction made is the first one examined. This allow her not to go too far back within a clause in order to find the desired prediction. Certain nonmandatory predictions are wiped out if they are not satisfied by the word immediately following the word that brought them about. Unused predictions that have not been wiped out are stored in a "hindsight pool." Limits are placed on prediction: In a two-clause sentence, a nominative noun in the second clause cannot satisfy a prediction for a subject of the first clause. When a sentence has been completed, Mrs. Rhodes' method asks whether any mandatory predictions remain unsatisfied. If there are unsatisfied mandatory predictions, the hindsight pool is inspected for alternative possibilities to the resolution of the sentence. Using this hindsight pool, another pass is made at the sentence to see whether the mandatory predictions can now all be satisfied. Further passes at the sentence could, of course, be made until all of the possible translations have been obtained. Mrs. Rhodes prefers, however, to stop after the first acceptable analysis has been completed. In this respect, her technique is at least as good as the other translation techniques which allow for only one possible evaluation, and she has certainly created the tools to detect syntactic structure.

At first glance, her technique seems more palatable from the point of view of programming than a multiple-pass method. Her pass at the sentence is straightforward; it considers and treats each word as it appears. Her search for predictions is always backwards and terminates with the most recently made useful prediction. In some senses, however, it is not too much more straightforward than the multiple-pass method. The multiple-pass method consists of finding the word, noting its predictions, and searching the sentence for other words that might have been predicted by it. Mrs. Rhodes' technique consists of finding a word and searching backwards through the sentence for other words that might have predicted it. Her technique approaches its maximum programming desirability when there is an extreme shortage of storage, for she handles each word in a systematic order and her search backward has a low probability of going to the very beginning of the sentence. Even then, she erases predictions after they have been utilized. Thus, storage requirements are reduced.

THE OUTPUT

Several machine-translation groups create two types of output: one simply to display the translation, and one for research purposes. The Ramo Wooldridge group uses a so-called "horizontal output" for the first purpose, and a "vertical listing" for the second purpose. The horizontal output consists essentially of lines of English words constituting the translation; whenever a Russian word has more than one English translation and the program has not made a selection, the English translations appear underneath each other, creating a multiple line of English at that point.

For research purposes, much more is needed than just the English words of the translation. The output shown in Figure 3 is a vertical listing displaying the information that was extracted by the program in the process of translation.

The lines consisting of periods and ones or periods and *x*'s between each line of text show the grammar code referred to in Figure 1. The difference between the ones and the *x*'s is that those grammar codes that contain a one stem from the dictionary lookup, while those containing *x*'s were either created or modified by the program.

The first column gives the text location of the individual words. Thus all this text comes from page F, lines 45, 46, 47, 48, and 49, and the numbers following the line number refer to the position of the word on the line. The next columns containing the numbers 40 and 41 on line 6 represent syntactic translation decisions. The group of six numbers following that column displays the syntactic analysis of the sentence; each digit indicates a particular syntactic condition that has been identified by the program. The next column represents the desired English word order: a number is assigned to each English word, indicating the position which it should occupy in the translation of the sentence (in this case, it is identical with the Russian word order). The column after that is a transliteration of the original Cyrillic. Finally, there is the English translation. If you draw a vertical line just to the left of the word GENERAL, you find the dictionary English to the right of that line. To the left of that line are words like *the, do, of the*; these are words supplied by the program. The asterisk on the lines with the words AMERICAN, BELIEVE, and PEOPLE, indicates that the exact Russian representations of these words were not in the TRW dictionary and that the grammar code and possibly the inflection of these words was supplied by the stem-ending analysis described above. The translations says:

```
X........ . . ......................... . ....X. X..................X...... . XX.XXX ...........................

 F47 4          020000 14  NE                      DO NOT                              I I A        3575
......1.. . . ......................... . .1.... ......................... . ...... ...........................

 F47 5          020000 15  VERIM                      BELIEVE                                       8814
.1....... . . ......................... . .111.. ......................... . ...... ...........................

 F47 6 01       000040 16  (TO                        THAT                             I            6050
.....1... . . ......................... . 11.... ......................... . ...... ...........................

 F47 7          001000 17  ONI                        THEY                                          3095
X........ . . ......................... . ....X. ..X...................X...... . XX.XXX ...........................

 F48 1 77       020000 18  VYRA$AQT                   EXPRESS                            A           348
.1....... . 1 ......................... . .11... ......................... . ...... ...........11.1.........1...

 F48 2          005004 19  MNENIE                  THE OPINION                                      6441
X........ . . ......................... . ...... ............X............ . ...... ...........................

 F48 3          001204 20  BOL*)INSTVA          OF THE MAJORITY                                     4609
X........ . . ......................... . ...... ........X................ . .....X ...........................

 F48 4          001204 21  AMERIKANSKOGO        OF THE AMERICAN                              *      6065
..1...... . . ......................... . .....1 .....1................... . ...... ...........................

 F49 1          001204 22  NARODA                     PEOPLE                                *       7280
1........ . . ......................... . ...... .....1................... . ...1.. ...........................
```

FIGURE 3

GENERAL PAUZR SENATOR GOLDVOTER TAKE (OR OCCUPY) THE IMPORTANT POSITION IN THE AMERICAN OBWVESTVE BUT WE DO NOT BELIEVE THAT THEY EXPRESS THE OPINION OF THE MAJORITY OF THE AMERICAN PEOPLE.

This, though far from being a perfect translation, is not ridiculous. A correct translation would read:

GENERAL POWERS AND SENATOR GOLDWATER OCCUPY AN IMPORTANT POSITION IN AMERICAN SOCIETY BUT WE DO NOT BELIEVE THAT THEY EXPRESS THE OPINION OF THE MAJORITY OF THE AMERICAN PEOPLE.

Studying the vertical listing, we found that the words GENERAL, PAUZR, SENATOR, GOLDVOTER, and OBWVESTVE had been missing from the dictionary. This was remedied by the program as follows: The analysis of the endings and of the neighborhood of the missing words by our missing-word routine indicated that GENERAL is a noun in the masculine nominative or the masculine accusative; that PAUZR, SENATOR, and GOLDVOTER are nouns with the unknown case, gender, and number, and OBWVESTVE is a noun in the neuter prepositional As shown in the vertical listing, appropriate grammar codes were created by the program and the syntactic analysis could proceed

We also found that the translation of the Russian word *I* as the conjunction *and* was missed, due to a glossary maintenance error that was committed just before this run. The vertical listing allowed us to detect this error.

Now to explain the vertical listing further. In the column representing syntactic analysis, the number 001000 indicates that each of the first five words (which all show this digit) are in a nominal block. Other numbers in the same column indicate that the sixth word is a predicate, the seventh and eighth words are nominal blocks that form an object, and the ninth, tenth, and eleventh words constitute a prepositional phrase, within which the tenth and eleventh words form a nominal block, that the thirteenth word is a nominal block, that the fourteenth and fifteenth words form a predicate, the sixteenth word forms a search boundary, the seventeenth word a nominal block, the eighteenth word a predicate, that the nineteenth word forms a nominal block and is part of two types of complement. This complement (used in the word-combination routine described above) extends from the nineteenth word to the twenty-second. The twentieth, twenty-first, and twenty-second words in addition constitute a nominal block, and the twentieth, twenty-first, and twenty-second are also in the genitive. The syntactic analysis has enabled the program not only to insert articles (some of which, as can be seen, are incorrect) but also the auxiliary *do* and the preposition *of* in two places. Without the syntactic analysis, the sentence would have read:

GENERAL PAUZR, SENATOR GOLDVOTER TAKE (OR OCCUPY) IMPORTANT POSITION IN AMERICAN OBWVESTIVE BUT WE NOT BELIEVE THAT THEY EXPRESS OPINION MAJORITY AMERICAN PEOPLE.

The code number 41 on line 6 indicates that, due to missing agreement codes, the routine was not sure it had identified the subject of the sentence. There was a possibility, as far as the program could see, of the first five words being the subject, and therefore no rearrangement took place.

The information presented in the vertical output is kept with other information on a magnetic tape that we refer to as the information tape. Each record on the information tape represents a sentence and each file an article. On each record, the first five and one-half lines contain the English information, the remainder of the sixth line contains information about stem length, the eventual English word order, whether the word was created by stem-ending splitting, whether the word participated in an idiom, and whether the grammar code was modified. Line 7 contains information about multiple-equivalent resolution. Line 8 contains information about the dictionary access number of the word, the form of the ending, and whether the word is potentially part of an idiom. Lines 9, 10, 11 contain the grammar code, lines 12, 13, 14, the Cyrillic. Line 15 contains information about the location of the word in the text and about surrounding punctuation, if any. Line 16 contains a record of insertions to the right that the routine has decided upon. Line 17 and part of 18 are used for recording insertions to the left; the remainder of 18 and all of 19 are used for a record of the syntactic decisions. Consequently, it is possible to create routines that will go over previously translated text in order to search for relationships that were not thought of at the time of translation.

As to the size of the program: the dictionary lookup required 6,000 computer instructions, and the syntactic analysis, 10,000 instructions. The dictionary lookup works at 180,000 words per hour and the syntactic analysis at 60,000 words per hour. That is, translation is done at the rate of 45,000 words per hour, or 750 words per minute, or 12.5 words per second.

Information retrieval

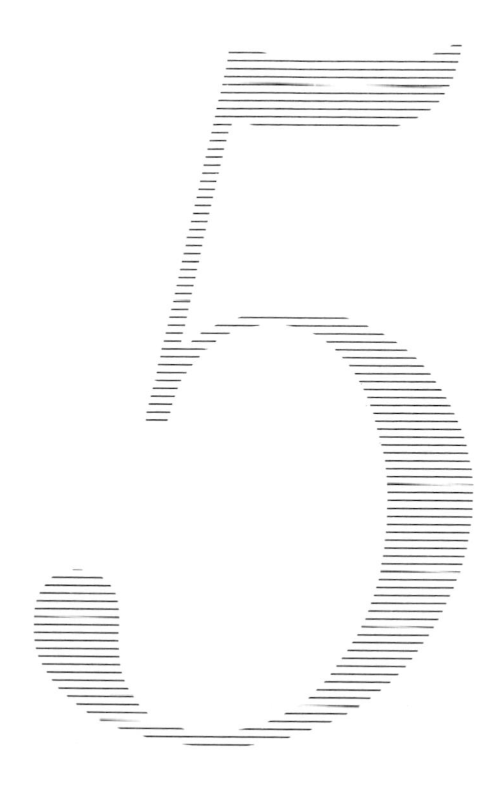

DON R. SWANSON

The formulation of the retrieval problem

From published literature one might reasonably infer that the problem of information retrieval has been often solved but never formulated. At least it appears that this problem has not been formulated in the particular way presented here. The purpose of this discussion is to examine the nature of the fundamental problems that arise in the interrogation of a body of natural-language text stored in a computer, and then show how essentially these same problems occur in conventional information-retrieval systems.

Let us provisionally assume that experience with existing libraries and retrieval systems does not necessarily constitute a reliable guide to the process of formulating and defining the problem. As a primitive starting point on which to base our formulation and definitions, we shall conceive of a warehouse full of information consisting of unindexed and unorganized articles, documents, and books. Suppose, further, that there exists a requirement for some information which the warehouse may contain. In principle, this information could be found if each document in the warehouse were examined individually by the requestor to ascertain its possible relevance to the question of interest; the only shortcoming of this technique lies in the total impracticality of reading essentially the entire text of all documents in the collection. Yet this viewpoint is useful and thought provoking, since it is by no means obvious that there exists any *other* way to attain what we may define as "perfect" retrieval. That is, if the requestor himself has the opportunity to examine and study each item in a collection, no other method could possibly lead to a more accurate determination of responsive retrieval documents. Direct examination of this kind can thus be adopted as a "standard of comparison" against which the performance of any information-retrieval method can be measured. The problem of information retrieval is to devise practical systems whose performance is high by the standard just defined. "Performance" must in some way take into account both the percentage of relevant information retrieved and the amount of irrelevant material also retrieved.

TEXT-SEARCHING MODEL

The foregoing notion of "perfect" retrieval is particularly useful if we can learn something about the intellectual task of ascertaining *relevance* for any particular document. As a way of approaching this formidable problem, let us interpose a computer between the requestor and the text of the "library" and then determine to what extent a practical "relevance-matching" procedure can be developed as a *nonintellectual* exercise. Once this primitive kind of matching of question to text is understood as a computer process, we can then determine whether the intellectual aspects are or are not important for practical information-retrieval purposes. Perhaps the chief virtue of this approach is that it permits one to distinguish between what is profound—that which the computer cannot do—and what is obvious—that which a computer can be programmed to do. The process to be examined is illustrated schematically in Figure 1.

The above viewpoint is not the only fundamental approach to defining the problem of information retrieval. It does, however, have the advantage of an apparently logical point of beginning from which it proceeds in a systematic way. The introduction of a computer in our model has nothing particularly to do with the question of automating information retrieval in a practical or economic sense, but rather serves the purpose of imposing a rigorous viewpoint on the entire process, whether or not such a process is ever really implemented by machine. The absolute ruthlessness of computers enforces a disciplined and consistent description of the task of information retrieval. Since a computer can perform only tasks which are precisely defined, then we necessarily must define information retrieval in a precise way when a computer is interposed between the human and the unindexed full-text library.

From the point of view of a machine, library text contains only strings of words and punctuation. Hence, this machine can accept search instructions from a human being only in the form of recorded words, together with certain specifications as to combinations, sequences, punctuation, and frequencies. (The machine may also be provided with a dictionary which can contain human-supplied codes for each word to reflect semantic or grammatical information about that word.) Thus, any attempt to retrieve information dealing with "concepts" or "subjects" must somehow be formulated in terms of words and their combinations. The problems that arise in attempting to do so are best explained with the help of

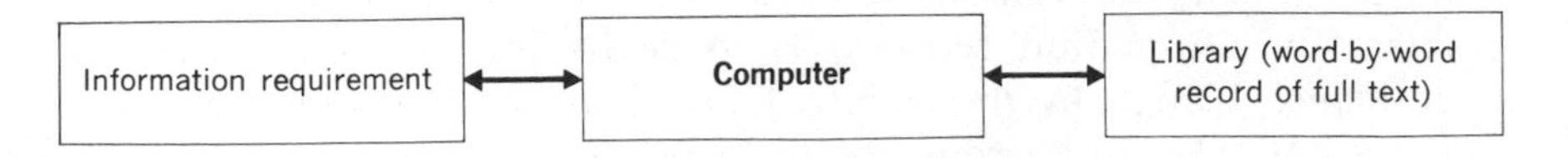

FIGURE 1 *Full-text library interrogation via a computer.*

a specific example. Let us consider an information requirement expressed as a question such as

> *What factors are critical to the commercial practicality of nuclear power?*

Strictly speaking, the model of Figure 1 implies that the full natural-language question be fed to the computer. We shall first examine segments of the input question and then later the problem of translating that question into the proper segments.

To decide whether a document, an article, or a book deals with nuclear power is, in general, a highly intellectual task, not at all amenable to rigorous formulation as would be required in order to instruct a computer to perform such task. Let us start with an aspect of this task which clearly is susceptible of mechanization and which ought to provide an approximate or partial solution to the problem. We hypothesize that any article dealing with nuclear power will probably contain the phrase *nuclear power* or some more or less synonymous equivalent of this phrase, such as *nuclear energy* or *reactor*. The task of searching for a specified phrase is one that can be performed by a computer. The process of searching text for the occurrence of a particular word or a particular phrase is "machinelike" in nature. This phrase-searching task is in sharp contrast to the nonprecise, intellectual, or nonmachinelike task of searching for material that is in some way or another "relevant" to the subject of nuclear power.

Now let us proceed further with this "partial solution" to the relevance problem and examine the two major types of difficulties which are likely to be encountered. First, it is easy to imagine that a highly relevant and important article may deal with nuclear power without employing that phrase or any of its reasonably near equivalents. Consider the sentence,

> *The ability to release enormous amounts of energy from minute quantities of matter should have a major impact on future technology.*

The smallest portion of this passage that makes an (almost) unmistakable reference to nuclear power is the phrase

> *release enormous amounts of energy from minute quantities of matter*

The problem is clearly not to be solved by providing the machine with a better synonym list. Second, the phrase *nuclear power* (or an equivalent) could occur in a context quite unimportant to the question—for example: The amount of *nuclear energy* released in the decay of most radioactive substances is several MEV. Thus, the second problem is that the specification of a word or phrase might lead to the retrieval of irrelevant information because of wrong context.

It is evident from these examples that there are at least two major problems which cause irrelevant information to be retrieved and relevant information to be missed. Is any process so elementary as searching for words or phrases therefore untenable as an approach to information retrieval? If we insist on a precise or rigorous solution to the problem—namely, a solution in which all relevant and only relevant information is retrieved—then the answer is probably yes, and in this case any information-retrieval system yet conceived or likely to be conceived would be inadequate. Fortunately our problem requires a practical rather than a rigorous solution. What percentage of the information within the library relevant to a given request will be found, and how much irrelevant information will be retrieved at the same time? This question is answerable only if it is somehow known independently (e.g., through direct examination of the library by the requestor) which documents within the collection are and which are not relevant to the given request. With this knowledge, the question can be answered through experimentation. Some experiments of this kind carried out on a relatively small scale have been reported by the author;[1] the answers obtained apply strictly to an experimental model library but may be suggestive of the type and magnitude of problems that may be encountered more generally.

Having discovered potentially serious difficulties in taking just one aspect of the original question posed—namely, *nuclear power,* selected from *What factors are critical to the commercial practicality of nuclear power?*—it is even more readily apparent that the problem is compounded when we attempt to instruct the computer to find material specifically relevant to the entire question rather than just to the phrase *nuclear power.* In particular, any reference to *commercial practicality* involves problems of equivalent expressions more difficult than does the phrase *nuclear power,* since the latter is a good deal more specific. Nonetheless, we may proceed with our approximation by speculating on sets of words or phrases roughly equivalent to *commercial practicality* such as *economic feasibility, cost per kilowatt, commercial profitability, private enterprise,* etc. Now, if the computer were instructed to hunt for all material which contains any member of this set of phrases and at the same time contains any member of the *nuclear power* set of phrases, then we are likely to retrieve a smaller amount of irrelevant information. However, since the process is not rigorous, such a more highly selective search necessarily implies also increased likelihood of missing relevant information. Furthermore, an entirely new problem is now apparent, which, if taken into account, could lead to still greater specificity. The fact that an article contains the phrase *nuclear power* and the phrase

[1]D. R. Swanson, "Searching Natural Language Text by Computer," *Science,* vol. 132, no. 3434, pp. 1099–1104, Oct. 21, 1960.

commercial practicality does not necessarily imply that the latter phrase applies to the former. The article might deal with theoretical calculations on nuclear power together with the commercial practicality of communication satellites. That is to say, the rather nonsophisticated but obviously machinelike specification of word and phrase cooccurrence within articles involves a neglect of specifying somehow the "relatedness" of the cooccurring phrases to one another.

Let us review the formulation of the search question and the statement of the information-retrieval problems which it exposes, since we shall show how these same problems occur in the field of information retrieval whether or not one adopts the computer text-searching model described above. Our search instruction to the computer constructed from the earlier stated question can be written as shown in Figure 2. The bracketed groups of words may be viewed as thesaurus groups (defined as groups of words essentially equivalent in meaning for purposes of information retrieval). A thesaurus and the alphabetic index thereto may be presumed available to the machine and so constitute a useful approach (in the context of Figure 1) to problems of semantics in information retrieval. However, difficulties may still be expected to occur.

As indicated, even if all documents were found in which the criteria shown in Figure 2 were fulfilled, irrelevant information might be retrieved and relevant information missed. These problems occur because, to begin with, a listing of synonyms and near-synonyms does not account for the fact that an idea may be expressed in a number of different ways which do not rely on synonymity. Furthermore, the idea of "nearness of meaning" or "near-synonymity" between two words or phrases is not immutable but often is a function of the context within which these phrases occur. For example, nuclear energy may be released through both fission and fusion; thus, in some contexts these two latter words may be essentially synonyms, whereas in others the difference may be of critical importance.

The fact that synonymity is a function of context lies at the heart of

Hunt for articles which meet the following criteria for word and phrase content: articles which contain

<table>
<tr>
<td>nuclear power
or nuclear energy
or reactor
etc. . . .</td>
<td>and at the same time contain</td>
<td>commercial practicality
or cost per kilowatt
or commercial profitability
or economic feasibility
or private enterprise
etc. . . .</td>
</tr>
</table>

FIGURE 2 *Example of a search instruction to a computer.*

the semantic problems of information retrieval and points up a potential weakness in the thesaurus approach. That is, if one provides the machine with a thesaurus, then the machine is clearly capable of matching a word or a phrase appearing in the original request with the identical word or phrase in the thesaurus. It can then select all words and phrases which are members of the corresponding thesaurus group as a basis for formulating a search instruction; in this case the machine indiscriminately accepts all members of the group as being essentially synonymous with the originally selected word or phrase. The fact that synonymity is a function of context implies that indiscriminate selection of an entire group is not strictly correct. Whether this weakness is serious can be determined only through experimentation, and such experimentation has shown thus far that the thesaurus approach is useful in practice despite its limitations. Even some of these limitations are susceptible of solution with a sufficiently sophisticated computer procedure for context analysis.

The second major problem area identified is *relatedness* between words or phrases. If these words or phrases occur entirely within a sentence, then the problem is, at least in part, one of syntax. Even though syntax is a subject about which much is known, it is not clear how much of this knowledge can be brought to bear in a practical way on the problem of information retrieval. Just as there may be many ways of expressing an idea without relying on synonyms, there are also many ways to form sentences which express the same idea but which are not at all similar or equivalent in syntactic structure. Furthermore, many aspects of relatedness occur between words of different sentences. We may again take a purely pragmatic approach and seek simple approximations which lead "in most cases" to the desired type of relatedness. For example, experiments have shown that if two phrases (or two words) from a retrieval request cooccur in an article, a useful criterion for determining whether that article is responsive to the request is the proximity of the two phrases in question. The likelihood that the two phrases exhibit the proper kind of relatedness appears to be much greater if they occur within a span of four to five sentences than if they occur much farther apart.[2] Of course, this approximation does not provide an answer to the classical question of distinguishing between documents dealing with exports from France to Germany in contrast to those dealing with exports from Germany to France. Clearly some documents with the wrong kind of relatedness will be retrieved by the procedure just described, but it can be argued on the basis of experimental evidence that the amount of irrelevant retrieval which occurs is not intolerable. The method furthermore has the advantage that it will not cause relevant documents to be missed. The con-

[2] *Cf.* D. R. Swanson, "Research Procedures for Automatic Indexing," *Machine Indexing: Progress and Problems,* pp. 281–304, Washington, D.C., 1961.

dition of *proximity* is much weaker than any specification of true relatedness (syntactic or other), and this weakness is clearly desirable in the absence of more accurate techniques. We shall presume, however, that the final process of selecting and separating the relevant from the irrelevant, the interesting from the uninteresting, and the important from the unimportant will be performed by human beings and in particular by the requestor himself for any given question.

In the foregoing analysis, it was assumed that the retrieval requirement began with a question cast in natural language; the search instruction, on the other hand, utilized only isolated words and phrases of that question. The simple form of the transformation from the original question to the search instruction illustrated in Figure 2 was dictated by the capabilities of a computer to perform the search function. In particular, no syntax-recognition feature was incorporated in the transformation, since it was not assumed that syntactic recognition would be included in the text search. Because of this simplicity, it is possible to outline a plausible method by means of which a computer could accept the natural-language question and formulate a search instruction similar to that which we have illustrated. Input of the question to the computer would be followed by a dictionary lookup; the dictionary would be coded in advance (through human effort) with a weight factor which reflects the difference between potentially important and unimportant retrieval words. This factor takes into account also the question of whether or not it is easy to avoid use of a word through other means of expressing the same concept. The important words and phrases so recognized in the dictionary-lookup process would then be used as entries to a thesaurus to permit construction of synonyms and near-equivalents. The same coded dictionary could include two- or three-word phrases as well as single words to permit the computer to determine whether to construct an entry from a word or from a phrase. This process implies, of course, that all phrases of retrieval interest must be anticipated in advance, clearly a formidable requirement. Accordingly, it is reasonable to include in the computer search process a rule which permits breaking a phrase up into single words if the search is unsuccessful for the phrase. The degree to which the method just described is likely to be successful is not yet known; it has been investigated experimentally by the author and will be reported on in the near future.[3]

Let us now turn from the model of Figure 1 toward more conventional considerations of retrieval. The approach described is not intended necessarily to suggest that full-text searching is an economical or practical

[3]*Cf.* D. R. Swanson, "Interrogating a Computer in Natural Language," to appear in *Proceedings of the Congress of the International Federation of Information Processing Societies,* Munich, August, 1962.

technique for information retrieval, but is presented in order to expose basic problem areas which can be shown in one form or another to characterize all information-retrieval systems.

The discussion based on Figure 1 has been elementary; it is hoped that some of its simplicity can be validly carried over to actual information-retrieval systems. A technique widely applied by scientists when confronted with an insolvable problem is to invent an easier problem that *can* be solved and then convince everyone that it is actually the problem they have. (As a matter of historical interest, this technique was developed by a few physicists during World War II and ever since has gone by the name of "operations research.") The problem "invented" in Figure 1 is not solvable, though hopefully its nature is understandable.

To bridge the gap between text searching and more conventional information-retrieval methods, a few additional remarks are necessary—first, on the question of automatic indexing, and second, on the question of hierarchical relationships among index terms.

AUTOMATIC INDEXING

In the foregoing process it was assumed implicitly that the computer searched the full text of the library collection for each retrieval question. Now, if we hypothesize that a large number of retrieval questions contain common words or phrases, then clearly it would be more efficient to anticipate such phrases in advance, perform the search for each only once (and perhaps all at once) and tag each document with a set of symbols that designate the words or phrases in question. The purpose of these tags is to permit more compact storage of the document in machine language (through more condensed storage of each word and avoiding recording of synonyms and repeated occurrences of the same word) and to permit greater efficiency in the over-all indexing-retrieval process. The same end product would obtain; efficiency is the only issue.

Now the question arises as to whether or not all possible words and phrases which may occur in retrieval questions can be anticipated. This task is formidable but not impractical. If, for example, we consider a single major technical field such as physics, the total vocabulary utilized in the published language of the field probably does not exceed 10,000 distinct words (not including phrases). About two-thirds of these can be recognized in advance as being, for all practical purposes, useless for information retrieval. These useless words can thus be incorporated in the thesaurus with a weight assignment of zero. Zero-weight words will then be ignored in both the question and the text.

The question of anticipating phrases is more subtle. The total number of possible combinations of two and three words which can be formed from a group of 10,000 words is, of course, enormous (about 100 billion);

the number that are syntactically and semantically acceptable within the constraints of natural language is unknown but is certainly many orders of magnitude smaller. The number is further reduced when only those phrases which occur repeatedly and which tend to behave as a unit are taken into consideration. In this latter case, experience probably provides a partially reliable guide; it is estimated that a 10,000-word vocabulary need be augmented by only a few thousand phrases. Thus it should be possible to construct a word-phrase dictionary of a relatively few thousand terms which largely covers the range of terms encountered in all questions that can be asked of the system. Thus, a single search of the full text together with the assignment of tags designating the anticipated list of words and phrases permits construction of a brief representation of the full text which is as adequate as the latter so far as information retrieval is concerned.

This process of condensing the full text to an abbreviated representation we define here as automatic indexing. The degree of condensation depends on several factors. First of all, each word may be replaced by one or several three-character designators of the "thesaurus groups" of which that word is a member. If it is found necessary to preserve information on proximity of words and sequences of words, then it is not enough to store only once a signal indicating the occurrence of a given word. Not only that signal but some indication of each position within the text in which the word occurred must then be stored. (Note that the issue of "vocabulary control" is circumvented. We have considered the indexing vocabulary to consist of a manageable number of terms that substantially spans the entire natural-language vocabulary.)

It should be noted that a thesaurus is somewhat more complex than may at first be apparent. Any given word will probably appear in several thesaurus groups, so that the automatic assignment of a thesaurus group based on detection of a specific word or phrase may involve ambiguity not necessarily resolvable by mechanical means. On the other hand, such ambiguity may be susceptible of partial solution based on automatic recognition of context.

The combination of terms that results from decomposing a natural-language question into a search instruction will itself provide some degree of context recognition. In a search of natural language for a conjunction of several terms, the probability is relatively low that the wrong meaning for one of the terms will appear in text with the correct accompanying terms.

Machine search of an automatically produced representation of natural-language text differs from full-text search only in the over-all order of the machine procedures which are used; thus, the conceptual problems of automatic indexing are identical to those of text searching.

SUBJECT HIERARCHIES

If an information-retrieval question contains a general term which subsumes many specific terms, should it be supposed that each specific term is necessarily responsive to the question? Conversely, if a specific term is requested, is an article on a more general subject which subsumes that term responsive to the question? Unfortunately these two questions do not have categoric answers, but depend largely on the motive, purpose, and intent of the requestor.

In most cases, the answer to the first question is yes (that is, if information on antibiotics is requested, it is presumed that an article on streptomycin is responsive) , and to the second question, no; a request for material on streptomycin should not be fulfilled with an article generally on antibiotics, or one on some other particular antibiotic such as bacitracin. This answer is based on intuition and experience, not on any particular compelling theoretical reason. This phenomenon introduces a complication into the thesaurus approach suggested earlier. A thesaurus group on antibiotics should contain all specific terms which that title subsumes, but the specific terms are appropriate only when the more general is specified. If entry into the thesaurus occurs from a specific term, the search instruction should *not* then be constructed out of the more general term or out of some different specific term. Thus, a sort of "directionality" or asymmetry is introduced into the thesaurus which implies that the structure of a given group is a function of the word on which that group is entered. If we were to imagine a five- or ten-level hierarchical structure, the whole question becomes enormously complicated, perhaps prohibitively so, owing to a proliferation of ambiguities. That is, any given term may be subordinate to several others, depending on the viewpoint with which that term is regarded. In conventional systems where these ambiguities occur within the framework of a classification scheme, their resolution is attempted by establishing conventions that must be agreed on by the indexers and the users of the system. In general, these conventions are not susceptible of the precise formulation that would be required in a machine system.

The fact that a retrieval question and a corresponding responsive document may be at quite different generic levels in some hierarchical structure gives rise to one of the most formidable aspects of the total information-retrieval problem. It may be noted, however, that a workable information-retrieval system can be designed which does not take into account at all the hierarchical structure of knowledge. Coordinate indexing systems generally have this characteristic, though the consequences of ignoring hierarchical levels are not known in measurable terms. Since the problem can be ignored to some degree, there may be ways of successfully introducing part of the hierarchical phenomenon in such a way that most of the complication is avoided.

Suppose, for example, that a system composed initially of an unstructured set of terms is reorganized to take into account two hierarchical levels. The effectiveness of the modified system can then be compared experimentally with the corresponding unstructured system. Furthermore, with only two hierarchical levels, the problem of classification ambiguity should be relatively manageable through adequate cross referencing. Thus, it is suggested here that retrieval experiments be performed with the objective of gaining insight into the problem of hierarchies by utilizing a simple structure consisting of two levels. It is of some interest to observe that an ordinary dictionary utilizes a two-level structure for the purpose of defining words. That is to say, a particular word is usually defined (at least in part) as a member of the next larger class under which it is subsumed. Furthermore, the *see also* cross references of certain subject-heading lists tend to introduce essentially a two-level structure. It is possible that the nature of language and the structure of human knowledge is such that a two-level structure might constitute an optimal mixture of effectiveness and simplicity.

CONVENTIONAL SUBJECT-HEADING SYSTEMS

Let us now examine more conventional library systems and consider whether or not their problem areas are similar to those which arise in the computer text-searching model of Figure 1. Because collections are too large to permit "perfect retrieval" through direct examination, it is necessary to create some kind of brief "representation" of the collection which is manageable in size for purposes of searching. This representation may be defined as an *index* or *catalogue* to the library.

In a conventional system the indexer or cataloguer may utilize an array of subjects organized in accordance with some systematic scheme for classifying human knowledge. In addition to such a classification scheme, an alphabetized list of subject headings may also be available. The alphabetic list may include subject headings which refer to a particular item in the classification structure as well as auxiliary subject headings which are not part of the structure. This description applies, for example, to the Library of Congress system. Other systems such as a single alphabetic subject-heading list are simpler.

In the process of indexing a technical article (by means of a simple subject-heading list), for example, the indexer will read the article, select or construct terms which seem to him descriptive of the subject matter, look such terms up in the alphabetized subject-heading list, and, if they are found, record the appropriate subject heading for each selected term. If the specific entry he seeks is not present, then he must substitute some more or less equivalent term or a more general term under which the original can be subsumed. In most cases he will be successful in finding what seems to him to be an appropriate entry. Whether or not a second indexer would come to the same conclusion and, more important, whether a requestor would follow the same line of reasoning is, of course, a crucial matter, and not at all obvious. There have been several attempts to measure the consistency with which different indexers will perform this kind of task; the results indicated a disturbing lack of consistency.

In the retrieval process, the requestor must, of course, translate his information requirement into a subject-heading representation, just as the indexer transforms each article acquired for the collection. Thus, the requestor and indexer communicate via the catalogue or index "representation" of the library. We may with justification picture information retrieval as a guessing game between the requestor and the indexer. The requestor, usually assisted by a reference librarian, tries to surmise the viewpoint of an indexer, but his ability to surmise is handicapped by not knowing the precise nature of the material which he seeks.

To gain understanding of the problems which arise in using a subject-heading system, consider next the relationship between the total technical vocabulary covered by the material in the library collection and the range of vocabulary spanned by the list of subject headings. We may load the question somewhat by asking whether or not these two vocabularies really differ in any significant way from one another. This is a difficult question because there are few descriptions of the way in which subject-heading lists are compiled, but it is true that for at least a number of systems the language of the subject-heading list is specifically tailored to the language of the documents being indexed and, in particular, to the titles of those documents. This fact tends to support the hypothesis that precisely the same kind of semantic problems arise in the use of a subject-heading list as arise in searching text for information addressive to a question.

Examination of a typical alphabetized subject-heading list reveals a cross-reference structure which, in general, provides a guide to adjacent hierarchical levels. Under any particular alphabetized entry, one may encounter a *see* reference to either a synonymous term or a more general term or a *see also* reference to either a nearly equivalent term or a subordinate term. In some subject-heading lists a notation *see from* is made under any given entry to indicate which other entries have referred to that one. These cross-reference tags serve for the subject-heading list the same purpose that thesaurus groups serve in the automatic-indexing process described earlier, provided such a thesaurus is assumed to contain at least two levels of hierarchical structure.

The questions of vocabulary coverage and the similarity of cross-reference structures to thesaurus groups furnish highly plausible evidence that the problems of generics and semantic ambiguities in the use of subject-heading lists for information retrieval are identical to those which arise in the computer searching of natural-language text. The argument, however, necessarily rests on intuition, plausibility, and experiment rather than on rigorous proof.

Let us now turn to the earlier question of relatedness among different terms of a request. In most subject-heading or subject-classification systems, this problem is bypassed altogether. It is true that two subject headings may be "coordinated" by asking for all documents indexed by at least those two headings, but in general it is not possible to specify a relationship between two different headings. Certain otherwise conventional systems do, however, take into account the question of relatedness through the use of so-called "role indicators." These indicators may be affixed to a term to denote the syntactic role which that term plays in some phrase accurately descriptive of the article being indexed.

Other methods in use, with human indexers, make extensive and accurate use of syntax and relationships. In *Chem Abstracts,* for example, an entire phrase is assigned as an indexing entry for an alphabetized listing of each term. All contexts of that term that have occurred in the indexed chemical literature are brought together for inspection by the requestor who may then select only those appropriate to his interest. A mechanized counterpart of this technique, as applied to titles alone, exists in the KWIC (keyword-in-context) listing of chemical titles.

The conceptual problem of information retrieval has been formulated in a fundamental sense; its solution is not likely to come from known mathematical disciplines but rather through experimental research addressed to the basic problem areas of semantics, generics, and relatedness of terms. The outcome of these experiments should lead to optimal design principles for information-retrieval systems. The heart of the conceptual problems encountered in text searching and automatic indexing lies in the thesaurus. Cross-reference structures of subject-heading lists play a corresponding role for conventional systems.

R. M. HAYES

Mathematical models for information retrieval

The purpose of an information system can be considered *to provide relevant responses to an environment.* That is, in a very general sense, the information stored in a file, when combined with a suitable program of operations to be performed on that information, can be considered as a set of responses to the environment of activity on the file. In this sense, although the file may consist of stored information concerning inventory items, stored documents, or humanly stored patterns of response, in each case it provides a response to some type of environment. This environment, for example, may be the set of changes, additions, deletions, interrogations, etc., involving the stored items.

The problems in designing such an information system revolve around the questions of *relevancy* and *economics*—first, the logical problems of determining relevancy; and second, the physical problems of providing the relevant responses at reasonable cost and time. Methods of solving these problems in the past have generally involved organizing the file in some predetermined fashion. The environment may then be examined in terms of its relationship to this predetermined organization, and logical relevancy completely determined in this way. Under these conditions, it is quite standard to "sort" the environment into the same sequence of organization as that provided for the file; in this way the successive responses for a set of environments can be provided at higher speed than a random search would provide. It is possible, on the other hand, to provide mechanisms for indexing or random access within the predetermined file structure and in this way solve problems where batching and sorting is precluded by the required response times.

In either event, however, economic operation is feasible only if the predetermined pattern of the file organization corresponds to the environment. Where it is not possible to so organize the file, linear scanning of the file is a necessity and the file operation becomes hopelessly slow and impractical. This lack of responsiveness is the major source of difficulty in present solutions to the information-storage and retrieval problem.

Hence the attempt must be made continually to fit the organization of the stored response to that of the environment, rather than vice versa.

The attempts to attack this problem of file organization in response to environment have been many and varied; researchers have included librarians, documentalists, and computer specialists. For example, the librarian, with fixed classification schedules, provides, in effect, an a priori estimate of the environment of requests, additions, etc. However, classification schedules are quite inflexible and tend to lose contact with the changing environment. Subject catalogues have been utilized as a more flexible response mechanism and can perform reasonably well in the treatment of additions to the file, but reorganization of the *existing* file in response to changing requirements is still difficult.

The recent developments in documentation, with newer systems for file organization, attempt to provide more flexible responsiveness of the entire file to the environment. This is done through techniques which, on the one hand, utilize more of the content of the document and, on the other hand, provide some degree of mechanization. Recent work in the area of information retrieval has therefore tended to emphasize these mechanization aspects in an attempt to increase the speed and accuracy of response through computer technology.

From this work, three problem areas have become evident. The first area concerns the recognition and representation of patterns in the environment. Questions relating to the selection of data to represent individual items or requests and to the recognition of interrelations among terms and items are significant pattern-recognition problems. The processes of selection are required primarily for reasons of economic necessity, since the data selected must be limited in some way for operation to be efficient. These logical problems have been the subject of investigation by a number of research groups. Automatic abstracting, formalization of language, etc., have all been concerned with this type of question.

The second class of problems relates to determining the relevancy to the environment of the stored patterns of response. In certain respects, this also represents a logical problem of pattern recognition but of a slightly different and probably more complex character. Again, these problems of relevancy have also been the subject of numerous investigations. However, they have only recently advanced beyond the stage of simple Boolean-logic relationships. The introduction of probabilistic techniques in the solutions of these problems has the potential of very promising results.

The third problem area relates to the organization of the responses in such a way that physical problems of response time and accessibility can be economically solved. Attempts to resolve these difficulties for cases where organization cannot be prespecified have led to an increasing interest in "self-organizing systems," including, for example, computer program models of the learning process, game-playing programs, theorem-proving programs, and the like. This work has been quite fruitful but has not been sufficiently extensive to represent the characteristics of mass-storage problems. There has also been activity in the development of neutral-net models, particularly in relation to the logical design of computers, but, although helpful in some respects, this research has been almost too specific in its consideration of individual logical elements to be useful for the mass-storage problem. The field of psychology has provided a whole set of models for inference, learning, and cognition in general. These models are very helpful, particularly as analogies, but have the difficulty of being too dependent on the still largely unknown characteristics of the human being.

There appears to be a very close relationship between the functioning of such a self-organizing large file and that of human beings. On the one hand, a file can be viewed as an analog of the mind, and since the human being is an effective retrieval device with fantastically large capacity, any insight into the functioning of the human being would provide tools for understanding desirable structures for large files. On the other hand, the human mind can itself be considered solely as a large file mechanism, a view that provides a significantly different understanding of the heuristics of human processing.

This concept of the human mind as a large, multiple-level file is not new. Jacques Hadamard has pointed out:[1]

> The ideas that lie at any moment within my full consciousness seem to attract of their own accord the most appropriate out of a number of other ideas that are lying close at hand, but imperfectly within the range of my consciousness. There seems to be a presence-chamber in my mind where full consciousness holds court, and where two or three ideas are at the same time in audience, and an ante-chamber full of more or less allied ideas, which is situated just beyond the full ken of consciousness. Out of this ante-chamber the ideas most nearly allied to those in the presence-chamber appear to be summoned in a mechanically logical way, and to have their turn of audience.
>
> It can hardly be doubted, and we shall be able to confirm this later on, that there must even be, in the unconscious, several successive layers, the most superficial one being the one we just considered. More remote is the unconscious layer which acts in automatic writing; still more those which allow inspirations such as we reported in the preceding section. Even deeper ones will appear to us at the end of this study. There seems to be a kind of continuity between full consciousness and

[1] J. Hadamard, *Psychology of Invention in the Mathematical Field,* Dover, New York, 1954.

more and more hidden levels of the unconscious; a succession which seems to be especially well described in Taine's book *On Intelligence,* when he writes: "You may compare the mind of a man to the stage of a theatre, very narrow at the footlights but constantly broadening as it goes back. At the footlights, there is hardly room for more than one actor. . . . As one goes further and further away from the footlights, there are other figures less and less distinct as they are more distant from the lights. And beyond these groups, in the wings and altogether in the background, are innumerable obscure shapes that a sudden call may bring forward and even within direct range of the footlights. Undefined evolutions constantly take place throughout this seething mass of actors of all kinds, to furnish the chorus leaders who in turn, as in a magic lantern picture, pass before our eyes."

ROLE OF MATHEMATICAL MODELS

The models described below represent the work of many different groups. They are described in the context of a single, integrating picture of information systems. This picture, since it is a quantified one, potentially can be a powerful tool for the analysis, comparison, and design of methods for file organization and reorganization in information systems, when placed in the hands of competent professional system designers.

A model as a design tool is one of its several possible roles in the development of a theory for this field. When the model is accepted as an adequate picture of a problem, the systems designer can specify the parameters of the problem in task-oriented terms and then ask a clerk or even a computer to develop the consequences as prescribed by the model. As usage and understanding of the model develops, it may be used by the less well-trained designers to solve completely problems of relatively noncomplex character. This has been the history of all such models, whether for servomechanism design, for linear programming, for decision making, or for any other purpose. Of course, when utilized in this way, there is grave danger that it will be misapplied and used as a crutch, but the gains from having such a tool available are substantial.

A second more subtle but more significant role of a model in the hands of the competent professional system designer is to expose the fundamental nature of a given problem. The model is again accepted as an adequate picture of the problem, but is used as a means by which the system designer can evaluate hypotheses about the parameters of the particular situation. The system designer can postulate some particular parameters and arrive at extremely complex consequences which he can then compare with his intuitive experience or experimental results. In this way, discrepancies between the consequences as developed by the model from the hypothetical problem description and the designer's intuition as to what results should be will pinpoint the erroneous hypotheses about the problem. In other words, the model becomes a means by which to clarify the basic assumptions concerning any particular information system.

A third role, which in certain respects is the most significant, is the use of a model as a step in developing a theory for information systems. In this role the model itself is critically examined and improved. Thus, since the model provides a mechanism for deriving consequences from hypotheses, if the consequences do not match experimental evidence or intuitive experience, either the description of the problem is incorrect and must be adjusted (and this is the second role described above) or the model is incorrect and must be improved. Again, this has been the historical experience with the development of models. In effect, the system designer will be operating as a scientist utilizing the scientific method for developing a theory for this field.

Scientific Method Scientific method, on which all of modern technology is based, involves essentially four steps in an iterative procedure. The first can be called the *judgment* step, in which the principal purpose is the formulation of the problem and the establishment of objectives and criteria of value. This is essentially an intuitive process dependent on the experience and knowledge of the individual researcher. Based on this preliminary view, the procedure then enters the second step—*data collection*—in which information pertinent to the problem is accumulated. In principle, this second step should be completely objective and independent of any particular formulations or objectives. In practice, however, data collection is very heavily biased, even though not deliberately so, by the old objectives which have been established.

As soon as sufficient data have been accumulated, the third step—*formulation of hypotheses and models*—is undertaken, which includes the establishment of measures of effectiveness with which the model is to fit the data. When the model fits the available data to the required accuracy, it is then used to develop necessary consequences from the hypotheses. Here the model acts independently of the physical world and the particular problem. This is the reason that mathematics is the principal source of models, since it is concerned with the analysis of structure, removed from the physical objective world, idealized, and independent of reality.

Therefore, predictions by the model are derived without reference to the actual physical situation but merely as consequences of the hypotheses. Having developed the consequences (which cannot be avoided, since once the hypotheses are accepted the consequences must also be accepted), the scientist must experimentally test their validity. This process, the fourth step in the scientific method, is the *experimental testing* of the model. The model is satisfactory to the extent to which the results verify the predicted consequences. To the extent that the consequences derived from and predicted by the model do not exactly fit what actually occurs, the mathematical parameters describing the physical situation must be corrected and the program iterated. If the inaccuracies are sufficiently great in comparison with the accuracy of measurement, the model must be reformulated or different hypotheses established. Under these conditions, the experimental phase represents a reiteration of the data-collection phase followed by a reformulation of the model which again must be experimentally tested. This process continues until the predictions are within the accuracy of the measurements. Later, as the accuracy of measurements improves, the process must again be repeated.

Mathematical Models In the scientific method as described above, the field of mathematics occupies a unique role. It must be emphasized that strictly speaking mathematics is not a science–it is not concerned with the scientific method; it is not concerned with experimentation nor with measurement. Mathematics is essentially a scholastic discipline concerned with the analysis of structure and the development of necessary consequences from hypotheses. The mathematician is essentially an analyst, not an experimentalist. Of course, much of mathematics is drawn from the intuitive understanding of physical process and most mathematical structures have resulted from the problems of modeling for a specific physical situation, but this merely represents the source of material on which the mathematician operates.

It is precisely because mathematics is concerned with the analysis of structure that it has represented the great source of models for the scientist and has been looked to for aid in the field of information systems. Mathematics provides differential equations as models of dynamic processes, probability theory as a model for statistical process, and algebra and topology as models of relationships. Each of these structures has been analyzed by mathematicians and the resulting theory makes it easy for the scientist to determine what consequences are to be expected from particular hypotheses.

It is important to understand the variety of measures available from mathematics and therefore the kinds of models that can be utilized by a theory of information-system design and file organization. The process of measurement has been described as the assignment of elements from some mathematical system to the set of physical objects, or events, of interest. That is, if $P = \{p_1, p_2, \ldots\}$ denotes a set of physical objects, then *measurement of P* means that a function (or rule) assigns to each element of P, such as p_i, an element b_i from some mathematical system $B = \{b_1, b_2, \ldots\}$. The nature of the set P of objects and the process for mapping it onto the abstract space B comprise the *operational* definition of measurement. This "explication by operation" is the point at which data gathering and the testing of predictions take place. On the other hand, the mathematical structure of the system B belongs to the formal side of measurement theory and is the domain of the mathematician. The structure of B is usually dictated by a set of rules or axioms which state the relationships among the implicitly defined elements of B.

The mathematical structures which can be utilized in this way have themselves been ranked in terms of the relative complexity of their structure. A mathematical model is said to be *nominal* if it has essentially no structure whatsoever imposed on it. An *ordinal* (partial-order) scale of measurement is implied if there is natural ranking of the elements in the mathematical system according to some attribute, and is appropriate if the physical objects being measured can themselves be partitioned into classes in such a manner that: (1) elements which belong to the same class can be considered equivalent with respect to the attributes of interest; (2) a relation can be defined between each pair of classes, such as *class x is contained in class y;* and (3) there is a degree of consistency in these comparative judgments so that if class x is contained in class y, and class y is contained in class z, then x is contained in class z. At the far extreme in this relative scale of complexity are those models which are essentially quantified and wherein the mathematical structure consists of the real numbers.

In most situations, the objective in developing a theory for a field is to continually increase the complexity, in the sense outlined above, of the mathematical structure and, in particular, to move from the purely nominal to the relational to the quantified. In this way, as the complexity of the model increases, it absorbs more and more of the complexity of the world into its own structure, and correspondingly reduces the difficulties in dealing with considerations not covered by the model. In the past, the models which have appeared appropriate to information-system theory have been almost solely relational. However, as we will try to show, it seems that the time is right to attempt quantification.

In the following discussion we will summarize the significant features of three mathematical structures—Boolean algebra, linear algebra, and probability—which have particular relevance to information-retrieval theory. This summary treatment certainly cannot substitute for the texts in these fields, but it can serve as a useful review and introduction to them. For our purposes, the discussion will also serve to define the notation and approach which we will use when applying these structures as models for information-retrieval processes.

Of the mathematical structures which have provided models for relationship, *Boolean algebra*—including its generalizations in the theory of sets and lattice theory—is the simplest one that provides an organization of elements adequate for an information-system theory. That is, it is simple in terms of requiring only the structures defined by a relationship between elements, but it is organized in the sense of exhibiting associations among elements. The foundations of Boolean algebra were developed first by the German mathematician Leibiniz in his formulation of a system of mathematical logic. Later contributions to such a systematized logic were made by Augustus de Morgan and George Boole around 1850. The first complete formulations were those by Russell and Whitehead in their *Principia Mathematica*, in about 1915,[2] and by Hilbert and Ackermann in their classic text on the subject, *Principles of Mathematical Logic,* in 1928.[3]

The concept *classes of objects* is the cornerstone of Boolean algebra; it is impossible to conduct logical reasoning without it. As we will show, the fact that two classes of objects may have things in common describes a relationship between the classes; the structure of this relationship is the subject matter of Boolean algebra. Similarly, the elementary logical properties of statements exhibit the same type of structure. Therefore, Boolean algebra is concerned with the structure of this relationship among, for example, different sets of items or, as another example, different statements about things.

Attempts have been made to devise a diagrammatic approach to the presentation of these relationships among classes. The first such diagrams were created by a nineteenth-century mathematician John Venn and are called *Venn diagrams.* Several are illustrated in Figure 1 for the operations defined above, and for various combinations of them.

Although we have discussed these concepts in terms of sets of things, the relationship they bear to logical statements is extremely close. For example, the logical statement *the object a of the class I is in the subclass X of I* is either true or false for each object a of I. Or, viewing this relationship between classes and statements about them in the reverse manner, the subclass of all things in I for which that statement is true defines the class X and the subclass for which it is false defines the class $\overline{X}$. In a very real sense, it is this relationship which makes Boolean algebra so applicable to information retrieval. Thus, if the class I is taken as the domain of documents of a library, then for a document to be in a subclass X might be taken as meaning that the term X has been applied to it. Therefore, the conjunction of terms, $A \cdot B$, defines the conjunction of the corresponding classes of documents and thus the documents to which both A and B have been applied.

[2]Bertrand Russell and Alfred North Whitehead, *Principia Mathematica,* 2d ed., University Press, Cambridge, England, 1925.

[3]David Hilbert and W. Ackermann, *Principles of Mathematical Logic,* Translated from the German by Lewis M. Hammond, G. Leckie, and F. Steinhardt, edited and with notes by Robert E. Luce, Chelsea Publishing Co., New York, 1950.

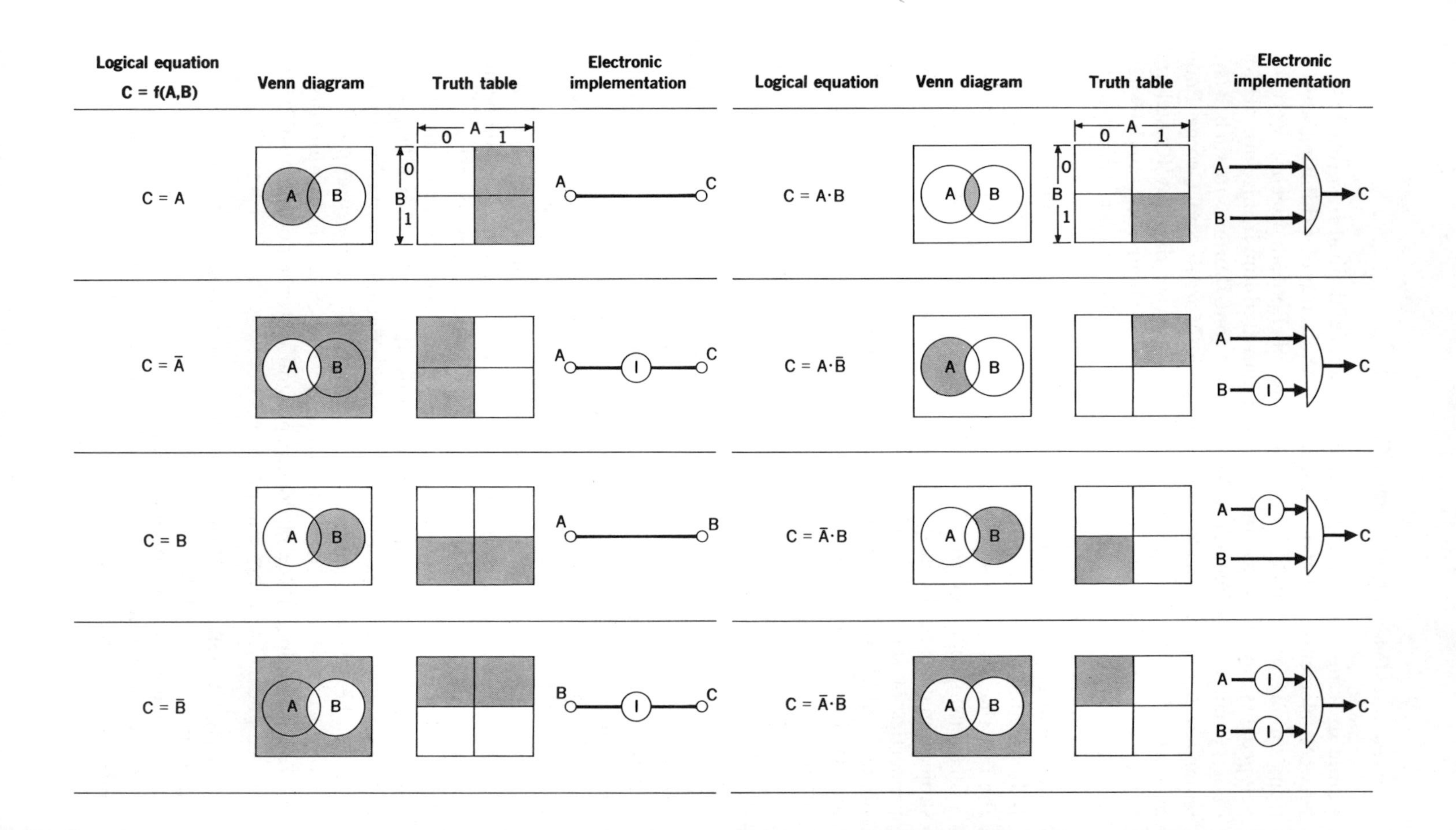

Logical equation
C = f(A,B)
Venn diagram
Truth table
Electronic implementation
Logical equation
Venn diagram
Truth table
Electronic implementation
C = A
C = Ā
C = B
C = B̄
C = A·B
C = A·B̄
C = Ā·B
C = Ā·B̄
A
B
0
1
C
I

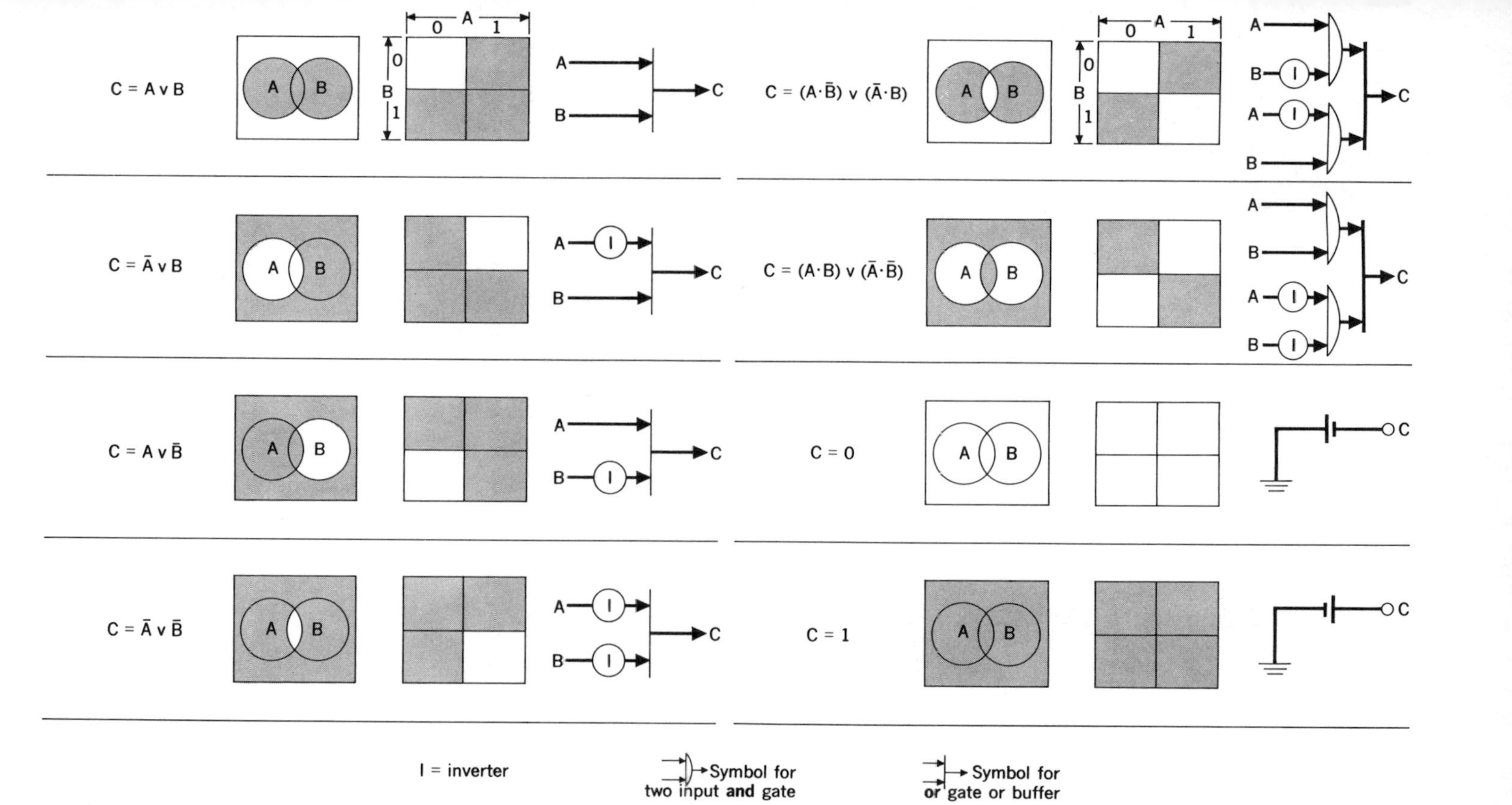

C = A v B
C = Ā v B
C = A v B̄
C = Ā v B̄
C = (A·B̄) v (Ā·B)
C = (A·B) v (Ā·B̄)
C = 0
C = 1
A
B
0
1
C
I
I = inverter
Symbol for two input and gate
Symbol for or gate or buffer

FIGURE 1

Indeed, for certain purposes, these postulates are more than sufficient and simpler structures are adequate. One which has received a good deal of attention in this respect is the *lattice*. The lattice, like Boolean algebra, describes relations among sets of things, or among logical statements, and indeed satisfies most of the abstract properties defined for Boolean algebra. That is, a lattice provides an inclusion relation among its elements which defines a partial order (so that the inclusion relation is reflexive, antisymmetric, and transitive), and for any two elements A and B in the lattice there are elements $A \cdot B$ and $A + B$ with the properties, respectively, that if any element X is contained in both A and B, it is contained in $A \cdot B$, and if any element Y contains both A and B, it contains $A + B$. In lattice theory, the sets $A \cdot B$ and $A + B$ are called, respectively, the *greater lower bound* and *least upper bound* of the two elements A and B.

Lattices can be represented graphically as structures consisting of nodes and links of the following character:

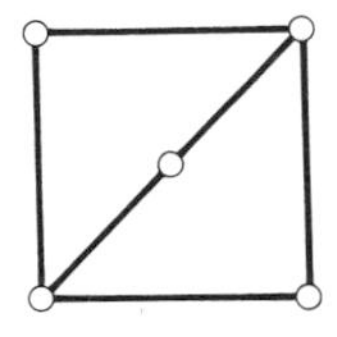

where the nodes (circles) in such a net represent the elements of the lattice and $A \leq B$ if A is below B and connected to it by a chain of links.

There are many possible steps which could be taken in the development of a quantified model for information-system theory from, for example, the simple counting of levels in a lattice to the complete measurement by a real-number scale. One particular quantified mathematical structure has been used as a model in science with particular frequency, and appears to be highly appropriate to this field of information-system design. This is the structure called *linear algebra*. This model has been almost universal in its application, not so much because physical processes are linear, but rather because it allows simplicity of representation. In particular, the most significant aspect of linear algebra is that the process of analysis leads to simple synthesis; that is, the effects of a combination of conditions can be determined as a simple linear combination of their individual effects.

Linear algebra is concerned with the nature of linear transformations on vector spaces, that is, with the change of quantities in such a way that preexisting linear relationships are preserved by the change. The fundamental quantitative tool of linear algebra is the *matrix*. Matrices are rectangular arrays of real (or possible complex) numbers, called the *elements* of the matrix, of the form

$$\begin{bmatrix} a_{11} & a_{12} & a_{13} & a_{14} \\ a_{21} & a_{22} & a_{23} & a_{24} \\ a_{31} & a_{32} & a_{33} & a_{34} \end{bmatrix}$$

The subscript notation for the elements provides a means for defining the location of the particular elements in the array: the first subscript defines the row in which it occurs, the second defines the column. Thus the element a_{ij} falls in the ith row and jth column. The "size" of the matrix is defined as the number of rows by the number of columns: n by m. When $n = m$, the matrix is said to be n-by-n square. For convenience, matrices are represented by shorthand, symbolic notations such as A, or (a_{ij}).

The operation of matrix product can be extended to other than square matrices, provided the rows and columns appropriately match so that the summation can be defined. In particular, an m-by-n matrix can be multiplied onto an ordered array of n numbers. For example,

$$A\bar{x} = \bar{y} \text{ means } \begin{bmatrix} a_{11} & a_{12} & a_{13} \\ a_{21} & a_{22} & a_{23} \\ a_{31} & a_{32} & a_{33} \end{bmatrix} \begin{bmatrix} x^1 \\ x^2 \\ x^3 \end{bmatrix} = \begin{bmatrix} y^1 \\ y^2 \\ y^3 \end{bmatrix}$$

Such matrix "equations" thus represent in compact form entire sets of simultaneous linear equations. If the ordered array $\bar{y}$ is known, then solution for $\bar{x}$ requires solution of the corresponding system of linear equations. The latter in turn requires that restrictions be placed on the matrix A. In particular, A must be "nonsingular"; that is, there must exist another matrix, A^{-1}, called the inverse, such that

$$AA^{-1} = A^{-1}A = I$$

A singular matrix is one which does not satisfy this condition. With a nonsingular matrix,

$$\text{if } A\bar{x} = \bar{y}, \text{ then } \bar{x} = A^{-1}(A\bar{x}) = A^{-1}\bar{y}$$

Such ordered arrays of n numbers, as $\bar{x}$ and $\bar{y}$ above, can be considered as what are called *vectors* in a *vector space*. In such vector spaces, measurements of *length* and *angle* can be defined as functions of the component numbers in the vectors. In particular, the length $\bar{x}$ of a vector and the angle between two vectors, $\bar{x}$ and $\bar{y}$, are given respectively in terms of

$$|\bar{x}|^2 = \sum_{i=1}^{n} (x^i)^2 = (\bar{x} \cdot \bar{x}) \qquad \cos(\bar{x},\bar{y}) = \sum_{i=1}^{n} x^i y^i / |\bar{x}| \cdot |\bar{y}|$$

Even if quantification can be introduced into information-system theory, however, significant problems arise because of the variability in the events being measured. In many cases a model cannot possibly handle the measure of an individual event because of this variability and, therefore, must treat measurements concerned with classes of events. *Probability theory* is the study of the distribution of the variable measurements over these classes, and the statistical techniques provide the methods for determining these distributions from the measurements made. In a sense, therefore, the probability distribution provides the mathematical model for variability of measurement, and statistical analysis provides the experimental tool for evaluating predictive performance.

To be specific, consider the probability that a given document will or will not involve a class of terms; or the probability that some number, k, of file items must be examined to find a relevant one; or the probability that a question of a particular type will be asked. In each case, a probability distribution presumably can be defined that describes these probabilities for each class of events (each class of terms, each number k, each class of questions). A standard example is the probability distribution for the occurrence of letters of the alphabet in English text, based on their relative frequency of usage.

Comparison with Operations Research Although we are attempting to develop quantified models for information retrieval, it can legitimately be questioned whether in fact the field of information-system design has reached the stage where quantification is possible. Certainly the element of judgment is a predominant factor in this field, and judgment is, almost by definition, an ill-defined operation. Determining the relevancy of a document to a request, determining the index terms appropriate to representation of document content, determining the most appropriate position of a document in a file—each of these largely depends on the knowledge, experience, and intuition of competent professionals.

On the other hand, the field of management-decision making is an almost perfect example of an area wherein judgment and informed experience are fully as critical as they are in information retrieval, and yet one where quantitative techniques and the scientific method have been successfully applied. The development of mathematical models for the management-decision process has been identified as "operations research." This work first received recognition perhaps twenty to twenty-five years ago in the attempt to quantify complex decision problems in the military field. It has since found broad application throughout government and industry. Fundamentally, operations research attempts to do for management-decision making exactly what we are trying to do here in the area of information-system design.

Basic to the application of any model in the scientific method—whether to engineering, to operations research, or to information-system theory—is a criterion for determining the degree to which such confidence is justified. This is done by providing as part of the model a measure of its own performance or effectiveness in predicting behavior. The aim of any mathematical model is to provide this measure of effectiveness. Most model theory follows immediately from the function chosen for measurement and the ways in which it will be maximized or minimized. Therefore, any time a model is posed, the first question that should be asked is: What is being measured, and what function is used to measure it? And the next should be how the model maximizes or minimizes this function.

The Role of Testing Programs In general, measurement produces sets of quantities, but the desire is to optimize some single objective of value. This means that the measure of effectiveness views value in terms of the established objective as a function of the set of individual measurements. Choosing the appropriate measure, and therefore the model, is not simple, particularly since there is usually a set of possible functions. Which of these possible measures of value should be used is a problem to be resolved between the physical, experimental scientist and the analytical model builder. Essentially, the model, the experimental data, and the measure relating the two cannot be divorced from one another.

A measure can be used in a number of ways. It can be used to predict, for example, that according to the measure of value, a system will perform to a certain level of effectiveness. An experiment can be used to test whether the system in fact performs to the predicted level of effectiveness. If the predictions consistently hold within the limits of accuracy of measurement then the measure can with confidence be used as a tool for synthesis, to design a system that is optimum according to the measure. This is, of course, a much more difficult step than the analytical creation of the model, but it is one that the scientist would like to feel can be taken.

Viewed in the light of scientific method, testing programs occupy the particularly significant role of testing the accuracy of predictions provided by the mathematical model. Used in this way, the purpose of tests is to evaluate a model in the physical situation which the model is attempting to represent. That is, given a physical situation, such as a particular file structure, the mathematical model will provide the measurement for the system efficiency and a testing program can then be used to test the accuracy and validity of the predictions from the model.

The other purpose for a testing program is to obtain the quantitative data concerning particular systems. Used in this way, the testing program will serve as the step of data collection to provide the raw information on which either to construct a model for later test and verification or to provide the input to an existing model for purposes of prediction, comparison, or design.

At times, testing programs have been used by information-system analysts to provide an evaluation of the relative effectiveness of two systems. However, unless this is done within the context of a proven predictive model, it is fallacious to extend the results of the test to a general evaluation of the systems. Without such a model, a test merely tells which of the two systems was more effective in the particular test situation; it will not in any sense describe which of the two systems will be more effective in any other situation. In fact, all too frequently there is an inherent bias due to the very character of the test situation in favor of one or the other of the systems being evaluated. In a sense, the situation is completely comparable to the descriptions of a high IQ as merely an indication of the ability to score well on IQ tests.

Thus, whether test data can be extended to other contexts depends on the accuracy to which some model, either explicit or implicit, will predict performance in other situations. It is therefore essential, before undertaking any testing program, to clearly state the model by which evaluation and generalizations are going to be made. At this stage, since no reliable model yet exists, the most desirable approach is to make the purpose of any test program to provide an evaluation of the degree to which the model does predict behavior.

Some experiments to test information systems in fact are in progress. The ASLIB group in Great Britain, under the direction of Mr. Cleverdon, is conducting one of these.[4] Dr. Don Swanson, at Thompson Ramo Wooldridge Inc., has also been conducting experimental tests.[5] A somewhat different approach is to examine existing information systems to determine the parameters of operation as they exist, and to verify predictions of their performance. This approach thus deals with total existing situations rather than artifically contrived ones, and has the concomitant disadvantage of including the great diversity of relationships which any real situation will exhibit. On the other hand, it has the advantage of dealing with systems which presumably have developed near optimum operation—under "biological" competition and survival of the fittest.

To be specific, existing libraries and commercial data-processing systems can be considered in this light. Whether these systems are actually efficient or optimum may be debatable, but if qualitative judgments of relative efficiency can be made, then the model should predict them. Unfortunately, almost traditionally libraries have lacked a cost-accounting

[4]C. W. Cleverdon, *ASLIB Cranfield Research Project.* Report on the first stage of an investigation into the comparative efficiency of indexing systems. The College of Aeronautics, Cranfield, England, September, 1960.

[5]Don R. Swanson, "Searching Natural Language Text by Computer," *Science,* vol. 132, no. 3434, pp. 1099–1104, October, 1960.

approach. There are, for example, virtually no accurate data on library operations, their time and cost. If this lack can be suitably filled—such a step appears essential if any solution is to be found to the library "problem"—libraries can represent the most suitable of experimental testing grounds.

In most of these library systems, the human being is utilized in many roles—as a decision maker and as a user of information, but also as a "machine" and as a cog in the system. It is therefore vital, if this approach of examining existing information systems is to be successful, to develop a clear picture of the human being in each of these roles. In this respect, there is a wealth of information, from psychology and elsewhere, with which to define the quantitative characteristics of human beings as information-transfer devices, viewed as machines. It is equally important, then, to understand the psychology of the human being as it relates to the decision process or as it relates to his need for information. This view is concerned with the human being as a definite participant in any process in his "role as a human being."

This information is valuable for another reason. The human being can himself be regarded as a successful information-processing system—particularly in ill-defined situations requiring judgment. Any model can therefore be tested for prediction of performance for the human being in such situations. In this view, the human being—if considered by the anthropomorphic analogy of files as similar to the brain—is recognized as a successful information system and used as a pattern for information systems. The concept is that an anthropomorphic file will also be successful on certain types of problems.

Limitations of the Scientific Method The scientific method has been perhaps the most powerful tool ever developed for increasing our knowledge. However, it has some significant limitations which must be recognized when we attempt to extend it to information-system theory as it has been extended to operations research. There are many situations for which the scientific method is not appropriate because the necessary data are not available; in other situations, the scientific method is unsatisfactory because the standards of measurement do not permit adequate comparison of predicted values with observed values.

If measuring instruments cannot accurately measure the parameters involved in the model, the derived results are unsatisfactory. To raise a specific example, the mathematical structure of linear programming can be used, as we have indicated, for management decisions such as determining the optimum product mix or the optimum transportation of products from warehouses to receiving points. The accuracy of the results obtained from a linear-programming problem, such as a transportation problem, are highly dependent on the accuracy of the initial data, such as the cost figures for transportation from given warehouses to given receiving plants. If these figures are inaccurate, not only are the results likely to be meaningless, they might be nonexistent, and the statement from the mathematical problem might be that there is no answer to the problem whatsoever. This is a very great possibility because of the size of some of these problems and the way in which error behaves in linear-programming problems of high order. Therefore, in any application of models—in particular, to the field of information retrieval for which no accurate measurements exist—the accuracy of the data is a highly significant consideration. On the other hand, the development of models may well stimulate the development of comparably accurate measurements by providing a framework for this prescription.

A second limitation is the availability of analytical tools on which to draw for the formulation of hypotheses and models. In general, these tools are drawn from the field of mathematics; however, mathematics is itself undergoing continual growth. There are structures which can easily be defined but which present-day mathematics cannot handle because of the limitations of present-day theory. Thus, under such conditions, although the model could be defined and might be completely appropriate to the data, there would be no reasonable method of developing predictions to be tested. However, it appears that at its present relatively unsophisticated stage, information-system theory will find present mathematics completely adequate.

Even with the availability of a theory, the availability of tools adequate for handling the computation may represent a limitation. The computer as a tool to help in the solution of large numerical problems represented a substantial forward step and allowed the application of mathematical models in many areas where they had not been possible before. But even now, certain combinatorial problems are beyond the capacity of even the largest and fastest computers.

Finally, a third limitation of the scientific method is the cost of experimental testing. There are times when it is impossible, for a number of reasons, to test the hypotheses. The cost of experimental testing is significant, particularly in the field of information retrieval. Some of the experiments which are now underway are very valuable experiments, very important experiments, very necessary experiments, but also very expensive experiments. The cost of getting literature into mechanized form for language translation, or for running experiments in information retrieval, are substantial. If any barrier really exists in the application of scientific method to this field, it is probably this one.

ITEM REPRESENTATION AND RELEVANCY

Definition of File Items One of the critical questions is defining what is meant by a file item and determining how to represent such a file item quantitatively. Our approach has been based on several premises concerning the organization character of files and the information stored in them.

The first of these premises is that the contents of a file should reflect the entire set of utilization so that file items in a library, for example, ought to consist not only of stored documents but also of some representation of requests, requestors, classes of users, indexers, words and terms, and all other things with which the library is concerned. Thus, most people think of the contents of the library as a set of documents. We think of the contents of the library as including also the set of *requests* which have been made in the past, even the set of *requestors* represented in one way or another. It should even include the words that are used in the library; thus the subject catalogue in a library contains not only representations of the documents, but representations of the words, indexes to the words, and even perhaps dissemination lists or profiles of file users.

The following factors will illustrate the significance of this premise, particularly with respect to the handling of requests.

1 The file must be responsive not only to requests, but also to the addition of new documents or other information since these represent just as significant a part of the processing load.

2 The character of response to a new document can be viewed as completely analogous to that of a response to a request and it may involve an output of, for example, relevant requestor data from a dissemination list or profile.

3 The storage of requests is potentially as significant as the storage of documents, since it indicates the statistics of usage and aids in the development of dissemination profiles and, perhaps most important, can provide past requests as responses to later requests which will be of almost as much value as formal documents.

4 The logical problems in determining the character of a request are analogous to those in determining the contents of a document and, in fact, one might ask a requestor to state his question in the form of a small essay.

A second premise on which our definition of a file item is based is that the contents of a file should be viewed as homogeneous in its character, so that there is no essential qualitative difference between a document, an abstract referencing that document, a request, or a requestor profile. The difference, if any, between items in the file in this sense should be a quantitative difference rather than a qualitative one. Furthermore, as a consequence of this premise, the response generated from a stored item may well be completely satisfied by the provision of an item from the file, such as the information from a card-catalogue card, which is quite removed from the information contained in the full document. Thus, with this premise, the difference between *document retrieval* and *fact retrieval* becomes a quantitative difference between various depths of acceptable response rather than a fundamental difference in the character of the file.

The third premise for our definition of a file item is that a quantitative model and measure for relevancy is possible. We have therefore utilized mathematical structures based on quantified measurement. Whether this is a valid view, particularly at this stage in the development of a theory, is highly debatable. Certainly there are not sufficient data on which to base a valid model, and therefore this view is largely an exercise in analysis. However, it is also significant that some step in this direction must be taken and that much of the most recent work in this field is consistent, as we will show, with the quantified model presented.

The fourth premise is that there is no essential relationship between the method for representing an item and the organization of groups of items into a file. We therefore consider the two problems of item definition and file organization as essentially distinct and different. This we feel has been obscured in the past by the fact that the representation of items by, for example, classification numbers, seemed to automatically predetermine the organization of such items in the file. There is absolutely no reason for this to be so except to the extent that the efficiency of a file organization might be related to the choice of terms. In this way, we make a distinction between, on the one hand, the *logical* problems in information retrieval which are basically the problems of relevancy—the problems of item representation, the problems of matching a document and a request, and the intellectual problems—and on the other hand, the *physical* problems in information retrieval.

To illustrate this last premise, visualize some kind of mechanical or human monster which could instantaneously and with absolute accuracy decide whether a given document, when looked at, was relevant to a request or not. Would one or would one not organize the file of documents? We claim that you *will* organize a large file, even though it is clear that we have removed all of the logical problems. The only remaining reason for organizing the file is for ease of physical access. The time to get to the document, to read the document, and so on, become the predominant considerations. The device may be able to make the decision instantaneously and accurately once it has read the document, but it still has to get the document and read it.

Basically, both the logical and the physical considerations must be recognized, but, in particular, the organization of the file appears to be essentially a physical problem. The reason for pointing this out is that most of the work in this field has been concerned with the very interesting intellectual problems of how to represent the information content of the document, and how to decide that it is the document wanted. But the more mundane, practical problems of how to get something out of a memory at reasonable time and cost are completely ignored.

Following from this is our fifth premise. We define organization as the grouping together of items (e.g., documents, or representations of documents) which are then handled as a unit and lose, to that extent, their individual identities. In other words, classification of a document into a classification slot to all intents and purposes identifies the document with that slot. Thereafter, it and the other documents in the slot are treated as identical until they are examined individually. It would appear, therefore, that documents are grouped because they are in some sense related to each other; but more basically, they are grouped because they are likely to be *wanted* together, and logical relationship is a means of measuring this likelihood. Therefore, the fifth basic premise is that we organize not just for reasons of physical necessity, but in particular we organize for the purpose of bringing items together that are likely to be needed at the same time. Finally, as a corollary to this premise, it seems that we organize not only on the basis of whether items are likely to be wanted together, but also on the basis of whether items are likely to be wanted. That is, we make readily available those items which are most likely to be wanted and make relatively inaccessible those items which are least likely to be wanted.

Proposed Model for Item Definition The model which we propose for definition of items is highly geometric in character and should be considered in such terms. Less visual approaches could also be adopted.

We interpret all items with which a file is concerned—whether stored documents, previous requests, users' profile, or words and terms—as the analog of physical bodies in a multidimensional space (not as physical documents such as a book on the shelf, but as "physical documents" in an abstract sense). That is, each such thing as a document or a person, in our representation of it, is a physical body in this space in the sense that it occupies volume and has a mass distribution. We can interpret this as the volume of knowledge encompassed by the document, the mass distribution (not necessarily uniform) in some sense representing the value of the contribution made by the document to each particular point of knowledge. We further assume that there is a measure of distance and angle in this space so that, given any two points in the space, there is a determinable distance between them and an angle they subtend from any third point. There is thus, for example, the means of measuring the distance from a request, which is such a physical body, to a document, which is another physical body, as the shortest distance between these two bodies. We might call this the *space of knowledge,* or the space of interest to the file system.

Such a view of file items is a highly intuitive one and certainly impossible to handle without some concrete representation. The first difficulty lies in the representation of the volume encompassed by a particular file item. The inherent difficulty is in representing any continuum. In general, the only way to do so is by means of discrete points. However, in principle, with mass and distance as defined quantities, it is possible to determine, for example, the center of gravity and other quantities related to the moments of inertia of a mass distribution. The adequacy with which discrete points represent a volume can then be quantified in terms of the extent to which the moments of inertia of the mass distribution are matched by those of the selected points. The obvious way of attacking this problem is to choose the discrete points at appropriate centers of gravity and represent the original mass distribution by mass concentration at these points. In the simplest case, this would mean the representation of a mass distribution by an equivalent mass at its center of gravity. More complex cases would require additional points adequate for the representation.

Thus, the representation of file items can be reduced in each case to the representation of a set of points in the space of interest. Still, if our premise of quantifiability is valid, points in the space must be given a numeric representation. There is a need, therefore, to introduce a coordinate system of some kind in order to provide a basis for such a quantified representation of the points. This would imply the specification of certain points in the space as coordinate points and then all other points in the space are identified in terms of them. Of course, this immediately raises the problem of the dimension of the space and the adequacy with which the points corresponding to file items can be quantitatively represented in terms of a finite number of points. In a sense, this problem is related to the question of how much of the information content of a file item can be represented by a finite number of criteria. This will be discussed later in more detail.

The present approach is to select a set of coordinate points and define the location of any other point by so-called "barycentric coordinates." In such a coordinate system, any point is represented as the center of gravity of a distribution of mass at each of the coordinate points. This allows for both the geometric location of the point and the assignment of mass at it. In particular, we can choose a set of key words in the space as our coordinate words. Each word is really a volume, but we will concentrate the volume at its center of gravity and choose that point as a coordinate point (realizing that, while we may choose a point as the representation of that word, the word itself is still diffuse in its meaning).

The concept of barycentric coordinates is a metric interpretation of the general concept of projective coordinate systems. It is based on an

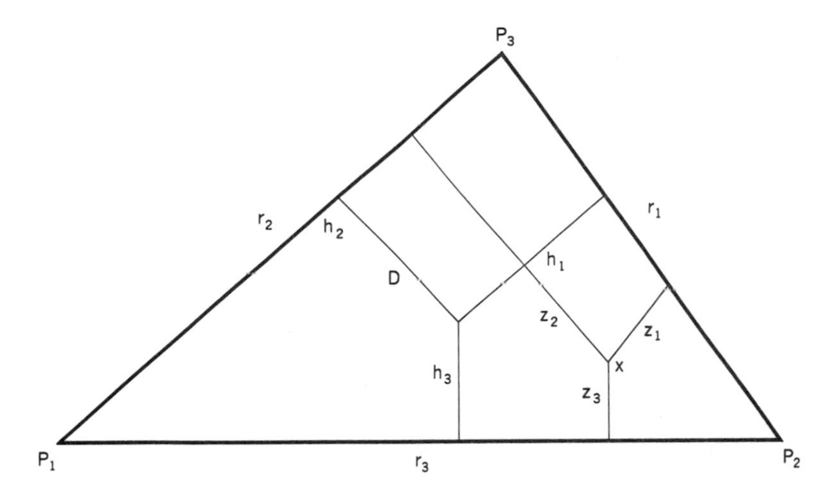

FIGURE 2 $m_1{:}m_2{:}m_3 = \frac{z_1}{h_1} : \frac{z_2}{h_2} : \frac{z_3}{h_3}$

ingenious mechanical idea developed by Moebius.[6] As the coordinates for a point P in the plane, he conceived of the distribution of masses at the vertices of a triangle in such a way that the point P became the center of gravity of the distribution of masses. It can be shown that these masses are proportional to the distances of the point P from each of the sides of the triangle (see Figure 2). By allowing negative masses (which we might interpret as the negation of a term), points can be defined not only within the triangle but throughout the plane. Although the concept of barycentric coordinates was initially defined in terms of the plane, it can clearly be extended to n-dimensional spaces.

A point of particular importance is the center of gravity of the entire mass distribution in the space because it is by choosing the center of gravity as an origin for coordinates that certain equations, particularly dynamic equations, become simplest. This point has the same character as any other point in the sense that it is a point of knowledge, but in effect, it might be considered as the center of interest of the library. Documents here may have very great value. In fact, it might be that it is the center of gravity precisely because the library has "works of. . . ." located at that point and has built everything else around it.

Before proceeding further, it is well to express this view of file items and their representation in more familiar terms. As indicated, the representation of a file item by a set of points is comparable to the representation of a document by the disjunction of a set of logical "phrases,"

[6]W. C. Graustein, *Introduction to Higher Geometry,* Macmillan, New York, 1946, pp. 156–173.

each of which attempts to represent the center of interest of some major section of the document. If the document is concerned with a fairly restricted topic, a single phrase may be completely adequate. If the document is concerned with several unrelated topics or an extremely diffuse one, then a correspondingly greater number of phrases will be required to adequately represent the document content. Each such phrase, in a well-defined sense, corresponds to a single point in the space of knowledge defined above.

To represent the information content of any such point in the space and, in particular, a logical phrase, we have previously chosen a set of key words. Each key word is interpreted as defining a point for assignment of mass in the space, so that the point of interest would be interpreted as the center of gravity of the mass distribution at the coordinate key-word points. The degree to which a key word was itself diffuse would be reflected by the difficulty in pinpointing its meaning to a single point in the space of knowledge. The barycentric coordinates then correspond completely to the assignments of relative importance of each key word to a phrase which is representative of the information content of some portion of a document.

The usual response to the proposal of a weighted indexing is one of shock, because indexing, classification, and abstracting are considered complicated enough as it is. However, even the present method of term assignment is simply a special case of weighted indexing. The assignment of one from a set of more than two weights really should not complicate judgment too much.

Several methods have been proposed for determining the weights assigned to terms. For example, Maron[7] suggested a judgmental evaluation of the probability that someone using the term wanted the document. Luhn's[8] technique of statistical indexing, since it generates a relative frequency for each term in the document, conceivably provides a mechanical process for assignment of weights. A possible generalization of this technique would combine the frequency values with Zipf's law[9] on probable frequency on the basis of length. Other techniques for deter-

[7]M. E. Maron and J. L. Kuhns, "On Relevance, Probabilistic Indexing, and Information Retrieval," *Journal of the Association for Computing Machinery,* vol. 7, no. 3, pp. 216–244, July, 1960.

[8]H. P. Luhn, "Potentialities of Auto-encoding of Scientific Literature," *IBM Report RC*-101, New York, May 15, 1959.

[9]See Edmundson, "A Statistician's View of Linguistic Models and Language-data Processing," earlier in this volume.

[10]R. M. Needham et. al., "The Information Retrieval System of the Cambridge Language Research Unit," *CLRU Internal Report.*

mining of the content-bearing sentences, phrases, and words of a document—such as those of Baxendale, Oswald, and the Cambridge Language Research Unit (CLRU) [10]—can similarly be used as mechanical processes for assignment of weights. Later we will propose a variant of the judgment approach—not as a day-to-day operational method, but as a tool for theoretical study.

With this view of document phrases as represented by assigned weights to key words, an interpretation is available of the role of the logical conjunction and disjunction of key words. That is, if the possible weights are limited to zero or one, then the conjunction of terms is equivalent to their having the weight of one in the representation of a point in the document or request. The role of disjunction—i.e., logical *or*—in document or request representation (i.e., the document covers A *or* B) can now be interpreted as implying that separate points are involved in representing the volume covered. In other words, if two points are needed in order to represent the information content of the document, the logical *or* is the tool for separation of a document into this set of points, each point being then perhaps equivalent to one phrase from the document. Thus, if a request is for $(A \cdot B) + (C \cdot D)$, it is concerned with the separate concepts $(A \cdot B)$ and $(C \cdot D)$, each identified by assigning the weight one to its respective terms. The generalization to other ranges of possible weights does not change this basic interpretation.

Having chosen a set of key words as coordinate points, the representations of the entire set of points of interest—whether concerned with points in documents, requests, terms, or requestor profiles—can be compactly arranged in a matrix:

Key words

$$\text{Points} \quad \begin{bmatrix} w_{11} & w_{12} & w_{13} \\ w_{21} & w_{22} & \cdots \\ w_{31} & \cdots & \\ \cdots & & \end{bmatrix}$$

The tools of linear algebra are then available, as we will show, for manipulating this matrix and interpreting relations among the rows (i.e., among various points in the space) or among the columns.

As defined here, the quantitative representation of points in the space involves a set of weights assigned to the selected key-word points. In certain cases the number of such key words may be quite large, perhaps on the order of 5,000 to 10,000 words, and it would normally be expected in such a case that many of the weights would be quite small; representation in this form will therefore normally be extremely inefficient. Under such conditions, one might establish a "cutoff" value for the weights and essentially treat all weights less than that cutoff value as zero; then the key words for which the assigned weights were greater than the cutoff value could be identified and the actually assigned weights attached to the identification. The resulting representation will normally be much more efficient. For example, if 5,000 words are used as coordinate points and a scale of four values allowed for each weight, then the representation of any given point in the initially defined form would require at least 10,000 bits. On the other hand, using the cutoff-value approach, it might be expected that, say, only thirty words would have assigned weights exceeding the cutoff value. The representation would then require $30\ (13 + 2) = 450$ bits, since each of the thirty words could be uniquely identified by 13 bits, and 2 bits would define the assigned weight. In summary, this approach identifies each of the significantly relevant key words together with its individual importance.

Definition of Relevancy For a number of purposes—answering requests, organizing terms, classifying and grouping points—it is essential to have some measure of the degree of association, relevancy, and closeness of terms or documents. Viewed in the framework of the model for definition of file items described above, this reduces to the problem of measuring the degree of similarity between two sets of numbers, such as two rows or two columns of the point-term matrix. From the experimental standpoint, the significance of these numbers and the extent to which the measure of their closeness coincides with the judgment of informed professionals is highly important, but from the analytical standpoint the problem is largely independent of the interpretation which these numbers may have. Most of the work which we will describe has been of the analytical kind without serious experimental testing of the extent to which it matches informed intuition.

All the suggested approaches can be viewed within the common framework of the point-term matrix which we have previously described. Usually they have limited their considerations to weights of one or zero. Considering this array of numbers there may be reason to feel that certain pairs of the rows or columns appear to be similar. The effort has been to develop various measures of the degree of similarity between rows, or columns.

The Cambridge Language Research Unit, in their paper on the "theory of clumps,"[11] stated it as follows:

> The basic step is to replace the original array by one calculated from it in which the entries are numbers measuring, in some defined sense,

[11]A. F. Parker-Rhodes and R. M. Needham, "The Theory of Clumps," *CLRU Report,* February, 1960.

"similiarity," "connection," or "overlap" of pairs of columns (or rows) computed from their respective columns (or rows) in the original array. They may be set up in an obvious way in a square symmetrical array, the *ij*th entry being the nearness of column A_i to column A_j. The concern is with the properties of such arrays, which may properly be termed *connection* or *association matrices.*

The Cambridge group discussed various ways of defining the nearness function of two columns, A_j and A_k. These included:

1 $N(A_j \cdot A_k) =$ *number of ones in both columns* A_j *and* A_k. This definition would be suitable if the number of ones in a column were fixed or at least narrowly distributed. Otherwise it is counterintuitive, for it would, for example, make the nearness of

1110001101111 to
1111110010000 the same as that of 1110100000000 to
1111000000000

2 $N(A_j \cdot A_k) + N(\bar{A}_j \cdot \bar{A}_k) =$ *number of places of agreement between ones and between zeros*—i.e., the nearness in a Boolean lattice. This is simply the number of places where the two agree; it avoids the defects of the first definition, but does not resolve sufficiently unless the same weight is given to agreement in a zero as in a one.

3 $\frac{N(A_j \cdot A_k)}{N(A_j + A_k)} = \frac{\textit{number of ones in both rows}}{\textit{number of ones in either row}}$. This attaches no weight at all to agreement in zeros and is therefore only suitable where the proportion of ones and zeros is low. It is the most obvious definition in those cases where, at least in principle, the columns are indefinitely long but the number of ones in each is fixed or (statistically) limited.

Tanimoto[12] similarly takes the document-term *n*-by-*m* matrix $R = (a_{ij})$. He denotes by A_j the *j*th column vector of R. He defines the similarity coefficient σ_{jk} of a pair of columns A_j and A_k, with respect to the given set of documents, by a form equivalent to the last definition above:

$$\sigma_{jk} = \frac{N(A_j \cdot A_k)}{N(A_j + A_k)} = \frac{\textit{number of attributes assigned to both}}{\textit{number of attributes assigned to either}}$$

In a similar way he defines the dual similarity coefficient s_{jh} of a pair of rows b_j and b_h with respect to the set of terms by

$$s_{jh} = \frac{N(B_j \cdot B_h)}{N(B_j + B_h)}.$$

[12]T. T. Tanimoto, "An Elementary Mathematical Theory of Classification and Prediction," *IBM Internal Report,* November, 1958.

Tanimoto calls the n-by-n matrix $S = (s_{jh})$ the *matrix of the similarity coefficients* of the documents B with respect to the set of terms A, and dually, $\Sigma = (\sigma_{jk})$ the m-by-m matrix of the similarity coefficients of the terms A with respect to the set of documents B.

Maron,[13] using the term-document matrix, suggested another of the several possible coefficients of association between columns. The particular coefficient he chose arises in the following way. Consider the columns A_j and A_k corrsponding to two terms, and determine the number of elements in each of four classes–viz., documents with a one in both A_j and A_k, those with one in A_j but not A_k, those with one in A_k but not A_j, and those without a one in either. The number of elements in each class is shown most conveniently in the table below.

	A_k	$\overline{A}_k$	
A_j	$x = N(A_j \cdot A_k)$	$u = N(A_j \cdot \overline{A}_k)$	$N(A_j)$
$\overline{A}_j$	$v = N(\overline{A}_j \cdot A_k)$	$y = N(\overline{A}_j \cdot \overline{A}_k)$	$N(\overline{A}_j)$
	$N(A_k)$	$N(\overline{A}_k)$	n

Thus x corresponds exactly to the value obtained from the first definition of CLRU (see above); y to the corresponding value for the number of common zeros; etc. Maron then proposed as a measure of association

$$M(A_j \cdot A_k) = \frac{(xy - uv)}{(xy + uv)}$$

Stiles[14] searched for a formula that would give a relative frequency–one that would measure the departure from the expected frequency of occurrence assuming no association. He decided on the following:

$$P(A_j \cdot A_k) = \log_{10} \frac{(|N(A_j \cdot A_k)\,n - N(A_j)\,N(A_k)| - (n/2))^2 n}{N(A_j)\,N(A_k)\;(n - N(A_{ji}))\;(n - N(A_k))}$$

where the expressions involved have the meanings previously defined. Stiles describes this formula as a form of the chi-square formula using the marginal values of the 2-by-2 contingency table and the Yates correction for small samples. If $N(A_j)\,N(A_k) > nN(A_j \cdot A_k)$, the association is negative. Such occurrences must be recognized during the computation process and the resultant association factors marked to indicate negative association.

[13]M. E. Maron and J. L. Kuhns, "On Relevance, Probabilistic Indexing, and Information Retrieval," *Journal of the Association for Computing Machinery,* vol. 7, no. 3, pp. 216–244, July, 1960.

[14]H. E. Stiles, "The Association Factor in Information Retrieval," *Journal of the Association for Computing Machinery,* vol. 8, no. 2, pp. 271–279, April, 1961.

Each of these cases dealt with document-term matrices whose elements are only zero or one. It is possible to extend each possible measure, among those considered above, to the general case where the elements can take on a spectrum of values from zero to one. For example, we might take the *dot product* of the two sets of numbers, $A \cdot B = \sum a_i b_i$, which reduces to the CLRU first measure when values of only one or zero are allowed. This extension, incidentally, makes even more evident the counterintuitive character of this measure. Similar extensions are evident for each of the other proposed measures. To provide them, we must define a generalization of the concept of A by letting its elements be $|1 - a_i|$, where a_i are the elements of A.

In Maron's work, this extension is implicit, since he allows a range of values to be assigned for the weight of a term with respect to a document. This weight, as we have indicated, reflects the probability of interest in documents with respect to the term.

Osgood[15] defines an approach of this character. He established a set of factors to which an individual is to assign weights of relevancy to various concepts. This is done by defining, for each factor, a scale of values from high negative to neutral to high positive. The value assigned by the subject can then be interpreted as a barycentric-coordinate weight for the given factor with respect to each concept. These are then combined in a matrix similar to the form we have used, with a range of values possible for each element. He proposed as the measure of association the correlation between columns as computed from the sum of the products of the differences of each element from the average values for its columns:

$$R(A_j \cdot A_k) = \sum_i (a_{ji} - \bar{a}_j)(a_{ki} - \bar{a}_k)$$

This geometric type of approach has a good deal of appeal, since it introduces the possibility of a "point of view." In the case of Osgood, it was the center of interest. Thus, it would seem that relevancy is not an absolute concept but is dependent upon the point of view. In this way, although the concept of relevancy among file items is obviously highly related to the distance between points in the space, we need not interpret relevancy in such simple terms. Suppose that we consider that file items are relevant, not in any absolute sense, but to the extent that they are considered as relevant from some point of view. Thus, we may measure the relevancy of two points, A and B, with respect to a third point, P, by the cosine of the angle subtended by them at that third point. This can be illustrated by Figure 3.

[15] C. E. Osgood, *The Measurement of Meaning,* University of Illinois Press, Urbana, Ill., 1957.

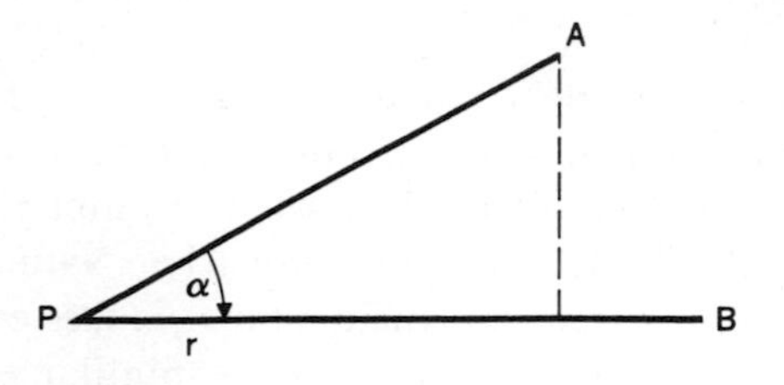

FIGURE 3 Rel $(A,B;P) = \cos \alpha = r\sqrt{PA}$

If properly interpreted, each of the previously described measures can be considered as a special case of this approach. For example, if the point P is chosen at the origin of coordinates, then $r = A \cdot B = N(A \cdot B)$, or the equivalent of CLRU's first measure (extended to the dot product to accommodate a range of coordinate values).

Of more interest perhaps is to interpret in this way the measures which were suggested by Osgood, Stiles, and Maron, by defining P as the center of gravity of the set of n points, so that

$$P = (\tilde{a}_1, \tilde{a}_2 \ldots, \tilde{a}_m)$$

Then in the case of Stiles and Maron

$$\tilde{a}_j = \frac{N(A_j)}{n} \cdot A_j \cdot A_k = N(A_j \cdot A_k)$$

and in the case of Osgood

$$\tilde{a}_j = \frac{\sum_{i=1}^{n} a_{ij}}{n} \cdot A_j \cdot A_k = \sum_{i=1}^{n} a_{ij}a_{ik}$$

Osgood's measure then provides exactly the dot product

$$r = (A_j - P) \cdot (A_k - P)$$

necessary for calculating the angle subtended at P. It can be reduced as follows:

$$\begin{aligned}\sum_{i=1}^{n} (a_{ij} - \tilde{a}_j)(a_{ik} - \tilde{a}_k) &= A_j \cdot A_k - \sum_{i=1}^{n} (\tilde{a}_j a_{ik} + \tilde{a}_k a_{ij}) + n\tilde{a}_j\tilde{a}_k \\ &= A_j \cdot A_k - n\tilde{a}_j\tilde{a}_k\end{aligned}$$

Similarly, Stiles' measure can be reduced as follows:

$$\frac{(|N(A_j \cdot A_k)n - N(A_j)N(A_k)| - (n/2))^2 n}{N(A_j)N(A_k)(N - N(A_j))(N - N(A_k))} = \frac{(|A_j \cdot A_k - n\tilde{a}_j\tilde{a}_k| - \tfrac{1}{2})^2}{a_j a_k (1 - a_j)(1 - a_k)n}$$

To reduce Maron's measure, define $\overline{A}_j$ as we have previously discussed: of a_{ij} is the *i*th element of A_j, then $1 - a_{ij}$ is the *i*th element of $\overline{A}_j$. On this basis,

$$N(A_j \cdot A_k)\, N(\overline{A}_j \cdot \overline{A}_k) - N(A_j \cdot \overline{A}_k)\, N(\overline{A}_j \cdot A_k)$$
$$= (A_j \cdot A_k)\,(n - n(\tilde{a}_j + \tilde{a}_k) + A_j \cdot A_k) - (n\tilde{a}_j - A_j \cdot A_k)$$
$$(n\tilde{a}_k - A_j \cdot A_k) = n\,(A_j \cdot A_k - n\tilde{a}_j\tilde{a}_k)$$

Thus, the three measures are closely related, differing only in the normalizations introduced by Maron and Stiles and in the minor correction for small n included by Stiles. They each relate closely to the angle subtended by two terms at the center of gravity of the points (documents) in the system. For example, given three terms A_1, A_2, and A_3, these angles could be interpreted in terms of the triangle shown in Figure 4.

Using this definition of relevancy, we can now define an operational procedure for determining the mass distribution required for the representation of a given point in this space as follows: Consider a document and an indexer for that document. We ask the indexer to evaluate the importance which each of the set of specified key words has with respect to the document. We interpret the values which he assigns as his view of the relevancy of those terms to the documents, and thus as the cosine of the angle subtended between each document point and the respective term points. This is illustrated by Figure 5, which shows two such terms, *A* and *B*, a document *D*, the indexer *P*, and the values which he would assign under this interpretation.

The values $(h_A, h_B, 0)$ then are proportional to the barycentric coordinates, at the points *A*, *B*, and *P* respectively, for the point *D* in the triangle defined by those points.

The degree to which the values h_A and h_B, determined by the relevancy numbers assigned by the indexer, would reflect the true weights required for representing the point in the space (AB) of interest is clearly a function of the position occupied by the indexer with respect to the space of

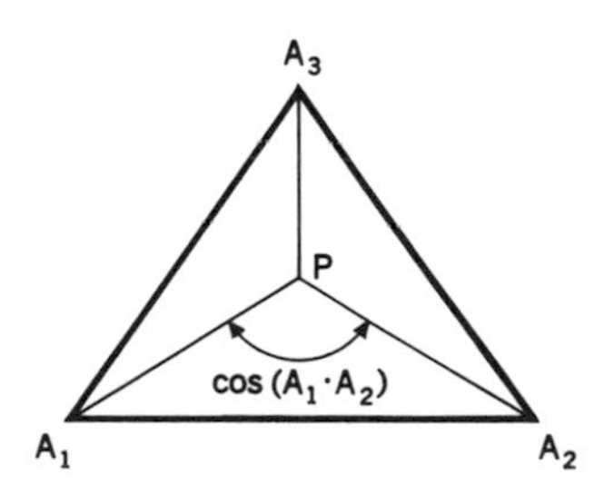

FIGURE 4

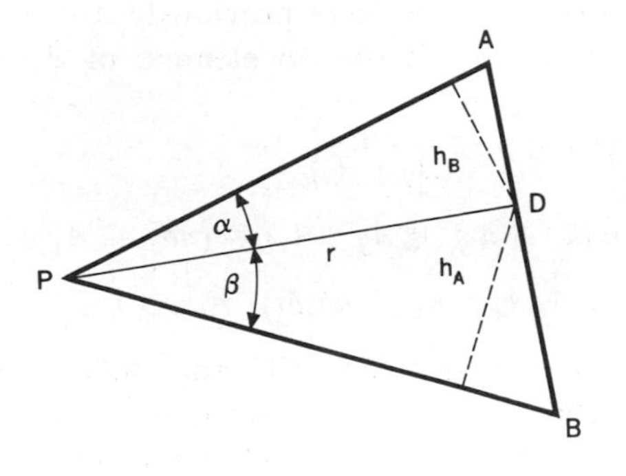

$$\text{Rel }(A,D;P) = \cos\alpha, \quad \frac{h_B}{r} = \sin\alpha$$

$$\text{Rel }(B,D;P) = \cos\beta, \quad \frac{h_A}{r} = \sin\beta$$

FIGURE 5

interest and the relevancy, cos $(\alpha + \beta)$, with which he views A and B. Thus, if his position with respect to the space of interest is relatively close to one of the key words, his evaluation will tend to be highly prejudiced. The ideal situation would be for him to be relatively equidistant from each of the points. Another observation to which this interpretation leads is that the more removed the indexer is from the space of interest, the closer will his evaluation be to the true weights. On the other hand, it should also be observed that the more removed he is, the less able he will be to discriminate among the terms. Thus, this interpretation allows for a means of measuring objectivity, bias, and lack of training.

Given this operational procedure which approximates the true weights required for representing a point by weights calculated from the relevancy values assigned by an indexer, two approaches are now available. One may ask several indexers similarly to evaluate the relevancy of key words to the same document and anticipate that an average process will eliminate the particular bias of the individual indexers. It would appear that this approach would not be the most fruitful, but one could attempt to determine the position which the indexer occupies with respect to the space of interest, by perhaps determining the importance with which he views the key terms and the mutual relevancy he assigns to pairs of them. With his position located in an absolute sense, the geometry provides a method for reducing his relevancy measures to proportional measures. Although this approach is certainly more complex than the first, it would appear to provide greater insight into the question of relevancy. Furthermore, with this approach, the handling of requests can be similarly treated. That is, the position of a requestor could be determined in the same way (such as Luhn's profile would presumably represent), the relevancy of documents to his requests could be evaluated, not in an absolute sense, but as he would view it.

FILE ORGANIZATION

Logical Organization As discussed earlier the purpose of organization is to bring together those items which are likely to be wanted together, and logical relationship is a means of measuring this. The question of establishing logical relationship can be approached in several ways, each with its own advantages in increasing the effectiveness of file organization. For example, one approach is to organize the terms on the basis of an a priori classification. This, of course, is the traditional approach of the various library classification schemes such as the Dewey Decimal, Universal Decimal, or the Library of Congress classifications. It is also the approach implicit in Ranganathan's facet analysis[16, 17] and Western Reserve's semantic factor analysis.[18] In each case, an intellectual examination of the field of interest to the library has resulted in an arrangement of the terms utilized to show their relationship to each other.

Although a priori organizations of terms have a great deal of appeal to those who feel that there exists an ideal structure to the physical world, they tend, as we have pointed out, to become more and more confining and to represent a straitjacket in any operational situation. Such specifications of term relationships are completely inflexible and incapable of responding to the character of changing usage. Because of this inflexibility, much of the theoretical work in the field of information retrieval has had the purpose of grouping documents or terms together on the basis of the character of usage. This work falls into two general classes: (1) those studies which consider only the relationships between terms and documents as exhibited by the document-term matrix; and (2) those studies which consider either or both of the association matrices which can be derived from the document-term matrix.

Thus, the assignment of terms to documents in itself provides a means for the organization of the set of documents into subclasses. In particular, one can define a cutoff value for the weight assigned to a particular term with respect to any document. Then, if the assigned weight exceeds that cutoff value, the document can be considered as a member of the subclass of documents defined by that term. In this way, if W_{ij} is the weight assigned to term A_j with respect to document D_i, and if E_j is the cutoff value for term A_j, then the class S_j is the class of all documents for which $W_{ij} \geq \mathrm{E}_j$.

[16] S. R. Ranganathan, *Philosophy of Library Classification,* Ejnar Munksgaard, Copenhagen, 1951.

[17] B. C. Vickery, *Faceted Classification: A Guide to Construction and Special Schemes,* ASLIB, London, 1960.

[18] J. W. Perry, A. Kent, and M. M. Berry, *Machine Literature Searching,* Interscience Publishers, New York, 1956.

In principle, this is the approach involved in all present coordinate-index schemes, recognizing that they have been based on the assignment of terms with weights of one or zero with respect to documents. It is also evident, however, in the use of a hierarchical arrangement of terms as a classification schedule for documents. In each case, the method considers that a document falls within the class of documents defined by a term if the weight assigned to the term is greater than zero.

In general, the process of set definition in this way will assign a single document to many different subclasses. Therefore, retrieval of documents will require specification of the particular class of interest as the logical (set-theoretic) combination of the subclasses. Thus, the methods of Boolean algebra or lattice theory are required for specification of the particular class of documents of interest.

Powerful though the document-term relationship may be as a tool for logical organization, the relationship implied among terms or among documents by the common assignment of terms to documents seem to have deeper significance than is utilized by the Boolean-algebra or lattice-theory approach. Thus we may feel that two documents have very similar assignments of terms and that this is only partially revealed by their common assignment to the classes of documents defined by each of the terms. This degree of association presumably would be displayed by a high value in the document-association matrix, derived by one of the measures previously discussed.

The general problem is to recover information about the possible groupings of documents (or terms) from the association matrices. The typical object in doing so is to use the groups found as classes for defining a generic relationship among terms, or as a classification for grouping documents. CLRU phrases their objective in the following terms: "What we want is a way of finding a partition into subsets with the property that there tends to be a stronger connection between two members of a group than between a member and a non-member."[19] This would replace the rigidity of a priori definition of relations by the flexibility of usage-determined relations.

A great variety of techniques exist for the *extraction* of significant factors from an association matrix. They include eigenvalue analysis, factor analysis, powers of the association matrix as an approximation to each, the CLRU "clump" approach, and others. Each of these produces factors which can be interpreted as derived concepts; these are described by relative weightings of the terms or documents from the original set. Any relative weighting of the original set of points can be represented by a single point located at the center of gravity of these weights. This

[19]Parker-Rhodes, *op. cit.*, fn. 11.

single point is identical in character to any other point in the space and, in particular, to any point which might have been chosen to represent a term or a file item; the only difference therefore lies in the method of its derivation. By application of this technique, any set of points related by their degree of association can, in effect, be grouped into a box labeled with the center of gravity of the set. By a repetition of this process, groups of "abstract-term" boxes can themselves be grouped and identified by a higher-order abstract of the same basic character which is itself a center of gravity, etc. Therefore, the technique of term or document grouping and the creation of abstract concepts provide a means for organizing the set of points in the space.

In principle, the number of new points is at least the same as in the original set, but a measure is provided of the information-content loss incurred by rejecting any portion of the set of new points. Typically, if there is any degree of association among the original set, there will be a tenfold or one-hundredfold decrease in their number with no appreciable loss of information content. Tanimoto[20] phrased it in the following terms: Suppose that the number m of objects is fixed, and ask what are the $k \leq m$ most important attributes of the set of objects? He answers this question by considering successive matrices in which the attributes of least significance have been eliminated. This procedure is repeated until there are exactly k attributes remaining or, alternatively, until the information loss is significant. In a similar fashion, given a fixed set of n attributes, one can find the $h \leq n$ objects which are best represented as possessing these attributes. One can also perform a reduction of both attributes and objects simultaneously if desired. In practice one should have a sufficiently large matrix R so that attributes and objects may be eliminated by the above process to reduce R to the desired dimensions without significant loss of information content.

In particular, for example, if the eigenvalues and normalized vectors

$$R\bar{x}_j = \lambda_j \bar{x}_j, \bar{x}_1, \bar{x}_2, \ldots, \bar{x}_m, \lambda_1, \lambda_2, \ldots, \lambda_m$$

of the term-association matrix were determined and listed in decreasing order of the eigenvalue, the resulting sequence of eigenvectors would represent classes of terms extracted from the association matrix. They can be used as a basis, or coordinate system, for the space. Any point can be represented as a linear combination of them:

$$\bar{x} = a_1\bar{x}_1 + \cdots + a_m\bar{x}_m$$

The extent to which a point could be considered as a member of the class defined by an eigenvector is measured by the magnitude of the

[20]Tanimoto, *op. cit.*, fn. 12.

corresponding component in its representation in such terms. In particular, the extent to which each of the original terms can be so considered is given in this way. The amount of information concerning the association between points in the space of interest which is provided by each class of eigenvector-defined terms can be measured by the magnitude of the corresponding eigenvalue. That is,

$$R\overline{x} = a_1\lambda_1 \overline{x}_1 + a_2\lambda_2 \overline{x}_2 + \cdots + a_m\lambda_m \overline{x}_m$$

The techniques of factor analysis, which are so commonly used in various psychological testing situations, can be regarded as generalizations of eigenvalue analysis, differing only in the character of the factors derived and the relative simplicity of the computational problem. Herbert Solomon described factor analysis in the following terms:[21]

> In the form in which factor analysis is most frequently encountered, it was motivated by the measurement of mental ability. However, factor analysis appeared in embryonic shape in connection with filing problems faced by Scotland Yard officials on the classification and identification of criminals. Galton, who was developing his ideas on correlation, became interested in the classification problem. He pointed out that the twelve Bertillon measures to be used for classification were not independent and proposed that the observed measurements be formed into a set of independent measures.

In the usual factor-analysis situation, the sets of measured data (such as responses to tests of mental ability) are associated with each other, and conjectures about the latent universe operating to produce the associations are mathematized. These mathematizations are the mathematical models in factor analysis. The most interesting from the standpoint of our work are the centroid method of Thurstone and the principal-factor method of Hotteling for multiple common-factor analysis.[22] In each case, the data are given the heavy burden of providing all the information without the introduction of a priori hypotheses concerning relevant factors. The major difference between the two consists in the computational basis for the estimation of the relationship between the original terms and the extracted factors. Details of the centroid procedure utilized by Thurstone can be found in his basic text on the subject. Fundamentally, it allows the determination of an infinite number of choices for the factors, but Thurstone feels that attention should be given only to the choice for which psychologically relevant interpretation can be given. Hotteling, on the other hand, suggests that attention should

[21] H. Solomon, *Mathematical Thinking in the Measurement of Behavior,* The Free Press, Glencoe, Ill., 1960.

[22] *Ibid.*

be given to the factors which correspond exactly to the eigenvectors, despite the fact that they may not have immediate psychological interpretation. Thus the eigenvalue-analysis approach can be considered as a special case of factor analysis.

The possibility of using powers of the association matrix is implicit in all approaches which consider second-order or higher-order effects. Thus the extent to which two terms are associated, as determined from their mutual degree of association with third terms, is described by the square of the association matrix. The behavior of high powers of the association matrix is therefore of considerable interest. This has been investigated in a number of papers.[23] Of particular mathematical interest is the fact that powers of the association matrix provide a method for the determination of its eigenvalues and thus represent an approximation to the methods of eigenvalue analysis and factor analysis.

CLRU's theory of clumps proposes the concept of *cohesion* across a partition of the set of terms into classes. For example, if two classes of terms, A and B, are considered, with $A_1, A_2, \ldots, A_k$ the terms in part A, and $A_{k+1}, A_{k+2}, \ldots, A_{k+h}$ the terms in part B, then the cohesion between them is given by the expression

$$\frac{\sum_{i=1}^{k} \sum_{j=k+1}^{k+h} a_{ij}}{\sqrt{\left(\sum_{i=1}^{k} \sum_{j=1}^{k} a_{ij}\right) \left(\sum_{i=k+1}^{k+h} \sum_{j=k+1}^{k+h} a_{ij}\right)}}$$

where a_{ij} is the association between terms A_j and A_k. By use of this measure, the partition of the original set of terms is made in such a way as to minimize the cohesion between classes. Each class then represents a classification of the terms included within it.

Whichever technique may be used to generate abstract concepts from groupings of term or document points, the process of abstraction not only produces a relationship among the points, but also can be utilized to reduce the complexity of representation of any given document point. Thus two separate representations of a document, one in the original form and the second in terms of the generated abstract terms, will have a qualitative difference in their character. This qualitative difference has been described by Yonker[24] in terms of his *descriptive continuum;* that is,

[23]David Rosenblatt, "On the Graphs and Asymptotic Forms of Finite Boolean Relation Matrices and Stochastic Matrices," *Naval Research Logistics Quarterly,* vol. 4, no. 2, June, 1957.

[24]Frederick Yonker, "The Descriptive Continuum: A Generalized Theory of Indexing," *International Conference on Scientific Information,* Washington, D.C., 1958.

he states that the terms to be used in representing document content can be arranged in a continuum ranging from what he calls "very short terms" (such as those represented by Calvin Mooers' descriptors or Taubes' uniterms) to somewhat "longer" terms (such as subject headings in a card catalogue or headings produced by combinations of descriptors or uniterms), to the "longest" type of term (this being the hierarchical classification).

The measure of "length of term" was never explicitly defined by him, but it can be interpreted as being related to the redundancy or mnemonic character of the term, or the degree to which the representation of a given term shows its relationship to other terms. Specifically, "short" terms are considered initially independent of each other and can be represented in binary notation by a number of bits equal to the logarithm to the base 2 of the number of terms. Combinations of terms may be represented in some compact way, such as superimposed random coding; but if their component terms are to preserve any degree of identity, representation will generally involve a larger number of bits than the number of combinations actually used would require. Similarly, description of a term defining a position in a hierarchical relationship will involve a highly redundant coding for the number of terms actually involved, in comparison with the total number of terms possible in the hierarchical structure.

Yonker and Taube attempted to show that the position of a particular choice of term type in this continuum determined, to all intents and purposes, the characteristics of the information system. In particular, they felt it determined such things as the depth of indexing, the number of criteria applied to the document, the degree to which terms could be permuted, etc. Their results seem to be valid, particularly with respect to the number of terms applied. For example, the number of terms normally applied to a document in a library card catalogue is in practice far smaller than the number of terms normally applied in the uniterm system, and in fact is normally far smaller than librarians feel ought to be applied.

In any event, the problem of organizing the terms used to represent the space relates directly to the choice of a coordinate system. The choice of a particular coordinate system may turn out to be not the most suitable one. It may therefore be desirable to change from one coordinate system to another, and one type of change of coordinate system is that involved in the attempt to reduce the number of coordinate points. As we have previously mentioned, there is the question of what the dimension of the space is and of the adequacy to which the points corresponding to file items can be quantitatively represented. Thus, how many points do we choose? How many key words are needed—10 or 10,000? Actually these questions cannot be answered, since one cannot say what the dimension of this space is, only what an *adequate* set of points is for file purposes. The approach through the association matrices seems to provide a method for determining adequacy.

A final approach is to organize documents on the basis of their mutual occurrence as determined from situations of circumstance. Thus, the fact that two documents have arrived at a library at effectively the same time to an extent implies a relationship between them which, in fact, is reflected by the closeness of the assigned accession numbers. Such an approach, particularly when used in conjunction with one of the others, is an extremely valuable one, although virtually unexploited, particularly where the environment has a high degree of consistency. Specifically, as new documents enter the system, a significant new parameter enters the determination of the degree of document association—that is, the distribution of activity. This means that in some sense the organization of documents should not only reflect the degree of logical association, it should also reflect the distribution of activity. Such an approach can be made the basis of an additional, relatively unexplored theory of file organization.

Activity Organization The problem in activity organization is to supplement the methods of logical organization by recognizing not just the likelihood that items will be wanted together, but rather that items will be wanted at all. Thus, from the previous discussion it is possible, using any one of the techniques of logical organization, to produce groups of related documents. In each case, the question of determining how many such groups of documents should be produced, or how many documents they should contain, or how many levels of successive groupings should be produced, can only be answered in terms of the desire to maximize, or optimize, some measure of effectiveness. As a possible measure of effectiveness, the *channel rate* or information rate obtainable from the information system appears to be particularly suitable (later we will also consider a measure based on the cost per operation). Such a measure immediately makes available the great wealth of mathematical literature on information theory concerned with precisely this type of question. Utilizing this mathematical structure requires very careful consideration of the question of which documents, groups of documents, groups of groups, etc., are most likely to be active. Determining this activity requires some measure of the probable distribution of activity.

To introduce the concepts of activity organization, it is necessary to consider a number of *distribution functions* over the space of interest and, in particular, over the set of defined abstract patterns. The first is the universe of the space, a function $u(x)$ which is uniform over the space and thus constant as a function over the space. The second distribution, and of more interest, is the volume $v(x)$ of items in this space.

With a variable concentration of documents, $v(x)$ is in effect a measure of the past concentration of activity. A third distribution, $w(x)$, is very similar to $v(x)$ except that it measures the worth distribution. Thus, there may be a very high concentration of documents in some area, but they may be worthless, whereas a very sparse set of documents may be such that each document is of vital importance. Hence $w(x)$, $v(x)$, and $u(x)$ are in general not equivalent.

The a priori probability distribution $p(x)$, the *probable activity,* is a fourth distribution. It says that over a long period of time a large quantity of requests or documents are going to come into volumes of space where $p(x)$ is large and a relatively smaller amount where $p(x)$ is small. For example, an engineering library might get a request on van Gogh, but most of the requests it handles are concerned with engineering topics. A related distribution, $q(x,t)$, is the conditional probable activity, given present activity at t. In other words, given the occurrence of a request in the area of knowledge t, $q(x,t)$ describes the "consistency" of the environment, since in a consistent environment the next stimulus should be fairly closely related to the immediate one.

These five functions—$u(x)$, $v(x)$, $w(x)$, $p(x)$, and $q(x,t)$ – are not necessarily equivalent. On the other hand, they are very frequently used as though they were equivalent, since the more easily determined of them may be utilized as an approximation to those which are difficult to determine. In particular, the distribution $v(x)$, in so far as it represents the past frequency of activity, is very frequently used as an approximation to $p(x)$, the probability of future activity.

To illustrate the significance of these distributions, consider the space as an analog to the twenty-six letters of the alphabet. The information rate which we will get from the twenty-six letters of the alphabet, provided their usage is uniformly distributed (i.e., assuming only $u(x)$ as the distribution), is about 4.7 bits. However, it is known that usage of letters in normal English text is not uniform; $p(x)$ describes the a priori distribution of the letters of the alphabet: E has frequency –, T with frequency – , and so one. Finally, $q(x,t)$ describes the conditional probability that, given some letter (such as Q), another specific letter (such as U) will occur.

The aim of activity organization is to produce a hierarchical arrangement of nested "boxes," or levels of groupings, which will represent a compromise among these various distributions in such a way as to optimize the selected measure of efficiency (such as channel rate). These sets of boxes become quite analogous to the structure of a normal classification scheme, although their method of derivation is dependent upon the character of usage rather than a priori decision. Thus, they can be visualized as in Figure 6.

Each box in Figure 6 represents a grouping at some level of abstraction, the level being described by the relative size of the box in the diagram. Thus, four levels are shown here, of which the smallest or lower level might possibly be the original documents themselves. If the cover of any box is removed, as shown in each upper left-hand corner, the interior of the box contains a nest of boxes of the same general character.

Each box is "labeled" by a pattern obtained from its contents—for example, by the point at the center of gravity of the patterns contained. In this way, what can be seen at any time is a set of patterns representing various levels of abstraction.

The actual "size" of the box at any given level is, of course, determined from the distribution of the documents themselves and the logical relationship which they bear to each other. It can be determined on the basis of any of the distribution functions $u(x)$, $v(x)$, or $w(x)$. On the other hand, the number of levels open at any time is dependent on the distribution $p(x)$ of probable activity. The aim is to produce boxes independent of their level of abstraction such that the integral of the probability, $p(x)$, of each box will be equal for all boxes which can be seen at any time. In the example shown, all the boxes which can be seen will therefore have the same probability of being utilized. This implies that the documents in the lower right-hand corner have the same probability

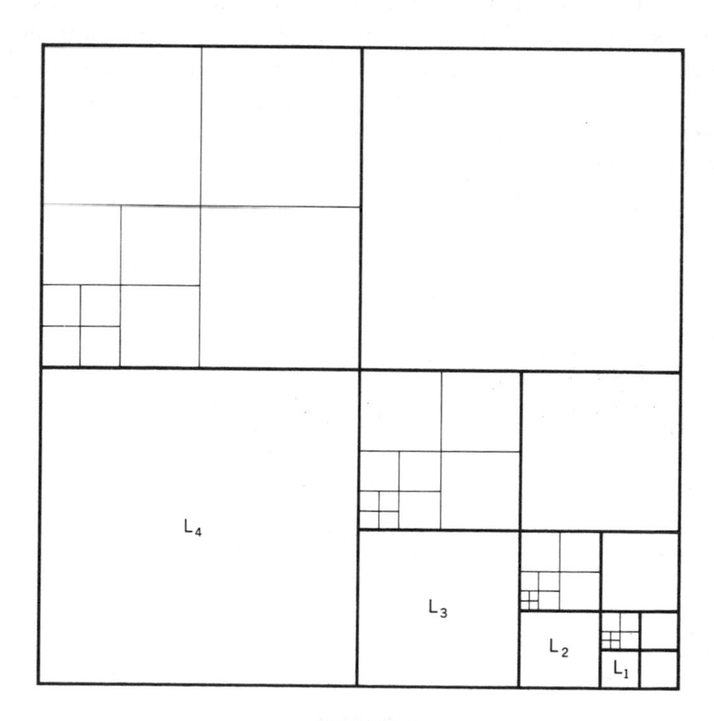

FIGURE 6

of being requested as the entire set of documents encompassed by the high-level abstraction in the upper left-hand corner. If the box in the upper left-hand corner were active, then the contents would be examined and would again consist of a set of boxes of equal probable activity. This process continues until the request is answered by the pattern representing a box at some level, ultimately by a document.

To take advantage of $q(x,t)$, we must organize the sequence of scanning of these boxes—looking at them in their order of probable relevancy. In other words, given $q(x,t)$ as a measure of the probable activity, arrange the boxes in the order corresponding to that measure. That means that in scanning them we will expect to come to the one of interest sooner than under an organization which ignores this distribution.

The determination of the actual relevancy of the given documents to an environmental situation and the selection of an adequate response involve the matching of the "request," for example, against the available box patterns and/or the location in the space of knowledge of the position which the request occupies. This process involves a scanning operation in which the pattern of the request is matched against the patterns of successive boxes. The selected box is then "opened" and the contents similarly compared.

It could be considered that such an operation takes place in parallel (with all available box patterns simultaneously matched), but this would beg the question. Instead, it could be considered that the scanning operation takes place sequentially, in a preferred order. It is for this reason that organization with respect to $q(x,t)$ is imposed on the boxes. That is, the preferred sequence of scan will possibly shift with the changing center, t, of activity.

The set of patterns describing the boxes which can be seen at any one time is equivalent to an index. The index is scanned (in the same manner) and indicates to which section of the space further attention should be paid. Access to the organization is an alternation of scanning

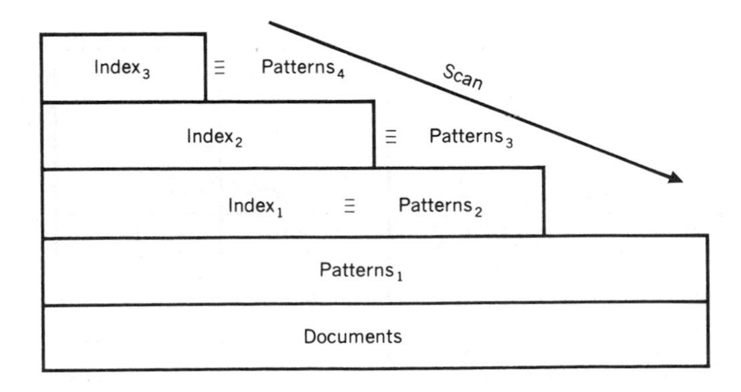

FIGURE 7

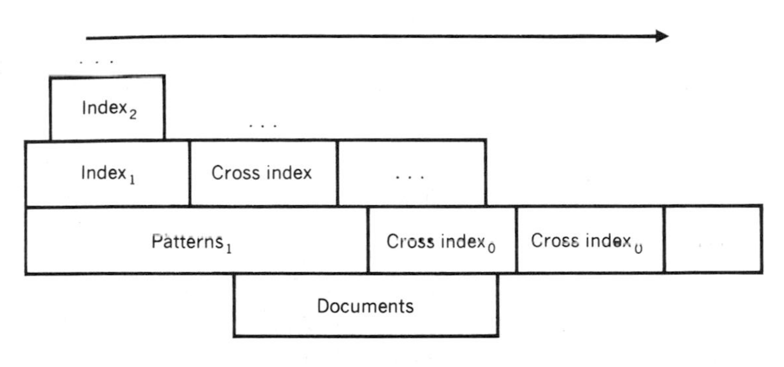

FIGURE 8

and physical indexing repeated until access is achieved (see Figure 7). The basis for organization by $p(x)$ is that in scanning an index at a certain level (say index$_2$) some of the patterns are references to groups of patterns in the next index level (index$_1$) and some are more basic, because of their volume of usage, and refer to patterns at a lower level (patterns$_1$).

As described, it has been assumed that where multiple points were required to represent a document, multiple points are represented at the pattern level. However, this frequently is not done (e.g. only one copy of the document is stored and that is located at the particular point defined by a classification slot). In such cases, references can be stored at higher index levels in the form of cross indexes. It should be recognized that such cross indexes are basically extensions to the set of document- or index-pattern points. Thus, the picture takes on the character shown in Figure 8.

LARRY E. TRAVIS

Analytic information retrieval

A recurrent theme in science fiction has to do with the ever-increasing volume of recorded information associated with expanding science, expanding technology, growing numbers of educated people, and increasing social complexity. What does the world do with all the films and tapes and papers and documents? Where are these things to be put and how are they to be used? One interesting story (perhaps analogous in more ways than one to the story which has people moving off to other planets because all the living surface on the planet Earth comes to be filled up with cemeteries) has the planet Earth hollowed out and made into one big library. The information in this library is randomly broadcast out into space over numerous channels—in hopes that every now and then somebody someplace will tune into some item of information which he might be able to put to use. We will consider here the problem of developing for access to information a means more efficient than random broadcast.

There has been a great deal of work done and material published on this problem of providing efficient access to information, referred to as the information-retrieval problem. It is a problem, of course, which has always been of concern to librarians. Recently, however, not only librarians but many others have come to take a very active interest in information retrieval for two reasons: (1) There has been within the last few decades, an explosive increase in the amount of information to which access must be provided, and the problem of providing *efficient* access has consequently become critical; and (2) the rapidly successful development of information-processing machines has presented the challenging—though yet to be proven feasible—possibility of extensive mechanization of the means of providing access to information.

Usually, discussion of the information-retrieval problem is couched in terms of providing a library user on some one occasion with documents which are relevant to his particular need for information on that occasion, and most of the work done on information retrieval has been on document retrieval. However, document retrieval represents only one special kind—albeit an important kind—of information retrieval. This discussion will be concerned with information retrieval in general, which we may call *fact retrieval.*[1]

We will first consider the meaning of *fact*; the explication here not only will be of use in the numerous philosophical discussions which involve the concept of fact, but also might be of use to people concerned with developing information-processing systems. Second, we will discuss a general characterization of a fact-retrieval system, a characterization which should be of use in providing a frame of reference for people concerned with designing and developing fact-retrieval systems. And third, the discussion will include comments and opinions that should be helpful in determining the limitations, capabilities, and feasibility of *automated* fact-retrieval systems.

FACT RETRIEVAL VERSUS DOCUMENT RETRIEVAL

Fact Retrieval Considered as Retrieval of Short (but Unprocessed) Texts To a large extent our discussion will be one level removed from facts themselves. Our main objects of concern will be symbol sequences of a certain kind, symbol sequences which might be said to express facts or to state facts. When we speak of a fact-retrieval system, it is, of course, these symbol sequences which are being stored, processed, and retrieved, and not facts themselves.

We may begin by considering the suggestion that a fact is simply what is expressed by a declarative sentence. Philosophers' objections that this can't be so, because then we would have to allow such paradoxical entities as false facts and fictional facts, are compelling; however, for the moment let us ignore them, because it turns out that the plausibility of this suggestion is closely related to the position that fact retrieval is only a special kind of document retrieval. This position is not very often explicitly asserted, but it is widely held, if only implicitly, as evidenced by the fact that many writers on document retrieval take their problem to be coextensive with the problem of information retrieval in general. To refute this assertion will thus be useful in itself as well as will contribute to our task of explication of fact retrieval.

Among writers on information retrieval, Bar-Hillel[2] has been especially insistent on the importance of distinguishing between the following: (1)

[1]Discussion in some detail of a system exemplifying many of the general principles discussed here is to be found in C. Kellogg, "The Fact Compiler: A System for the Extraction, Storage, and Retrieval of Information," *Proceedings of the Western Joint Computer Conference,* pp. 73–82, New York, 1960.

[2]Y. Bar-Hillel, "A Logician's Reaction to Recent Theorizing on Information Search Systems," *American Documentation,* vol. 8, pp. 103–113, 1957; "Discussion on the Paper by Dr. L. Mehl," *Proceedings of a Symposium on Mechanization of Thought Processes,* pp. 781–783, London, 1959; "Some Theoretical

finding books or documents or articles relevant to a subject, e.g., relevant to control of frost damage in Southern California; and (2) eliciting a specific answer to a specific question, e.g., to the question *Have plants ever been frosted in Santa Monica?* or *What has been the lowest temperature in Santa Monica so far this winter?* He suggests calling systems for doing the first "reference-providing systems" and systems for doing the second "data-providing systems." We shall call the first *document retrieval* and the second *fact retrieval.*[3] We shall conclude that it is convenient to think of document-retrieval systems as a species of fact-retrieval systems; however, our immediate task is, in effect, to show that it is misleading and confusing to think of fact-retrieval systems as being only a species of document-retrieval systems.

Perhaps one of the reasons that the distinction between document retrieval and fact retrieval is often muddied and that fact retrieval is taken to be only a special kind of document retrieval is that libraries typically perform both functions at least to a degree. Reference librarians are often called on to answer such questions as *What is the capital of Ethiopia?* or *What is the name of the congressman from California's twenty-sixth district?* Such questions are to be contrasted with *What authoritative books and articles does your library contain on the subject of movement of gold across international boundaries? What are some documents reporting study of decision making under risk?*[4]

Now, what is the difference between what a librarian does in one case and what he does in the other? It might be said that while document retrieval and fact retrieval are both concerned with answering questions, document retrieval is concerned with answering general questions and fact retrieval with answering specific questions. Ask a knowledgeable person a general question: *What is X like? What do you think about X? What has been done on the problem of X?* You are likely to get a fairly

Aspects of the Mechanization of Literature Searching," in W. Hoffmann, (ed.), *Digital Information Processors,* New York, 1962, pp. 406–443.

[3]Bar-Hillel has also suggested calling systems for doing the first "literature-search systems." This, however, would be misleading because typically the whole sequence of steps which is called a literature search may very well involve both document retrieval and fact retrieval—e.g., discovering relevant documents and then reading them to get an answer to a particular question such as *What results, if any, have been obtained from testing application of drug D to tumors of type T?* A final terminological point: we take *fact retrieval* and *analytic information retrieval* to be synonymous expressions.

[4]A friend who is a technical librarian and who has had experience with both types of people tells me that almost a sure criterion for distinguishing between an engineer and a scientist is that an engineer expects a librarian to answer for him the first type of question, while a scientist expects from a librarian only an answer to the second kind.

long, discursive answer, a large part of which is tangential or irrelevant to the particular question asked. This is not a reflection on the particular human being answering the question. If it is a reflection on anything, it is a reflection on the typical human memory, which is highly discursive. Here the important point is that the vague and general answer given to a general question is somewhat analogous to getting a document or documents in response to a general question addressed to a library. The questioner is subjected to and must examine much tangential and irrelevant material in order to get to points directly relevant to his question.

On the other hand, if when a person is asked a specific question (*Is X heavier than Y? How many attorney generals have been younger than Kennedy? Who was secretary of agriculture in* 1939?), his response is substantive, it is specific (*no, three, Wallace*). This is the kind of response expected of a fact-retrieval system. So perhaps the difference between document-retrieval systems and fact-retrieval systems is primarily one of (1) degree of specificity of questions addressed to the system and (2) volume and direct relevance to the questions of the answers provided.

Another approach which supports the conclusion just suggested is the following: Consider a linear ordering of natural-language "texts" according to their length. Let *X/Y/Z* represent a chain based on this ordering, i.e., *X/Y/Z* means *X is longer than Y, which in turn is longer than Z.* Such a chain might be the following: (1) all publications in a subject field *Sf*/ (2) all volumes of journal *J* about *Sf*/ (3) a particular volume *V* of *J*/ (4) a particular number *N* of *V*/ (5) a particular article *A* in *N*/ (6) a particular section *Sc* of *A*/ (7) a particular paragraph *P* in *Sc*/ (8) a particular compound sentence *Sn* in *P*/ (9) a particular clause in *Sn*. It might be suggested that the only difference between document retrieval and fact retrieval is that the former is primarily concerned with recovery of texts in the vicinity of (4), (5), and (6), while the latter is primarily concerned with recovery of texts in the vicinity of (7), (8), and (9). The plausibility of this suggestion is increased when it is recognized that existing library services which conventionally would be classified as fact-retrieval services do largely consist of providing particular sentences or paragraphs word for word as they are recorded in the library store. Particular paragraphs (or citations of such) are the output of libraries using so-called deep or analytical indexes (e.g., certain law libraries). And the reference librarian is likely to respond to a request for specific information by reading a sentence or a paragraph word for word, very likely one extracted from a dictionary or an encyclopedia of some kind.

Fact Retrieval Considered as Retrieval of Processed Data If someone wishes to mean by "fact retrieval" simply the retrieval of sentences or short texts word for word as they were stored and by "document retrieval" simply the retrieval of longer texts word for word as they were stored, he is of course free to do so. He must, however, allow that there is an interesting kind of information retrieval which is neither document retrieval nor fact retrieval, viz., information retrieval which is not limited to output of texts word for word as they were recorded in the file and which may subject texts (natural language or other) to more or less intensive analysis and processing before responding to a question. A distinction must perforce be made between an information-retrieval system which has only rote memory and one which has something more. It will be convenient to refer to the retrieval of unprocessed texts as document retrieval whether the texts involved are short or long and to reserve the concept of fact retrieval for systems which are capable of processing in one form or another the texts stored in their files. (As will be seen shortly, document-retrieval systems can be considered as a subclass of fact-retrieval systems, but the distinction being made here can be kept clear if it is remembered that the texts which are processed by a document-retrieval system considered as a fact-retrieval system are texts *about* the documents on file, not the texts *of* the documents on file.)

In rejecting the position that fact retrieval is only a special kind of document retrieval concerned with short documents, we put aside the suggestion that a fact is simply what is expressed by a declarative sentence. We shall be concerned instead with amplifying and examining a more defensible suggestion: A fact is a nonarbitrary association of an individual (or of an ordered group of individuals) with a datum (i.e., with a sequence of symbols).

Let us consider some members of the extension of fact-retrieval systems as we refer to them here. One would be a system which simply takes input which is a coded version of such natural-language expressions as *Los Angeles to Sacramento,* 7 *minutes; Los Angeles to Boston,* 4 *minutes; Las Vegas to Los Angeles, collect,* 4 *minutes.* Rather than outputting part or all of these expressions (though it may, if requested, be able to do this also) it answers questions with expressions quite different from those comprising its input. A possible response might be *Mr. J. Green, you owe your telephone company* $23.17. The more interesting fact-retrieval systems, however, are able to analyze and to process in ways several orders of magnitude more complicated than the way required for this response. There are fact-retrieval systems which, given information in store, can from this information combine, summarize, generalize, draw inferences, discover relationships, suggest hypotheses, test hypotheses, etc. The best examples of such high-powered fact-retrieval systems are certain human beings. (Of course, many, if not most, human beings behave more like malfunctioning document-retrieval systems whose main output is a garbled but otherwise unprocessed version of their input.)

The class of fact-retrieval systems illustrated above is so large and ill-defined that attention must be limited to a more precisely defined subclass if adequate treatment of technical details is to be possible. The discussion will hereafter be limited to artificial systems specifically designed to respond to questions. Further, in order to get clear about the fundamental structure of such systems, we shall consider only systems without capabilities of inductive inference, learning, concept formation, and other such capabilities which entail structural reorganization in response to input.[5] It is important to clarify the structure of such systems before proceeding to the higher-order problems posed by systems with evolving structure. The subclass of fact-retrieval systems with which we are concerned may be termed the class of *structurally fixed question-answering* (SFQA) *systems.* Exactly what is meant by this expression will become clear as the discussion proceeds and as examples of such systems are adduced. At this point the following clarifying remarks will suffice:

1 Let us take some examples of question-answering systems which would *not* be structurally fixed. Consider the following (possible) dialogue:

> HUMAN *Does X have Y?* (question *Q*)
> QUESTION-ANSWERING MACHINE *According to Source S, X obtained Y on Date D.*
> HUMAN *Don't bother me with such unreliable information. Tell me instead that you don't know.*

Suppose the machine modifies its processing programs so that next time when it is asked *Q* and it has no relevant information additional to that provided by *S,* it answers *I don't know.* In at least a simple-minded sense this machine could be said to have learned. Suppose the machine modifies its processing programs so that, not only with *Q* and *S* specifically, but also with sources such as *S* and questions such as *Q* it answers *I don't know.* In at least a simple-minded sense this machine could be said to have formed a concept.

2 In actual practice, of course, the structure of the artificial systems we are talking about will of practical necessity be constantly changing,

[5]The author is inclined to agree with Bar-Hillel that proposals concerning artificial systems or machines with such capabilities are "science fiction type" (Bar-Hillel, *op. cit.*, fn. 2) but I do not agree with his apparently pejorative use of this characterization. Research in connection with such proposals will almost certainly be—to a limited extent already has been—fruitful, not because practical machines (e.g., "inductive inference machines," *cf.* C. N. Mooers, "The Next Twenty Years in Information Retrieval: Some Goals and Predictions," *Proceedings of the Western Joint Computer Conference,* pp. 81–86, New York, 1959) will issue from it in the next twenty years, but rather because it is a strategic way to approach basic research on the subjects of inductive inference, learning, etc.

but only as a result of human intervention. What is primarily meant to be precluded by the modifier *structurally fixed* is *self-modification of structure.*

We shall consider six aspects of SFQA systems in our characterization of them. Given that they are systems for storing, processing, and retrieving information, we shall consider:

The language used to carry the information
The file used to store the information (the data file)
The indexes and dictionaries which provide access to the data file (the language files)
Kinds and methods of input of information into the data file
Kinds and methods of retrieval of information from the data file
Kinds and methods of display of retrieved information

LANGUAGES FOR STRUCTURALLY FIXED QUESTION-ANSWERING [SFQA] SYSTEMS

The Domain of Discourse We shall call the class of objects about which an SFQA system contains information *the domain of discourse of the system.* This domain of discourse, in other words, is the class of individuals which are described by the system, the class of individuals about which the system is able to answer (at least some) questions. To indicate the possible use of SFQA systems, let us consider possible domains of discourse. For a police system, the domain might consist (primarily)[6] of people with criminal records. For a system concerned with making conveniently accessible the medical histories of patients, the domain might again consist (primarily) of people. Other systems whose domains would consist (primarily) of people would be those for answering questions about corporation or government personnel experience, capabilities, performances, etc. For a chemotherapy research system, a (primary) member of the domain of discourse might be a particular experiment—e.g., an experiment designed to test the effect of a particular chemical compound on a particular kind of tumor. For a legal system, the domain of discourse might consist (primarily) of court decisions or of laws or of sections of laws.[7] For a business intelligence system, the domain of discourse might consist (primarily) of inventory items or of products (perhaps competitors' products) or of retail outlets. For a meteorological system, the domain of discourse might consist (primarily) of areas on the earth's surface (e.g., degree squares). Finally, for a library system, the domain of discourse might consist (primarily) of documents.[8] In many cases,

[6]This qualification will be explained below.

[7]*Cf.* L. Mehl, "Automation in the Legal World," *Proceedings of a Symposium on Mechanization of Thought Processes,* pp. 755–779, London, 1959.

[8]To relate this to our earlier discussion of the difference between document retrieval and fact retrieval, we consider document retrieval to be a special kind of

however, where the domain of discourse of a question-answering system ostensibly consists (primarily) of documents, it will be convenient to think of the system in another manner. Such cases arise when the documents involved are not described as wholes and in a general manner but rather their contents are intensively analyzed for assertions to be stored in the system; the domain of discourse thus would consist not of the documents as such, but of the objects referred to by these assertions. (A good mark of such a system is undemocratic treatment of the documents involved. In such a system, the same amount and kind of information is not stored for each document; how much and what kind is stored for a particular document depends entirely on the objects the document talks about and what it says about them.) Thus, in the case of the question-answering system being studied and developed by the Patent Office[9] it is best to think of the domain of discourse as (primarily) consisting not of the patent disclosures themselves but rather of the mechanisms, processes, substances, etc., which are the subjects of the disclosures.

In the actual design of a question-answering system, various and difficult problems arise concerning the extent to which the domain of discourse should be restricted. We shall assume that for any given system there is some relatively homogeneous class of objects which comprise the objects of primary concern for users of the system, e.g., the class of criminals, the class of patients, the class of laws, etc.[10] These objects of primary concern we call the *primary members* of the domain of discourse. It becomes necessary in even the simplest of systems, however, to store information

---

fact retrieval. The usual kind of document-retrieval system is to be considered a kind of question-answering system where the answers desired are the names of particular individuals in the domain of discourse, i.e., the names of certain documents which satisfy certain conditions.

[9] *Cf.* S. M. Newman, *Problems in Mechanizing the Search in Examining Patent Applications,* Washington, 1956; *Storage and Retrieval of Contents of Technical Literature,* Washington, 1956; "Storage and Retrieval of Contents of Technical Literature, First Supplementary Report," *Patent Office Research and Development Report No.* 4, Washington, 1957; "Linguistic Problems in Mechanization of Patent Searching," *Patent Office Research and Development Report No.* 9, Washington, n.d.; "Analysis of Prepositionals for Interrelational Concepts, Preliminary Study," *Patent Office Research and Development Report No.* 16, Washington, 1959.

[10] The assumption does not reduce the generality of what we say in any important sense. We make the assumption only for purposes of simplifying our presentation. It should not be difficult for the reader to figure out how the presentation would have to be modified to account for systems containing information about distinctly different kinds of objects—e.g., patients *and* hospitals—where objects of one of the kinds can in no sense be considered as parts or complexes of objects of another of the kinds.

about parts of these primary members, about complexes composed of several primary members, and about occurrences in which these primary members are involved. It is extremely awkward linguistically to treat this as information directly concerning the primary members themselves. (Perhaps a more helpful way of stating this problem is to say that some of the sentences carrying the information in the system, if stated in a natural and idiomatic manner, have as their subjects and objects, not the names of primary members of the domain of discourse, but rather the names of parts or complexes of these primary members or the names of occurrences in which these primary members are involved.) Consequently it becomes necessary to introduce into the domain these parts, complexes, and occurrences. In the case of a medical system, we might introduce brains, livers, etc., in addition to the patients who are the primary members; we might introduce complexes of patients related to each other in certain definite ways, e.g., a complex consisting of a man, his wife, and their children; and we might introduce occurrences in which patients are involved, e.g., an operation a patient has had, an accident he has been in, or a case of measles he has suffered.[11]

[11]The distinction between complexes composed of several primary members and occurrences in which more than one primary member is involved is not a precise one. In everyday talking, whether we treat the subject of some assertion as a complex or as an occurrence often appears a matter of arbitrary choice; thus if we assert something about a man and wife, we may be free to treat this as information about a marriage (an occurrence) in which they are involved or as information about a family (a complex) which they constitute. A rough distinction might be made on the basis of how long something lasts, but this provides no easy means of distinguishing a short-lived complex from a long-lasting occurrence. While this is an important problem, for purposes of this discussion we shall make no distinction between complexes and occurrences; what we say about treatment of one in a fact-retrieval system applies to treatment of the other. A subject of information in such a system need not be designated as an occurrence or a complex, and it is sufficient simply to mark it as being an occurrence/complex relative to primary members of the domain of discourse.

In allowing complexes and occurrences (i.e., sets of primary members connected together by some definite relationship or, in the case of some occurrences, specially characterized unit sets each containing only a single primary member) in a domain of discourse, we are already requiring for our language something logically stronger than a simple first-order functional calculus. No special trouble arises, however, until we introduce into a domain classes that are only intensionally defined, e.g., in the case of a medical system we might wish to introduce into our domain the class of patients with diabetic ancestry or the class of patients who have had their tonsils removed. Theoretical and practical problems do occur when a domain of discourse is broadened in this manner, and they are apparently unavoidable in any question-answering system of reasonable sophistication.

For variables ranging over members of a domain of discourse we shall use symbols from the sequences

$$x, x_1, x_2, \ldots ; y, y_1, y_2, \ldots ; z, z_1, \ldots ; w, w_1, \ldots$$

For names of the members of a domain of discourse we shall use symbols from the sequences

$$a, a_1, a_2, \ldots ; b, b_1, b_2, \ldots ; c, c_1, \ldots ; \mathrm{d}, \mathrm{d}_1, \ldots$$

Facts Involving Individuals in the Domain of Discourse In order to define what we mean when we talk of facts, we first have to define three auxiliary expressions, *datum, datum type,* and *fact function.* By *datum* we mean some particular finite sequence of symbols. Examples are symbol sequences such as "11010001101101110", "439.7", "*QA*610.6*G*", *green,* "16$*/*T*", etc. by *datum type* we mean a set of data all of the same form, e.g., the set containing the *separate* data *F, F, F, F,* etc.[12] By *fact function* we mean a grouping which associates, for each moment of time and according to some definite rule, each member of a domain of discourse (or each n-tuple of members for some n) with one and only one particular datum type. Each association in such a grouping we mark off with angular brackets. Examples of fact functions are the sets

$$\{< a,t_1, \text{“} + 1\text{”} >, < b,t_1, \text{“} - 1\text{”} >, < c,t_1, \text{“} - 1\text{”} >, \ldots\}$$

and

$$\{\ldots, < a,t_3, \text{“120/90”} >, < b,t_3, \text{“130/90”} >, < c,t_3, \text{“135/95”}\}$$

The associations which constitute any particular fact function are determined by the meaning of some term, i.e., the definite rule which determines the associations in any particular fact function is derived from the meaning of some term. Such a term we call a *predicate.* By *fact*

[12]The distinction being made here between the meaning of *datum* and the meaning of *datum type* corresponds to the conventionally made distinction between a symbol token and a symbol type. However, we shall speak imprecisely in some cases and shall consider a symbol-sequence token and several of its transforms as being the same datum, e.g., a numeral "10" assigned to some individual as an indication of its length will be considered the same datum in human-readable form, in decimal form on punched cards, and in binary form on magnetic tape. Similarly, all these different representations of the numeral will be considered as belonging to the same datum type. What ties the different representations together and makes it convenient, even necessary, to consider them as all being the same datum is that they all carry the same meaning, i.e., in the example suggested, they are all indications of the length of some particular individual and they are all completely translatable one into another by definite and well-defined transformation operations.

we shall mean a member of a fact function, i.e., (in the nontechnical terms which we are using) a fact is taken as some one item in the grouping which is a fact function. Thus, given the above examples of fact functions,

$$< b,t_1, \text{“} -1\text{”} > \qquad \text{and} \qquad < a,t_3, \text{“}120/90\text{”} >$$

are facts.[13] In order to assert the existence of a fact we identify a predicate and assert that, in the fact function determined by this predicate, a particular individual or *n*-tuple is associated with a particular datum type at a particular time. Assume that the predicate determining the first example above is *P*. Then to assert the existence of the first listed fact in the example we would say,

P *of* a *at* t_1 *is* "+ 1"

We should examine more closely the form taken by expressions which assert the existence of facts, expressions such as

P *of* a *at* t_1 *is* "+ 1"

This expression has the same form as such ordinary-language expressions as

the length of a is five feet

or

the price of a is four dollars

The language of mathematics also provides us with expressions of this same form; for example,

the sine of a is .45

or

the square root of a is 4

[13] In the technical terms of set theory, we define a fact function for unary predicates as a function associated with a particular unary predicate in a way such that the domain of the function is the Cartesian product of some given domain of discourse and the set of moments of time such that the range of the function is a set of datum types, and such that the value of the function for any ordered couple in the function's domain is assigned to the couple according to some definite rule derived from the meaning of the predicate. A fact is then simply taken to be a member of a fact function. Modifications necessary to generalize this definition to *n*-ary predicates for any *n* are obvious.

In mathematics the expression

the sine of a is .45

is abbreviated as

$sin\ (a) = .45$

In the present discussion a fact assertion, for example,

P of a at t_1 *is* "+ 1"

will be correspondingly abbreviated

$P\,(a,t_1)$ *is* "+ 1"

The one important difference between the fact assertion and its counterpart from trigonometry is that the subexpression to the right of the identity sign (= or *is*) is bounded by quotation marks in the case of the fact assertion but not in the case of the trigonometric expression. This is a consequence of our definition of fact functions and facts. Fact functions associate sequences of symbols with individuals or *n*-tuples. Thus

$P\,(a,t_1)$ *is* "+1"

asserts that a certain fact function associates the symbol sequence "+ 1" with *a* for the moment t_1; it does *not* assert that this fact function associates the number + 1 with *a*. The trigonometric expression, on the other hand, asserts an association of *a* with the number .45, *not* an association of *a* with the numeral (the symbol sequence) ".45".

To understand how the meaning of a predicate determines a fact function, we begin with the simplest kind of predicate, a predicate whose meaning divides the domain of discourse into three classes—a class of objects which have a certain property, a class of objects which do not have that property, and a class of objects which cannot meaningfully be said to have or not to have the property. Thus the predicate *biwinged* would divide a vehicular domain of discourse into planes having two wings, planes not having two wings, and vehicles which are not planes. Or the predicate *schizophrenic* would divide a domain of discourse consisting, among other things, of people and their parts into people possessing the symptoms of schizophrenia, people not possessing these symptoms, and objects (brains, livers, etc.) which cannot meaningfully be said to have or not to have the symptoms of schizophrenia. Consider such a predicate *P* and its defining property on the basis of which the domain of discourse can be divided into three classes. We can think of a fact function's being formed for P by successively taking each moment m of time[14] and then, in turn, successively taking for m each individual i in the domain of discourse and associating with i for m one datum type if i has the defining property at m; associating with i for m a second datum type if i does not have the defining property at m; and associating with i for m a third datum type if i cannot meaningfully be said to have or not to have the defining property. A useful choice of datum type for the first case is "+ 1", for the second is "— 1", and for the third is *NA*. It should be clearly understood, however, that *yes, no,* and *not applicable;* or *T, F,* and *NA*; or "1", "0", and "— 7" would do quite as well.[15] Suppose we choose "+ 1", "— 1", and *NA*. Then the expression

$P(a)$ *is* "+ 1"

asserts that a has the defining property.[16] The expression

$P(a)$ *is* "— 1"

asserts that a does not have the defining property. And the expression

$P(a)$ *is* "*NA*"

asserts that a cannot meaningfully be said to have or not to have the defining property.[17]

[14]It is, of course, a physical impossibility actually to list all members of a fact function, even a fact function of the simplest kind. This is, however, quite beside the point of our characterization of a fact function as a theoretical construct.

[15]Henceforth in our examples we shall use "+1", "—1", and *NA* as the datum types assigned in the case of predicates where the choice of datum type indicates presence, absence, or nonapplicability of a simple binary property. This should not be construed as meaning that for the examples the choice of the particular datum types is nonarbitrary. It is done only so that the stipulation of datum types used can be avoided each time an example is adduced.

[16]In many of our examples for the sake of simplicity we omit reference to time.

[17]In every case in the present discussion we use an expression such as $P(a)$ as a name (of a function value) rather than as a sentence. Divergence from widespread convention is justified on grounds that (1) ambiguity will not arise because expressions such as $P(a)$ will not be used as sentences, rather the synonymous expressions asserting existence of facts will be used; and (2) it is very convenient to treat all predicates on a par, i.e., to form functors from predicates corresponding to binary, classificatory concepts in exactly the same manner as they are formed from predicates corresponding to quantitative and other kinds of concepts. The second point will be amplified in the sequel.

Perhaps a word or two should be said relating the present proposal to technical philosophy: The proposal is related to but not identical with the traditional position that a fact is what is designated by a true sentence. One reason

In this discussion the term *fact functor* (or where no confusion will result, the term *functor*) refers to an expression of the form $P(x,t)$. We shall use the term *datum identifier* to refer to an expression of the form $P(a,t_1)$, i.e., an expression which results from a functor when the variables in the argument places of the functor are replaced with names of particular individuals. As is apparent from what has been said, no fact functor has fewer than two argument places. Even a functor based on what in ordinary language is a simple one-place predicate (i.e., a predicate expression which contains no objects and requires only a single subject) has two argument places, one for the name of an individual in the domain of discourse and one for a time indicator. We shall sometimes, however, omit reference to time when it is not necessary for the point of discussion and shall elliptically write fact functors and datum identifiers, e.g., $P(x)$ and $P(a)$, without any argument place for time.

We have seen how the meaning of a simple one-place predicate determines a fact function and what kind of a fact functor is formed from such a predicate. Let us examine the fact functions and functors associated with more complicated kinds of predicates. A completely general definition of fact involves possible use of functors with more than two argument places; possible use of functors formed from predicates for other than binary, classificatory concepts; and possible use, for datum types with which a fact function associates individuals or *n*-tuples, of sequences of symbols much longer and more complicated than the sequences *T, NA, yes,* "0", "+ 1", etc. Allowing many-place functors is simple enough. The point is that the entities with which a fact function associates datum types need not be single members of a domain of discourse but may be *n*-tuples of such single individuals. Thus the two-place predicate *father* might result in a fact function which associates "+ 1" with a 2-tuple (an ordered couple) of individuals when the first is father of the second; which associates "— 1" with such a 2-tuple when the first is not father of the second; and which associates *NA* with such a 2-tuple when it is meaningless to assert that the first is father of the second. The fact functor associated with this predicate would be *father* (x,y,t) and we would assert the existence of a fact determined by the predicate with an assertion such as

father (*J. Green, T. Green,* t_1) *is* "+ 1"

for lack of identity is that the present proposal would allow $< a,t_1,$ "— 1" $>$ as a fact, whereas the traditional position would say that, rather than determining the form which a fact takes, falsity determines the nonexistence of a fact. A more important reason for lack of identity is that in addition to facts determined by presence or absence of a property (truth or falsity of a sentence), the present proposal postulates facts of much more complicated types. These more complicated types of facts are discussed in the sequel.

A functor with even more argument places is

situated on a road between (x,y,z,t)

which might be used in a fact assertion such as

situated on a road between (Los Angeles, New York, Cleveland, t_1*) is* "— 1"

A point to be noticed in the use of many-place functors and datum identifiers is that the order of occurrence of names in the argument places is significant. Thus

father (J. Green, T. Green, t_1*)*

is an expression different from

father (T. Green, J. Green, t_1*)*

and identifies a different datum.

A general definition of fact involves (1) possible use of functors formed from predicates for other than binary, classificatory concepts, and (2) possible use, for datum types with which a fact function associates individuals or *n*-tuples, of long and complicated symbol sequences. A fact function may be, in effect, an empirical measure function,[18] a naming function, or any other kind of function which assigns sequences of symbols to individuals or to *n*-tuples of individuals. In a fact function which is an empirical measure function the definite rule according to which datum types are associated with individuals or *n*-tuples is a set of procedures involving measuring instruments and possibly calculations. Such a fact function is the one determined by the predicate *length* for which the

[18]C. G. Hempel ("Fundamentals of Concept Formation in the Empirical Sciences," *International Encyclopedia of Unified Science,* vol. II, no. 7, Chicago, 1952) would probably respond to the present suggestion as he responds to a related suggestion by Stevens—i.e., by asserting that an empirical measure function could not be what we have called a fact function because the former does not assign symbols to individuals or *n*-tuples of individuals as does the latter. Rather than assigning numerals, he says, it assigns numbers. It is possible, however, to consider an empirical measure function as one which assigns numerals rather than numbers so long as we are careful in our manner of speaking and do not obscure the fact that the numeral assigned to an individual or *n*-tuple by an empirical measure function is assigned because of properties possessed by the number which the numeral names and not because of properties possessed by the numeral per se. A more serious theoretical difficulty arises in cases where it may be desirable to conceive of measure functions as associating individuals or *n*-tuples with real numbers. There are not numerals for all real numbers. This is not a practical difficulty, however, because for practical purposes one can consider such functions as assigning numerals which name approximating rational numbers.

corresponding fact functor is *length* (x,t). The symbol sequences which this function associates with individuals in the domain of discourse are numerals. A fact in this fact function might be $< a, t_1, \text{“200”} >$. We would assert the existence of this fact with the expression

length (a,t_1) *is* "200"

A fact function also based on empirical measurement but requiring a functor with more argument places is the one whose functor is

distance between (x,y,t)

The datum type which a fact function associates with individuals or *n*-tuples may be more complicated than a simple numeral. Thus the datum types involved in the fact function determined by the predicate *blood pressure* have the form "130/90". We would even allow such complicated datum types as digitally expressed electrocardiographs. A fact in a fact function using such complicated datum types might be $< a, t_1, \text{“-------”} >$, where in the place of the dashes we have a very long series of numerals representing observations of a continuous time series, and we would assert the existence of this fact with the expression

EKG (a,t_1) is "-------"

Finally, the datum types associated with individuals or *n*-tuples by a fact function need not be numerical sequences but might be alphabetical or partly alphabetical and partly numerical. These possibilities are illustrated by the following expressions, all of which are assertions of the existence of facts in permissible fact functions:

christian name (J. Green, t_1*) is "John Thomas"*
address (J. Green, t_1*) is* "1333 *Westwood Boulevard, Los Angeles* 24"
price (a,t_1) *is* "$103.99"

In general, any finite sequence of symbols can occur as a datum type in a fact so long as the sequence is of a kind appropriate for the fact function involved. It is convenient to think of there being a single fact function for an entire family of properties rather than of there being a separate function for each separate member of such a family. This means that we use sequences of symbols such as *red, green,* etc., as datum types assigned by fact functions, and rather than having a fact assertion

red (a,t_1) *is* "+ 1"

we have one such as

color (a,t_1) *is "red"*

It might be suggested that it is also only a matter of convenience to think of fact functions, functors, and assertions so that we have fact assertions such as

length (a,t_1) *is* "10,000"

rather than

10,000 *units long* (a,t_1) *is* "+ 1"

The suggestion is correct but the convenience involved is very great. It is helpful both practically and conceptually to use expressions such as the former rather than the latter. The practical reason is that the number of predicates in our language must be kept at a workable level. To have infinitely many predicates, as we would have if we used expressions of the latter kind, would be to exceed this level. The conceptual reason is that it is necessary for certain purposes to distinguish between symbols which *represent* data and symbols which *interpret* data. That is, it is necessary for certain purposes to distinguish between symbols which *carry information* and symbols which *control information processing*. (Any particular symbol or sequence of symbols may, of course, serve sometimes in one role and sometimes in another, depending on context.) Given our present definitions, symbols which occur in datum identifiers, both in the predicate designator and in the argument designators, are serving in an *interpretive* role, and those which occur as data indicating a fact-function assignment are serving in a *representative* role.

Fact Assertions and Fact Denials So far we have said that, given a fact $< a, t_1,$ "19AQ" $>$ as a member of a fact function for a predicate R, we assert the existence of this fact with an expression such as

$R\,(a,t_1)$ *is* "19AQ"

In the actual case, however, one is seldom interested in a singular fact, for a singular fact as we have defined it has to do only with a single moment of time. We introduce the concept of a fact history by which we mean a set of facts such that (1) all the facts in the set belong to the same fact function; (2) all the facts in the set involve the same member or n-tuple of members of the domain of discourse; and (3) the set contains all the facts in this function and about this member or n-tuple for some continuous interval of time. An expression which asserts something about a single fact history we call an *atomic fact assertion*. In general, an atomic fact assertion has the form

$R\,(x_1, \ldots, x_n, I)$ *is* "$S_1 \ldots S_m$"

where a designation of a time interval is put in the place of I and the part of the expression represented by *is* "$S_1 \ldots S_m$" may be a fairly complicated expression depending on the nature of the datum types assigned by the fact function determined by R. The only restriction put on the part of the expression represented by *is* "$S_1 \ldots S_m$" is that it refer to the datum types assigned by the fact function for R and that it refer to them definitely enough so that the fact assertion in which it occurs is either true or false. An example of an atomic fact assertion is

R (*a*, 1-27-61) *is* "18" *or* "19"

which says that for every moment m in the day 1-27-61, $R(a,m)$ is either "18" or "19". Another example is

R (*a*, *before* 1-27-61) *is less than* "18"

which can be interpreted as meaningful if we assume a particular meaning for *is less than* in reference to the numerals assigned as datum types by the fact function for R.[19] Depending, of course, on the range of these numerals, a possible interpretation is that for every moment m prior to the day 1-27-61, $R(a,m)$ is in the range of positive-integer numerals from 1 through 17. It may be that an expression such as

Q (*b*, 1-27-61) *is less than "John"*

though it has the proper form, is not a permissible atomic fact assertion because the phrase *is less than* does not have a definite meaning relative to the symbol sequences assigned as datum types by the fact function for Q. How it is determined in an SFQA system whether such a phrase has a definite meaning will be discussed later.

An expression which negates an atomic fact assertion we call an *atomic fact denial.* An expression which is a truth-functional combination of atomic fact assertions and/or atomic fact denials we call a *molecular fact assertion.*[20]

[19]It should be noticed that this meaning corresponds to but is not the same as the meaning of the phrase *is less than* in reference to numbers.

[20]We would have to add a fairly long section to our present discussion if we were to go into all the details concerning molecular fact assertions which are of importance for an SFQA system. We shall attend mainly to atomic assertions in the present discussion with only a few general observations about molecular assertions. A point worth noting is that sometimes a molecular fact assertion might be synonymous for all practical intents and purposes, with a certain atomic fact assertion. This would be so, for instance, in the case of a given atomic assertion and a molecular assertion which is the conjunction of two atomic assertions each of which asserts what the given atomic assertion does, but refers only to a bounded half of the time interval referred to by the given assertion. The conjunction may say nothing about the bounding moments which divide the original interval, but these may represent an unobservably small span of time and hence be of no practical significance. Another point worth observing is that so long as we have not introduced quantification over fact assertions,

Predicates of an SFQA System Language We have said little about the linguistic nature of the predicates which occur in fact functors and datum identifiers and whose meanings determine the assignments of datum types made by fact functions. These predicates may be syntactically quite complicated or may be single ordinary-language terms. Whether they are complicated or simple will depend on the requirements and limitations of the particular SFQA system involved. Examples of simple predicates are those in the functors *length* (x,t), *direction* (x,t), *male* (x,t), *schizophrenic* (x,t), etc. Examples of more complicated predicates are those in the functors *distance between* (x,y,t), *railroad served* (x,t), *protected by burglar alarm* (x,t), etc. Examples of even more complicated predicates are those in the functors *number of engine nacelles on* (x,t), *vehicles on roads serving* (x,t), *number of vehicles on roads serving* (x,t), etc. Let us examine some of these examples and see what considerations would be involved in deciding to use a syntactically complicated predicate in an unanalyzed manner as opposed to using, in effect, a combination of simpler predicates. We introduce the expression

$$\eta x\ (P(x)\ is\ \text{“}S\text{”})$$

for indefinite descriptions—i.e., to mean: an individual x such that the

we can conveniently divide fact assertions and denials according to levels. On the first level we place atomic assertions and denials and conjunctions of atomic assertions and/or atomic denials. On the second level we place truth-functional combinations of first-level expressions, on the third combinations of second-level expressions, on the fourth combinations of third-level expressions, etc. It is possible to reduce all expressions on third or higher levels at least to second-level expressions by putting them in what is called disjunctive normal form. In the terms presently being used, a second-level expression in disjunctive normal form is a disjunction, all of whose disjuncts are first-level expressions. The point is that in an SFQA system it is convenient to treat all molecular fact assertions as second-level expressions in disjunctive normal form. We can also mention here the practical problems involved in introducing, in an SFQA-system language, quantification over fact assertions; e.g., (1) the problem of how and where to store quantified assertions relative to how and where particular fact assertions are stored and (2) the retrieval problem of efficient consultation of the part of the file storing quantified expressions whenever information is being retrieved about some particular individual in the domain of discourse. Such problems are so serious that often it is best to avoid quantification altogether, at least within the part of the SFQA system with which humans have no contact; to use a disjunction, with a disjunct for every member of the domain of discourse, instead of an existentially quantified statement; and to use, instead of a universally quantified statement, a conjunction with a conjunct for every member of the domain of discourse to which the statement applies, i.e., to every member which is not excluded by a protasis. However, this course is not usable if membership in the domain of discourse is indefinite.

datum assigned to x by the fact function for P is S. Then, rather than using the unanalyzed *railroad served* (x), we might use

serves ($\eta\gamma$ (*railroad* (γ) *is* "+ 1"), x)

In terms of ordinary language expressions, this is equivalent to saying *a railroad serves x* rather than saying *x is railroad served.* Another way of portraying the syntactical structure of the predicate *railroad served* would be with an existential quantifier—i.e., the quantifier in the expression $\exists x$ ($P(x)$ *is* "S") interpreted to mean: there is an individual x such that the datum assigned to x by the fact function for P is S. Then rather than using the unanalyzed *railroad served* (x), we might use

$\exists y$ ((*railroad* (y) *is* "+ 1") *and* (*serves* (y,x))

In terms of ordinary language expressions, this is equivalent to saying *there is a railroad which serves x* rather than saying *x is railroad served.* A third method of breaking down this predicate *railroad served* into simpler predicates would occur in an SFQA system which has proper names for railroads.[21] In such a system, in place of such a single unanalyzed assertion as

railroad served (a) *is* "+ 1"

there will be two separate assertions

railroad (b) *is* "+ 1"

and

serves (b,a) *is* "+ 1"

In one of these three ways, then, we would avoid using in an unanalyzed manner a syntactically complicated predicate like *railroad served* and use instead an explicitly articulated complex of the simpler predicates *railroad* and *serves.* Of the three methods, the third is almost certainly to be preferred if the SFQA system involved satisfies the conditions necessary for its use. The value of using either of the first two methods is that the syntactical structure of a complicated predicate may be exploitable in retrieval. It should be observed that the expression which portrays the syntactical structure of a complicated predicate need not be used whenever that predicate is used. Rather, the syntax-revealing expression need occur only once in some dictionary, and at other places in the SFQA system the predicate can be represented by a simple expression which the dictionary defines.

[21]As will be explained in the next section, the practical meaning of an SFQA system's having proper names for railroads is that the system has separate subfiles for storing fact assertions about separate railroads.

That there happened to be three (and only three straightforward) different methods for breaking down the predicate *railroad served* was an accident of the particular predicate. The indefinite-description operator and the existential quantifier may enter into the syntactical resolution of a complicated predicate in ways quite different from the ways they enter into resolution of *railroad served.* Thus *vehicles on roads serving* (*x*) might be replaced with

$\exists y$ ((*vehicle* (*y*) *is* "+ 1") *and* (*on* (*y*,ηz ((*road* (*z*) *is* "+ 1") *and* (*serves* (*z*,*x*))))))

or it might be replaced with

$\exists y \exists z$ ((*vehicle* (*y*) *is* "+ 1") *and* (*road* (*z*) *is* "+ 1") *and* (*on* (*y*,*z*) *is* "+ 1") *and* (*serves* (*z*,*x*)))

There are other possible replacements as well. A functor such as

number of vehicles on roads serving (*x*)

or

average length of vehicles on roads serving (*x*)

has an even more complicated syntactical structure and to portray it we would have to introduce a class-abstraction operator.[22]

DATA FILES FOR SFQA SYSTEMS

Storage of Data An SFQA system works with what we have called fact assertions. Speaking roughly, it can be said that such a system exists for the purpose of storing, processing, and retrieving these assertions. More precisely, what such a system stores, processes, and retrieves are data which, according to these assertions, represent fact-function assignments of datum types to individuals or *n*-tuples of individuals in the system's domain of discourse. A central part of the system will be the stored-data file. This data file, other files (discussed in the next section, "Language Files for SFQA Systems"), and programs of an SFQA system must be organized so that when the system is presented with a datum identifier it will know where to find the identified datum and how to interpret it. There are, of course, many ways in which the data file of an SFQA sys-

[22]The use of existential quantifiers to help portray the syntactical structure of predicates in an SFQA-system language is not the same thing as using them to range over fact assertions in such a language (see fn. 20). Further, introducing the class-abstraction operator to help portray the syntactical structure of predicates is not the same thing as introducing into our domain of discourse classes only intensionally defined (see fn. 11). In one case these operators bind variables within predicates and in the other they bind variables occurring in the argument places of functors formed from predicates.

tem can be organized. The optimal organization will depend on the primary functions of the system, and it may prove advantageous to have different parts of the file organized differently so that one part can respond efficiently to one kind of demand and another part to another kind. Heterogeneous organization of this kind might entail duplicating data and storing the same datum in several different places in a file. We shall consider the alternative possibilities of data-file organization[23] with a few general clarifying remarks.

An SFQA system will, in effect, have a proper name for each known member of the domain of discourse. This may be a numeral or it may be a sequence of alphabetic symbols—e.g., *John Green* (though it is unlikely that such a sequence would uniquely designate in a system with a very large domain of discourse). The only requirement for such proper names is that each one must uniquely designate.[24] We can think of the data file as containing a separate subfile for each individual for which the system has a proper name. Of course, the physical organization of an actual data file may be such that parts of the subfile for any given individual are physically quite separate from each other. This is the case, for instance, if all data identified with datum identifiers using the same predicate are stored together. On the other hand, if all the data in the subfile for each individual are stored together, it may be unnecessary actually to represent the proper names of individuals within the file, because physical locations of the subfiles can be utilized as implicit names. Subfiles might be stored in sequence along a tape, for instance, so that the storage sequence corresponds to the sequence of serial numbers naming the individuals. It is important to recognize that within its data file, an SFQA system needs, in one form or another, proper names of the specific individuals about which it is able to answer questions as a means of relating data that refer to the same individual. A serious practical problem for an SFQA system is that when new data are being entered into the file it may sometimes be impossible to associate them with previously entered data with the result that the existence of a relevant subfile may

[23]*Cf.* Kellogg, *op. cit.,* fn. 1.

[24]The names used in an actual system may or may not carry information, e.g., information about the geographical locations of the individuals named. If they do, it is important to think of the naming function of the name as separate from the information-carrying function and to think of the latter as resulting in an atypical (and probably quite compact) storage of certain fact assertions. For instance, if the SFQA system is a document-retrieval system and Library of Congress (or UDC) call numbers are used as proper names for the objects in the system's domain of discourse, it is important to distinguish between the naming function of the call numbers (which function could be performed quite as well by arbitrary serial numbers) and the categorizing function of the call numbers.

not be determined and a new subfile is mistakenly created. Such a case might arise, for instance, when information is being entered in a police-data file about the perpetrator of a newly reported crime. Obviously, a primary goal of some SFQA systems is coalescence of separate subfiles into one, subfiles which are separate because of lack of information. For at least some kinds of SFQA systems there are input techniques available which reduce to a minimum spurious addition of new individuals to the domain of discourse (see the last section of this discussion).

Finally, consider the following principle of data-file organization: When the domain of discourse consists of parts of primary members as well as the primary members, it will almost certainly be found advantageous to have nesting within the data file which reflects the part-whole relationships involved—i.e., to have the subfiles for parts included within the subfiles for the respective primary members (or for the larger parts).

Storing and Utilizing Second-order Information We have said that an SFQA system stores data which, according to certain fact assertions, represents fact-function assignments of datum types to individuals or n-tuples of individuals in the system's domain of discourse. It is important to recognize that our knowledge of the datum types which a fact function associates with individuals according to the meaning of a predicate may be quite incomplete. A fact assertion does not assure the existence of a fact. The fact assertion may be true or false. Consequently, it is necessary for an SFQA system to handle second-order information and probably to make it explicitly available to users of the system so that they have a means of determining the credibility and dependability of the answers with which the system provides them. In general, we can say that if an SFQA system is to be complete, it must store an identification of the source for each fact assertion, an indicator of the reliability of the report represented by the assertion, and the time of the report. Thus, in a complete system the form of the information which is stored in the case of any given fact assertion is the following:

S,R,T: $P(x_1, \ldots, x_n,t)$ *is* "$S_1 \cdots S_m$"

Such an expression is equivalent to

At time T source S reported that $P(x_1, \ldots, x_n,t)$ is "$S_1 \cdots S_m$"; the reliability of this report is indicated by R.

We have already discussed the nature of the fact assertion. Consider now the nature of the triple S,R,T which precedes it.

S ranges over sources. What the sources are will, of course, depend on the particular SFQA system and on the kind of input used for getting information into store. The sources may be persons, documents, measuring instruments, or something more complicated—e.g., the complex of a-particular-person-reading-a-particular-document. In the case of large

SFQA systems it may be helpful to set up what amounts to a separate, subsidiary SFQA system to keep a record of sources. Thus, if the main system is one for storing patients' medical histories, the subsidiary system may be for recording data about doctors, their training, their specialties, the fees they charge, how well their diagnoses have been borne out by later events, etc. One of the primary uses of such a subsidiary system would be for determining what should be stored in the place of *R* when a particular source originates a fact assertion which is to be entered into the data file of the main system.

R ranges over indicators of reliability. The importance of entering indicators of reliability directly into the data file of a SFQA system is obvious to anyone who has had any practical experience with the problems of fact retrieval. The information put in the place of *R* can take many forms. In cases where the reliability of the answers is crucial because they provide the basis for consequential decisions, the larger part of a data file may be filled with this second-order information. Consider the following examples. Reliability information might indicate such things as: *S*'s degree of confidence in his own report if *S* is a person; *S*'s probable error if *S* is a measuring instrument; *S*'s dependability as determined by whether later experience confirmed *S*'s earlier reports; conditions under which *S* made its report; etc. A reliability indicator *R* might have the simple form "±950" in a case where *S* is a measuring instrument; the simple form ".9" in a case where a human source *S* is estimating the probability of the correctness of his association of "+1" with some individual; or the very complicated form of a series of sentences in ordinary language where a human source *S* is entering reservations about, and qualifications to, some fact assertion which he is entering into the data file. Consider a case where the objects in the domain of discourse are documents and the source is a librarian attaching descriptors to these documents. The librarian might enter for document *d* the fact assertion

about computers (*d*) *is* "+1"

but then enter as *R* the statement

d purports to cover all computers but emphasizes pre-1955 *and American-made models.*

A theoretically significant result of introducing source indicators and reliability indicators to be carried along with fact assertions in an SFQA system is that they provide a basis for applying purifying programs to the fact assertions stored in the system—i.e., for resolving contradictions among different assertions, for culling out unreliable assertions, etc. They also sometimes provide a justification for retaining contradictory assertions in store. Assume that the expressions *probable* and *possible* are usable as reliability indicators for fact assertions containing the predicate L. Then it is imaginable that one would want to keep in his file both of the following expressions even though the fact assertions involved are contradictory:

S_1, *probable,* T_1:L *(a, before* t_1*)* *is* "5"

S_1, *possible,* T_1: L *(a, before* t_1*)* *is* "7"

T ranges over times. T as the time a fact assertion is reported must be distinguished from the time of the fact history referred to by the assertion. The relationship between T and the time t of the asserted facts provides the basis for a simple tense system: If T is before t, the tense of the fact assertion involved is future; if T overlaps t, the tense is present; and if T is later than t, the tense is past. More information would have to be entered into the data file before there would be a reflection of the perfect tenses in natural languages.[25]

Storing Relational Information Certain special problems occur in connection with the storage of relational information in an SFQA data file. Relational information is that information identified by a datum identifier which refers to two or more members of the domain of discourse–i.e., which has argument places for names of two or more members. Examples of such datum identifiers are *distance between (a,b)*, *father (a,b)*, *adjacent (a,b)*, etc.

There are numerous ways in which such information can be entered in a file, and, since the best way will vary with circumstances, they all should be listed. In the following paragraphs, the phrase *relation place* applied to a member of the domain of discourse refers to the location of its name in a relational datum identifier–i.e., indicates whether the name is in the first argument place or the second or the third, etc.

1 The method of interfixes is the method proposed by Newman for the Patent Office SFQA system which is under development.[26] In effect, for each individual i of those referred to by a relational datum identifier, this method stores in the subfile, first, the identified datum, e.g., "+ 1"; second, the relation place of i in the identifier; and third, an interfix number. The same interfix number is stored in each of the subfiles and a retrieval program can discover which individuals are related to which by matching interfix numbers. This "blind retrieval," as Newman calls it, might be workable if the range of subfiles within which an interfix number can be matched is somehow restricted,

[25]See H. Reichenbach, "Analysis of Conversational Language," *Elements of Symbolic Logic,* New York, 1947, pp. 251–354.

[26]See Newman, *op. cit.,* fn. 9.

as it will be in the Patent Office system (i.e., it will be restricted to the small group of subfiles resulting from a particular patent disclosure), but it could be highly inefficient in cases where the related individuals can be any of the individuals in a large domain of discourse.

2 For each individual *i* of those referred to by a relational datum identifier, the method of proper names stores in the subfile, first, the identified datum, e.g., "345" (in case of an identifier like *distance between* (*a,b*)); second, the relation place of *i* in the identifier; and third, the proper names of the *other* individuals referred to by the identifier (and, in some cases, their respective relation places). Thus, continuing the same example, "345", "1", and "*b*" might be stored in the subfile for *a*, and "345", "2", and "*a*" might be stored in the subfile for *b*. The desirability of using this method in many cases provides one of the many good reasons why an SFQA system must have a proper name for each of the individuals in its domain of discourse.

3 In some cases it is important to know only that a particular individual *a* is related to others in a certain way, not to which particular individuals *b, c,* etc., it is so related. In such cases, it is necessary only to store in the subfile for *a* a datum and a relation place and to make no definite reference to *b, c,* etc. Sometimes in such cases, even though it is not necessary to identify *b, c,* etc., it is useful or necessary to describe them in some way. This can be done by storing in the subfile for *a* indefinite descriptions (see the earlier discussion of predicates) as the method of proper names would store proper names (and also storing, in some cases, the relation places of the individuals referred to by these descriptions). This procedure of indefinite reference, in effect, uses as an identifier of a datum in the subfile for *a* an expression such as

adjacent (*a*η*x* (*slum area* (*x*) *is* "+ 1"))

rather than such an expression as *adjacent* (*a,b*). If in some given SFQA system it is never necessary when using a relational predicate to make definite reference to some of the individuals to which the predicate applies, then there are grounds for introducing a syntactically more complicated predicate requiring fewer argument places. Thus if the two-place functor *adjacent* (*x,y*) always occurs in situations where stored information corresponds to the example involving an indefinite description, it will be advantageous to use in its place the one-place functor *adjacent to a slum area* (*x*). The complicated structure of this new predicate will, of course, be displayed in some of the language files of the system.

LANGUAGE FILES FOR SFQA SYSTEMS

The Function of Language Files We have seen that a fact assertion has the form *P* (*x*, . . .) *is* "*S* . . . ". The answers which an SFQA system provides for users primarily consist of the data represented by "*S* . . . ".

However, in providing these answers the system must operate on the predicates represented by *P*. The larger part of the processing of a typical SFQA system will be the processing of the *interpretive* symbols represented by *P* rather than the processing of the *representative* symbols represented by "*S* . . . ". This processing of *interpretive* symbols is necessary to determine where *representative* symbols are to be found and how they can and should be handled after they are found. A distinction exists between SFQA systems of the type we are characterizing and conventional "scientific" data-processing systems, and also between such SFQA systems and conventional "business" data-processing systems. In the first case the distinction is that the large part of the functioning of SFQA systems is data identifying, whereas the large part of the functioning of "scientific" systems is concerned with arithmetically manipulating data after they have been identified. In the second case the distinction is that, though a large part of the functioning of "business" systems may be data identifying, this is done by means of straightforward searching through fixed formats and well-ordered files, while for SFQA systems data identifying may involve much more complexly ordered files and may not be achievable with some few fixed search routines used over and over again; on the contrary, the search routines used are likely to vary greatly depending on the particular questions which the system is called on to answer. In sum, these distinctions mean that the large part of SFQA system functioning is likely to be data identifying and, further, that this data identifying is likely to require a relatively complicated language (to provide access to complexly ordered files) and to require relatively many and complicated routines for processing this language. SFQA systems are thus properly classed as language-data-processing systems.

SFQA systems require language files in order to perform the language-data processing necessary for data identification. These language files should be clearly distinguished from the data files discussed above. The extent to which operation and maintenance of these language files is automated will vary from one SFQA system to another. If such a file stores its contents in human-readable form and can be consulted by human beings without their having to use any of the data-processing machinery of the SFQA system involved, it may be called an *external language file*. An example of an external language file would be a human-readable dictionary relating predicates in an SFQA-system language to terms not in the language. Such a dictionary would be consulted by system users to determine what answers the system might provide for them and how to interpret these answers. Language files which provide linguistic information for the machinery of an SFQA system are called *internal language files*. The present discussion will be primarily concerned with internal language files, though it should be understood that in actual systems human beings may, for economy, manually perform with external files many of the functions here discussed as being performed mechanically.

In general, there are two kinds of SFQA-system language files: those which control the operation of predicates upon data and those which control term interrelationships.

Files for Controlling Predicate Operation on Data Data-control files contain the information needed by an SFQA system for proper interpretation of data once they have been located in the data file. In effect, these data-control files define predicates of the system language in terms of what these predicates say about the data in whose identifiers the predicates occur. For instance, a data-control file may say, in effect: (1) When the predicate P occurs in a datum identifier—e.g., $P(a)$ – the identified datum will be either "+ 1", "– 1", or NA; (2) as a value in an expression of Boolean arithmetic, if the datum is "+ 1" it is to be treated as "1"; and if it is "– 1" it is to be treated as "0"; (3) the datum will be stored in a certain format; etc. It should be clear from the above example that the particular sequence of symbols which are assigned by the fact function for a particular predicate enter definitely into the meaning of that predicate for an SFQA system (i.e., enter into the "machine meaning" of the predicate), though choice of the particular sequences which will be used (e.g., choice of T and F as opposed to "+ 1" and "– 1") may be arbitrary from the standpoint of the meaning of the predicate in human discourse.

Two more examples of predicate machine meanings will be helpful. The machine meaning of the predicate *length* will include the range of the numerals which it can help to identify and will include the units of measurement to which these numerals refer. It is from this machine meaning that the machine will know how to compute with these numerals—e.g., how to compute a volume expressed in a specified kind of unit. In the case of the predicate *color,* the machine meaning will tell the machine how to treat the datum types *red, green,* etc., (discussed earlier); e.g., it will tell the machine whether these different datum types represent an unordered classification, whether they represent a classification into mutually exclusive classes, whether they represent some kind of ordering which can be reflected in what is done with data of these types, etc.

In addition to including data-control information of the type indicated in the preceding paragraphs, the machine meaning of a predicate includes (1) indications of how the machine is to interpret reliability indicators used for fact assertions containing the predicate, so consequently, for any predicate there are restrictions imposed on fact-assertion sources concerning the form which these reliability indicators can take; and (2) indications concerning how the machine is to interpret, when used in connection with the predicate, certain operators occuring in fact assertions and retrieval requests—e.g., the operator *is less than.*

Files for Controlling Term Interrelationships Term-analysis files contain information making explicit and connecting the meanings of predicates in an SFQA-system language as well as information connecting the meanings of predicates in the language with meanings of terms not in the language. These are the files which would be the focus of programs charged with inferential retrieval—i.e., with retrieval of fact assertions not explicitly stored in an SFQA system but logically implied by fact assertions which are so stored. The main content of term-analysis files corresponds to what Carnap calls "meaning postulates"—i.e., postulates which explicitly assert restrictions on, and properties of, the meanings of terms, and which explicitly assert relationships among the meanings of different terms.[27] One of the reasons that there is at least an appearance of plausibility in the currently popular suggestions concerning machines which draw and test useful, nontrivial logical inferences is that the high speeds of operation of contemporary and prospective computers make it thinkable that a machine could consult and utilize the very many meaning postulates and empirical statements necessarily involved in such inferences.[28] A serious practical obstacle to the creation of such a machine is getting the required meaning postulates and empirical statements into store. The problem of getting the empirical statements into store—the problem of inputting fact assertions—will be discussed in the next section. The problem of getting meaning postulates into store is that of compiling the term-analysis files. Let us here look at the form of some of the contents of these files:

1 There should be information concerning the logical properties possessed by the predicates being defined. For instance, there might be

[27]The introduction of Carnap's concept of meaning postulates into the present context is due to Bar-Hillel.

[28]See J. McCarthy, "Programs with Common Sense," *Proceedings of a Symposium on Mechanization of Thought Processes,* pp. 76–84, London, 1959, for a suggestion concerning an "advice-taking" machine capable of deciding what to do by drawing inferences from statements about goals and means—i.e., from statements only implicitly containing instructions for the machine. Also see Y. Bar-Hillel, "Discussion on the Paper by Dr. J. McCarthy," *op. cit.,* pp. 85–87; *op. cit.,* fn. 2, pp. 781–783, for an indication of the awesomely difficult problems involved in creating an "inference" machine. It should be understood that an SFQA system of the kind being presently discussed might be very useful even if its powers of inference are severely limited—e.g., even if all it can do is retrieve explicitly stored assertions and manipulate arithmetically the *representative* symbols which it thus obtains (see the last section of this discussion).

information that the predicate D is transitive—that is, in regard to D's fact function F for any individuals x, y, and z, if $< x,y,t_1, \text{"}+ 1\text{"} >$ and $< y,z,t_1, \text{"}+ 1\text{"} >$ are in F, then $< x,z,t_1, \text{"}+ 1\text{"} >$ is also in F.

2 There should be information concerning the syntactical structure of the predicates being defined (see the earlier discussion of predicates). It is this information which indicates how predicate components are bound together into complex predicates. These predicate components may or may not themselves be independent predicates of the SFQA-system language. An example will indicate the usefulness of this syntactical information. Suppose the language has in it the one-place predicates *vacuum-tube computer* and *computer console*. It is important that a distinction be made between the role of the component *computer* in one case and its role in the other case. When the datum identifier *vacuum-tube computer* (*a*) occurs in the file, it identifies *a* as being a computer; but when the identifier *computer console* (*a*) occurs, it identifies *a* not as being a computer but as something intended for use with computers. This distinction will be reflected by the entries in a term-analysis file which show the syntactical structure of

vacuum-tube computer (*x*)

as

(*computer* (*x*)) *and* (*contains vacuum tubes* (*x*))

and the syntactical structure of

computer console (*x*)

as

(*console* (*x*)) *and* (*used with computers* (*x*)) [29]

In the actual case it may be necessary further to resolve the components *contains vacuum tubes* and *used with computers*. Resolution of the latter is likely to require concepts beyond those of purely extensional logic.

3 There should be information concerning generic-specific relationships among the predicates being defined, as well as information concerning generic-specific relationships of the predicates being defined with terms not in the SFQA-system language. In some cases this information is the same as the syntactical information discussed in the preceding

[29]The use by Western Reserve documentalists of role indicators (see J. W. Perry et al., *Machine Literature Searching*, New York, 1956) to indicate the difference between the uses of *computer* in the two predicates of our example does not involve anything different in principle or intention from what is being here proposed, though it does involve a different notation.

paragraph; for example, the display of syntactical structure of the predicate *vacuum-tube computer* shows that there is a generic-specific relationship between *vacuum-tube computer* and *computer*.[30] It is necessary, however, to include in the term-analysis files generic-specific information beyond that included in the display of syntactic structure. This information takes the form of scope notes; that is, it indicates what specific subclasses are included in the scope of a general class according to the intended meaning of a certain general predicate and, to a certain extent at least, what specific classes are excluded from this scope. Thus scope notes may indicate that the class designated by *ship* includes the subclasses designated by *liner, freighter, tanker,* etc., but excludes the classes deignated by *canoe, raft,* etc. The subclass designators may or may not be predicates in the system language along with the general-class designator. It should be clear that, especially in the case of scope notes indicating exclusion, there are no limits to the number of scope notes there might be for any one general predicate; practical limits are determined by the intended use of the SFQA system and the probable usefulness of the notes, given the retrieval requests that are likely. These same considerations determine what particular dimensions will be used for subdividing general classes. Thus it may be decided that it is necessary to store a scope note indicating that *mammal, reptile,* etc., designate subclasses of the general class designated by *animal*; but that it is unnecessary to store a scope note indicating that *carnivore, herbivore,* etc., also designate subclass of the general class designated by *animal*.

4 There should be information concerning the relevance of predicate meanings to each other. This information takes the form of cross references exemplified by the *see also* notations in conventional library catalogues. Cross references can not be determined in a vacuum, because relevance of meaning is not an absolute matter, but must be determined on the basis of the expected uses of the particular fact-retrieval system. Thus in one kind of system containing information about baseball it might be appropriate to have a cross reference associating *number of home runs* with *stadium dimensions,* whereas in another kind it would be appropriate to have instead a cross reference associating *number of home runs* with *number of runs batted in*.

5 There should be information concerning the relevance of meanings of predicates in the system to meanings of terms not in the system. This information is analogous to the *see* notations in conventional library

[30]Conversely, the display of the syntactical structure of the predicate *computer console* shows that the relation between *computer console* and *computer* is not a generic-specific relation but a relation of another kind. It is worth remarking that, given the very many kinds of relations which can obtain among meanings of terms, undue attention is devoted to the generic-specific relation by writers on information retrieval.

catalogues. The same considerations apply to compiling this information as apply to compiling cross references among predicates in the system language: Which external terms qualify for *see* references depends on expected uses of the system.

Storing Synthetic Term Connections in SFQA Language Files There might be, in SFQA language files, information concerning synthetic connections among predicates in the system language. It is here that a fact-retrieval system of the sort being discussed might utilize the connections among terms asserted by certain low-level empirical generalizations. Probabilistic as well as deterministic connections might be reflected in these empirically based cross references. Thus in a medical data system there might be a reference from *manifests hypertension* to *suffers from headaches.*[31] One of the reasons in favor of storing synthetic as well as analytic term connections in SFQA language files is the notorious difficulty of determining whether any given connection of terms is analytic or synthetic. Clearly the analyticity–syntheticity of a particular term connection varies from user to user and from context to context. Whether it is important that the distinction be made in the context of a particular SFQA system will depend on the system. One would think that in a system concerned with legal matters, for instance, making the distinction might be necessary, while in a system concerned with medical case histories, for instance, it might not be. If the *see* and *see also* cross references discussed above are entered into SFQA files in a manner corresponding to their occurrence in conventional document-retrieval catalogs (or in telephone directory yellow pages), no distinction will be made between a *see* or *see also* cross reference based on an analytic connection and one based on a synthetic connection.

METHODS OF GETTING FACT ASSERTIONS INTO AN SFQA SYSTEM

Magnitude of the Input Problem As has already been indicated, a very serious practical problem in the case of any actual SFQA system is that of getting fact assertions into the system. The only case in which a complex,

[31]The introduction of information concerning synthetic connections among terms into SFQA language files raises a whole host of problems which we haven't solved and of which space does not allow discussion here. It should be noted that often when people talk of science as being concerned with the discovery of facts they refer to the discovery by science of general laws and not to the discovery by science of *particular* facts of the kind with which we are presently concerned. It is the reporter, the physician, the historian, or the police detective whose primary task is discovery of such particular facts. For the scientist in his most typical function, the role of such facts is instrumental, not the role of primary product. The storing and retrieving of information about *general* facts is a problem quite different from the storing and retrieving of information about *particular* facts—quite different and much more difficult.

artificial system of the kind being discussed here can possibly be justified practically is the case where the system stores a very large number of fact assertions, more than can easily be remembered by any one person and more than can be arranged conveniently and referred to efficiently in a handbook.[32] Such cases do arise with patient medical histories, criminal records, government records, business-intelligence records, etc., but when they do arise the problem of input becomes critical.

At a general level, there are three different types of input procedures, the first of which is the most promising practically, but the third of which is the most interesting theoretically: (1) direct input of *representative* symbols by human beings or measuring instruments; (2) input of information in a simplified and rigidly structured standard language; and (3) automatic analysis of natural-language text.

Direct Input of Representative Data Direct input of *representative* symbols is exemplified by a human being's inputting directly into an SFQA system, in order, the numerals "5" and "3"; or by analog-to-digital equipment's converting the alternating heights of a mercury column to the numerals "130" and "90" and inputting these numerals directly into an SFQA system. Of primary concern to us at the moment is how these data are to become properly identified within the system.

One method of identification is to have the system ask questions of the data sources. Thus the occasion of the human being's inputting the numerals "5" and "3" might be that the machine has in effect asked him, *What was the score at the end of the seventh inning in the Yankee-Pirate game of October* 7, 1960*?* It is this question which determines the datum identifier. When the answer is received, the fact assertion stored is something like[33]

seventh-inning score (*Yankee-Pirate* 10-7-60 *game*) *is* "5/3"

And the input from a measuring instrument of the numerals 130 and 90 might result from a doctor-and-instrument's having been asked on January 30, 1961, *What is J. Green's blood pressure?* When the answer is re-

[32]It is true, of course, that the possibility of rapid updating is also an advantage, relative to the usual handbook, of artificial SFQA systems. However, it may not be an advantage relative to a handbook which is very frequently updated and reprinted, perhaps as frequently as editions of a newspaper are changed. The utilization of computers with auxiliary high-speed printing equipment for such frequent handbook reprinting provides an interesting alternative solution to some of the same problems toward which SFQA systems are directed. It should be investigated, especially for cases where the users of the facts are few, e.g., for cases where the users are the high-level decision makers of a corporation or a government agency. Such a process would be expensive but not necessarily more so than the processes of an SFQA system.

ceived, the fact assertion stored is something like

blood pressure (*J. Green,* 1-30-61) *is* "130/90"

The questions asked by such a system are directly related to datum identifiers. Any expression which is a datum identifier—e.g., *P* (*a*) – becomes a potential question *P* (*a*) *?* simply by addition of a question mark. If the method of input is question asking, additional internal language files of the kind discussed in the previous section become necessary. These files might indicate to the machine: (1) what kind of input to expect in connection with each particular predicate, so consequently, data sources must know what kind of input to provide, e.g., whether to respond with *yes* or *no,* or with numerals in a particular order, or by manipulation of measuring instruments, etc.; (2) how frequently, on what occasions, and of what sources each particular question should be asked; (3) how the datum provided in response to each particular question is to influence the asking of related questions—for example, if the datum provided in response to *hurricane* (*a*) *?* is "+ 1", then the machine may determine from the language files that it should ask *direction of movement* (*a*) *?* and that it should avoid asking *underground* (*a*) *?*. What must be contained in these files will be determined, of course, by the degree to which question presentation is automated.

There are numerous avantages to using question asking as the method of input for an SFQA system. One is that it provides a highly effective method of keeping the language under control. The predicates of fact assertions entering the system are predicates with meaning for the system—i.e., with appropriate entries in the language files. A second advantage is that question asking provides assistance to data sources in determining what data are of importance to the users of an SFQA system and, if question presentation is automated, in determining what data are out of date and need replacement. Given that SFQA systems are primarily justifiable in connection with files of data that exceed the capacity of single human memories, there are likely to be so many datum identifiers required for such a file that human memories would be incapable of recalling each identifier in the right context and of retaining the necessary information concerning the complex relations among identifiers. The method of question asking exploits the capabilities of data-processing equipment to assist human memories in these tasks. A disadvantage of automated question asking is that extremely complicated machine programs are required to insure that the right question will be asked at the right time in the right place. A disadvantage of question asking, automated or not, is that the language of such a system must be fixed and

[33]This example illustrates a case where occurrences—e.g., games—are members of a domain of discourse.

consequently imposes severe restrictions on what reporters can report. Some of the most serious effects of this disadvantage can be alleviated by allowing reporters to enter, along with a fact assertion, free-text remarks consisting of reservations and qualifications; these free-text remarks have the function of reliability indicators, discussed earlier. A better way to alleviate these effects, better because it does not tend to prevent efficient operation of the system, is development of a flexible and sensitive set of procedures for modifying the language and language files in response to indication by reporters that they have something of significance to report which cannot be expressed in the existing language of the system.

An example of a question-asking system is the one proposed in 1952 by Bar-Hillel for standardizing the contents of scientific reports.[34] It is best to think of the system he proposed as being one where the data sources are humans-reading-documents and where the domain of discourse consists of the objects discussed in the documents. He probably did not have in mind, however, an automatic presentation of questions to the reporter as does Kellogg in his discussion of another example of such a system.[35] Where question presentation is not automated, a question-asking system can be considered an example of a system with the second type of input (input by writing reports in a standard language) as well as an example of a system with the first type of input (direct input of representative symbols). It exemplifies both types because what reporters do in such a system is to enter a datum directly into the machine and at the same time indicate its identifier—i.e., tell the machine what question it is that the datum answers. An interesting example of an actually existing and operating SFQA system which uses nonautomated question asking is the military inventory control system of the Office of the Assistant Secretary of Defense for Cataloging.

Input of Information in a Standard Language The second method of input to be considered represents a halfway house between direct input of *representative* symbols and input of unrestricted natural-language text. This is the method where human beings write, for the system, reports of facts in a simplified and rigidly structured standard language. The reporters are told, in effect, that they can say what they have to say and when they want to say it so long as they limit their language to a specified vocabulary of predicates and proper names combined in certain specified ways. An example of such a system is one where the domain of discourse consists of documents and the reporters (librarians) are given a predetermined set of predicates (descriptors) with which they can indicate the contents of these documents; they further are told that conjunc-

[34]See Bar-Hillel, *op. cit.,* fn. 2.
[35]Kellogg, *op. cit.,* fn. 1.

tion is the only permissible method of descriptor combination and that there is a maximum number of conjuncts which can occur in the report about any one document. It would be possible, however, to allow a much more complicated standard language than this one. Given machine capabilities to rearrange syntax, to break apart and to combine sentences, to detect synonyms, etc. (all of which are required in machine-translation systems with any sophistication at all), the restrictions imposed on reporting language might be surprisingly liberal. The advantages of imposing some restrictions on terms which reporters can use and how they can be combined are that programs and files for implementing these machine capabilities can as a result be less complex. In the actual case, then, the problem is the discovery of some compromise point where the restrictions are not so severe that the language is impossibly difficult for reporters to learn and use and where, on the other hand, the programs and files are simple enough to be practical. Whether there exists such a compromise point is a question which only experience can decide. Experience which is available tends to an affirmative decision. Such experience comes from such things as conventional police-reporting language, the existence of which would seem to indicate that without too much difficulty human beings can be taught to report factual descriptions in a succinct, telegraphic language of limited vocabulary and limited syntactical variety; and in a language sufficiently limited in these respects that a machine can be programmed, without too great difficulty, to translate these descriptions into fact assertions as defined in the present discussion. Once we reach the point of removing the limitations of vocabulary and syntax, we have input of the third type—i.e., input which requires automatic analysis of natural-language text.

Translating Natural Language into the Form of Fact Assertions In several cases where more efficient fact-retrieval systems are urgently needed, the information from which the retrieval must be made presently exists in the form of a very large volume of natural-language text. If the development of more efficient systems were to take the direction of the development of SFQA systems of the kind we have been discussing, then almost certainly techniques would have to be developed for the automatic translation of natural language into the formalized language which we have characterized. Input techniques of the two types we have discussed up to this point might be usable in systems where the large part of the information going into the SFQA data file is acquired after the system exists and is ready to receive information, but it is highly unlikely that these two techniques could efficiently be applied to the conversion of a large volume of already existing natural-language information into information in SFQA-retrievable form. Human beings could be put to the task of reading the natural language and then directly inputting the garnered data, or of reading the natural language and then summarizing what they read in a restricted standard language, but their task would be impossibly large in some cases.[36] The alternative is automatic analysis of the natural language. This alternative, however, represents at the present only a speculative possibility and is mentioned here primarily because it raises interesting theoretical problems. Operational realization of the alternative is far in the future. Work of direct relevance to the problems involved includes Reichenbach's logical analysis of conversational language,[37] Harris' work on application of linguistic transformation theory to information retrieval,[38] Simmons' work on the problems of constructing a data-processing system which could answer questions about what it reads in a primer,[39] Newman's work on development of a "ruly English" for Patent Office retrieval,[40] and some work on machine translation from one natural language to another.[41] All we need consider here is a brief outline of the kind of theoretical problems which are involved.

According to linguistic transformation theory, it is possible successively to apply various transformations to any natural-language sentence and

[36]For instance, in the case of the Patent Office with its problem of converting to machine-retrievable form the information in 3 million domestic and 5 million foreign patent disclosures.

[37]See Reichenbach, *op. cit.*, fn. 25.

[38]See Z. S. Harris, "Linguistic Transformations for Information Retrieval," *Proceedings of the International Conference on Scientific Information*, pp. 937–950, Washington, 1959.

[39]See R. F. Simmons, "Synthex: An Approach Toward Computer Synthesis of Human Language Behavior," in H. Borko (ed.), *Computer Applications in the Behavioral Sciences*, Englewood Cliffs, N.J., 1962, pp. 360–393.

[40]See Newman, *op. cit.*, fn. 9.

[41]It should be observed that, in general, machine translation from one natural language to another is quite a different thing than the machine translation suggested here—i.e., machine translation from a natural language into a highly formalized language of fact assertions. Where the goal is translation from natural language to natural language it is not necessary that the machine be sensitive to what might be called "rhetoric" in the source-language text; the rhetoric of the source-language text can be carried unanalyzed and unchanged into rhetoric of the target-language text. As a matter of fact, one test of successful machine translation from natural language to natural language is the degree to which the rhetoric involved remains unchanged. But in the case of machine translation into formalized fact assertions, the rhetoric must be analyzed and at least partially discarded; i.e., the machine must "get at the facts" and it is hindered in doing this by rhetoric. By "rhetoric" is meant an author's phrasing and emphasizing and organizing of his text on the basis of the particular audience he is writing for—i.e., on the basis of what he thinks will surprise the audience, what he thinks needs explanation even though it be common knowledge, what points he thinks will meet resistance, etc.

thus to produce a transform (probably consisting of several separate sentences) which says the same thing as the original sentence, but in which each of the sentential components is one of a very few simple canonical forms—so-called *kernel* sentences.[42] These transformations could be applied automatically by an information machine—assuming that the machine has access to a sufficiently large file of permissible transformations. Further transforming, of kernel sentences into fact assertions of the kind we have characterized in the present discussion, would be the next step, and this step also should be mechanizable—given a sufficiently large dictionary of the logical structures of various natural-language expressions. Let us consider what this last step would look like in terms of a particular example. The kernel sentence

They built John an office.

might be transformed into

$$\textit{built}\,(a,b,\eta x\ (\textit{Office}\ (x)\ \textit{is}\ \text{``}+1\text{''}),t_1)\ \textit{is}\ \text{``}+1\text{''}$$

assuming that *a* and *b* are the proper names used within the system for John's institutional benefactor and for John, respectively. The transformation would become significantly more complicated if we add an adverb to the original sentence, even though the sentence would still be considered of the same canonical form. The effect of some adverbs would be to determine what goes in the argument place for time. Thus the transform of

They built John an office immediately.

might be

$$\textit{built}\,(a,b,\eta x\ (\textit{office}\ (x)\ \textit{is}\ \text{``}+1\text{''}),\ \textit{soon after}\ t_0)\ \textit{is}\ \text{``}+1\text{''}$$

On the other hand, in line with an earlier suggestion concerning treatment of families of properties,

They built John an office posthaste.

might be transformed into

$$\textit{built}\,(a,b,\eta x\ (\textit{office}\ (x)\ \textit{is}\ \text{``}+1\text{''}),t_1)\ \textit{is}\ \text{``posthaste''}$$

An adverb of a kind requiring still another treatment is exemplified in

They built John an office gladly.

This case appears to require the introduction of an occurrence into the domain of discourse (see the second section of this discussion) – i.e., the

[42]For a discussion of transformation theory, see Stockwell, "The Transformational Model of Generative or Predictive Grammar," in Part 1 of this volume.

occurrence of *a*'s building *b* an office in some time interval *I*. If we refer to this occurrence with the proper name *c* then the formalized fact assertion might be simply[43]

gladly (*c*) *is* "+ 1"

The relationship among *a, b,* and *c* would have to be the object of a different fact assertion.

Such is the nature of the problems involved; much theoretical work remains to be done before a machine is produced which will transform natural-language text into machine-retrievable fact assertions. Some of the problems, besides those connected with adverbs, which remain to be solved include

1 How should truth-functional connections among kernel sentences be treated?[44] Assuming that kernel sentences are transformable into fact assertions, truth-functional connections among kernel sentences could be reflected in truth-functional connections among fact assertions, but there are unsolved problems concerning how these should be handled.[45]

2 How should subjunctive conditionals in the original natural language be transformed? This is probably just one example of a general problem concerning the mechanical processing of natural language: Is there any way to enable machines to translate, to interpret, to analyze sentences, the adequate processing of which requires reference to other sentences which are not explicitly stated (in the case of subjunctive conditionals, to certain general laws) ? It will be a great day when machines are developed which can "read between the lines."

3 How should kernel sentences in intensional contexts be processed? For instance, how should the kernel sentence

They built John an office.

be processed when it occurs in

Tom believes that they built John an office.

The introduction into our characterization of an SFQA-system language of source indicators and reliability indicators probably provides a basis for handling this kind of situation, but there are many details to be worked through. These indicators probably also provide the basis for handling the metalanguage expressions which frequently occur in natural-language text, e.g., in the sentence

To put it simply, they built John an office.

[43]For a related but different logical analysis of adverbs see Reichenbach, *op. cit.,* fn. 25.

[44]*Cf.* Bar-Hillel, *op. cit.,* fn. 2.

[45]See fn. 20.

but again there are many details to be worked through.[46]

4 How can objects of logical types higher than that of the primary members of a domain of discourse be described and accounted for in an SFQA-system language and file? The sentence

One hundred women participated.

represents a very simple canonical form for transformational analysis but represents a very complex logical form because its logical subject is an intensionally defined class—i.e., the class of individuals who are women and who participated. The introduction of such entities into the domain of discourse of an SFQA-system language tremendously complicates file structure and retrieval programs.

RETRIEVAL AND DISPLAY OF INFORMATION IN AN SFQA SYSTEM

Capabilities and Limitations of Noninferential Retrieval We have already mentioned that empowering an SFQA system with significant capabilities of inference is extremely difficult. However, systems without such capabilities can still do many interesting and useful things, and we here mention a few:

1 They can retrieve data by using explicit datum identifiers and then, before displaying the data to human users of the system, perform arithmetical operations on the data to discover statistical characteristics. This arithmetical manipulation of data by data-processing machinery represents nothing new, but its marriage with an efficient and flexible system for identifying and getting at large quantities of data of many different kinds will almost certainly be fruitful. As is well known, a serious bottleneck in conventional applications of data processing is data input. One of the primary functions of an SFQA system is to get a large amount and assortment of data into a form where the data will be directly accessible to a computer; as indicated in the previous section, the problem of input is critical in an SFQA system as well as in conventional data-processing systems, but once data have been entered they remain accessible to be consulted and manipulated on many different occasions and in many different ways. The following are examples of questions whose answers will require an SFQA system to manipulate data statistically after their identification:

[46]In the first (and probably in the last) attempts to transform natural-language text into fact assertions by machine, there almost certainly will be a residue which the machine is unable to resolve. This can be stored and printed out in the same manner as the free-text remarks, consisting of reservations and qualifications, which are entered in the SFQA file by reporters who are generating information in the form of fact assertions. The volume of this residue will, roughly at least, be an inverse measure of the success of the automatic analysis.

TO A MEDICAL-DATA SYSTEM *How many patients were diagnosed as ill with Asiatic flu in* 1960?

TO A BASEBALL-RECORD SYSTEM *What has been the average height of New York Yankees since* 1943?

TO A PUBLIC-HEALTH SYSTEM *Has there been a decrease since July in the average daily number of newly reported polio cases in city A?*

TO A BUSINESS-INTELLIGENCE SYSTEM *Are the reported profits of Competitor A significantly correlated with his reported expenditures on modernization?*

Some possible uses, other than direct question answering, to which automated SFQA systems might be put are those of automatic trend analysis and automatic calculation and reporting of deviation from norms. Thus, such a system might report to a doctor without his having requested the information:

J. Green has gained 27 *pounds in the last two months.*

2 SFQA systems might be justified simply because they provide rapid access to information, even if all they can retrieve is explicitly stored information. Thus if a doctor needs to know in a hurry the answer to

Has J. Green ever manifested allergy to penicillin?

an SFQA system might respond almost immediately, whereas a manual search through nonautomated files might take hours or days. All that need be involved is direct retrieval and display of a single, explicitly stored fact assertion, yet the system would be providing a most useful service. Probably even more in the areas of government and business than in the area of medicine is there an immediate need for particular items of information—e.g., when an official or a manager must make a decision in a hurry and wants quickly to marshall relevant facts on which to base his decision.

3 An important use of SFQA systems which requires only trivial powers of inference is in connection with problems of identification and similarity. The Patent Office, for example, has to take a description of an object for which a patent is desired and compare this description with thousands of descriptions of previously patented objects in order to test for degree of dissimilarity. Given the descriptions in the form of conjunctions of fact assertions, the comparison is a task for which an SFQA system is eminently suited. A related problem is the problem of identification, where an SFQA customer needs to know the name of an idividual who satisfies a certain description or needs to know if an individual who

satisfies one description is identical with an individual who satisfies another description. Thus, a question of a type, the answering of which would be a reasonable use to which to put an SFQA system might be

> *Is the individual x such that (F (x) is* "+ 1" *and G (x) is greater than* "7" *and R (x,a) is* "− 1") *identical with the individual y such that (P (y) is* "160" *and N (y) is* "114 57*th Street, Akron, Ohio*")?

In some cases the system might retort with something like

> *Your first description is insufficiently precise. (You are illegally using the definite-description operator.) There are* 43 *objects in my domain of discourse which satisfy the description.*

It should be noticed that very often users of an SFQA system will not know the proper name (see above) used within the system for an individual and will be able to refer to particular individuals only with descriptions. Thus the following dialogue might be typical:

> HUMAN (Describes an individual.) *Who is this man? Does he have a criminal record?*
> MACHINE *I have a record of two men fitting your description. Does your man have a missing right index finger?*
> HUMAN *No.*
> MACHINE *Your man is ______. His system number is ______. He does not have a criminal record.*

Inferential Retrieval A relatively powerful kind of inference which would not be too difficult to build into an SFQA system, if the system has a definitely determined domain of discourse, is finite induction. Thus such a system might be able to answer such questions as

> *Is there any individual x such that P (x) is greater than* "7"?

> *Are all individuals x such that L (x) is* "+1" *also such that D (x) is* "*blond*"?

> *Are more than* 50 *per cent of the individuals such that L (x) is* "+ 1" *also such that D (x) is* "*blond*"?

A primary problem in building an SFQA system with more powerful inferential abilities is the problem of explicitly storing all the required factual information and information about connections among meanings of terms. Almost all human reasoning is in the form of enthymemes. An argument which appears completely straightforward to a simple-minded human being may be completely impossible for a machine to create without consultation of a very large file of factual assertions and a very large dictionary of term interconnections, and there would probably have to be, in this file and in this dictionary, information which human beings would consider too obvious to be worth storing.[47] Nevertheless, a properly designed SFQA system might be of significant assistance to a human being charged with drawing and testing inferences. By consultation of its language files and its data file, such a system might be able to engage in a conversation of the following kind:

HUMAN *Do* you *infer that X is guilty of crime Y?*
MACHINE I *can't infer so, but I am in possession of the following information which may be of some use to you in deciding whether* you *can infer so:* _______

This might very well represent an area where techniques of heuristic programming can be fruitfully applied. Thus the dialogue might continue:

HUMAN *What you gave me is of little use. Try again.*
MACHINE (After search through its language and data files for five more minutes.) *How about this:* _______

Techniques of Retrieval and Display There is a great deal to be said about retrieval and display techniques, but we can do no more here than mention some interesting possibilities. Users of an SFQA system may be required to ask their questions of the system in a language of limited vocabulary and restricted syntax or they may be allowed to use a relatively free language approximating natural language.[48] If the latter alternative applies, to answer questions the system will have to make extensive use of its language files which relate terms not in the system to terms which are. And a very frequent response of the machine is likely to be something like

I don't possess any fact assertions concerning exactly what you ask for. However, I do have fact assertions utilizing the following terms near-synonomous with terms used in your request: _______, _______. *Are you still interested?*

[47]An interesting exercise for someone unfamiliar with logic is to consider how many implicit premises, factual and semantic, are involved in drawing the "obvious" conclusion *John has $5.35 on his person* from the explicit premises *John has a five-dollar bill in his billfold* and *John is carrying a quarter and a dime in small change.*

[48]The work of Green and his colleagues on SFQA systems is primarily concerned with machine analysis of questions asked in an English-like language and with appropriate machine response on the basis of this analysis. See B. F. Green et al., "Baseball: An Automatic Question-Answerer," *Proceedings of the Western Joint Computer Conference,* pp. 219–224, New York, 1961.

The human being might rephrase his request and try again. After several exchanges he should be able to discover what information useful to him, if any, the system possesses and exactly how he should phrase his question about this information.

The fact that the problem of display is here mentioned only slightly is not intended to imply that it is unimportant. It would be possible to design an SFQA system so that users are overwhelmed with undigestible information when they make a request. A central function of such a system—viz., to provide users with just the particular items of information that are relevant to their purposes—is defeated if these particular items are not displayed to them in a conveniently usable manner. A measure of success of the system is the degree to which the machine and not the human does the searching. In the case where the system can answer a question by simply divulging a particular fact assertion which it has in store, there is no problem. But in many cases its answer cannot be so direct, as indicated by several of the examples in the previous paragraphs. Often the best the machine will be able to do is provide information relevant to a question asked, rather than directly answer the question, and in other cases even a direct answer will call up many, perhaps hundreds, of particular fact assertions. Mooers suggests the fascinating possibility of having SFQA systems write short essays in response to questions.[49] Thinking about such machine performances might be a fruitful way of pursuing the study of generative grammars, but almost certainly in actual cases of SFQA systems the more useful method of displaying the kinds of facts to which an SFQA system can be effectively and justifiably applied will be the more prosaic method of tables and charts and graphs.

[49]See Mooers, *op. cit.*, fn. 5.

Overview

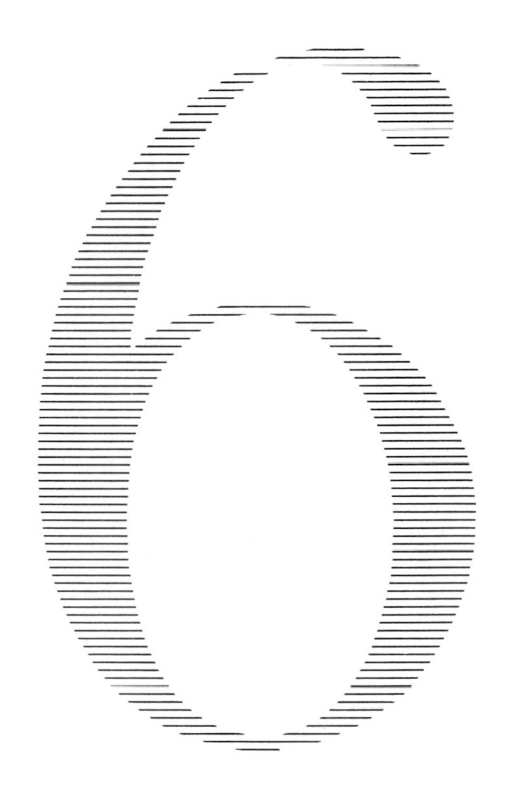

PAUL L. GARVIN
W. KARUSH

Linguistics, data processing, and mathematics

The two disciplines most closely concerned with language-data processing are linguistics and mathematics (including mathematical logic). The purpose of this final discussion is to explore how these two disciplines relate to each other and to language-data processing.

Much emphasis has lately been given to the significance of mathematics for the modeling and processing of natural language (some of this is reflected in the preceding discussions), and a good deal of effort has been devoted to attempts at expressing linguistic relations in mathematical terms. The extent to which these attempts are mathematically ambitious varies; some confine themselves to the use of a few mathematically flavored terms, some go as far as to use the apparatus of axiomatics, complete with definitions and theorems. It is clear that the attraction of higher mathematics for linguists is increasing. However, the mathematics actually in use at this time in operating—that is, not merely planned or proposed—language-data processing systems is unoriginal (e.g., some applications of statistics, or the Boolean algebra of computer instructions). On the other hand, approaches with serious mathematical ambitions have so far yielded only negligible practical results. Often, such approaches are mathematically contrived and turn out to be linguistically sterile. Does this mean that mathematical theory is useless in natural-language research, or does it mean that the mathematics has so far not been applied properly or that the needed mathematics has not yet been developed? These are the questions which we shall attempt to answer by examining the relation of the discipline of mathematics to natural-language research, particularly language-data processing and linguistics.

We propose to do this by comparing the two disciplines in the following respects:

1 The explicit methods of reasoning
2 The aims, as shown by the criteria used to evaluate contributions
3 The mode of investigation of particular research problems

Finally, we shall discuss the place of mathematics in an empirical field of science with particular reference to natural-language research.

METHODS OF REASONING

The soundness of an argument in mathematics rests upon deduction; in an empirical discipline, it rests upon induction as well as deduction. The general question of the relationship between deductive and inductive method has already been discussed in Karush, "On the Use of Mathematics in Behavioral Research," earlier in this volume. Here we shall be concerned with this question as it applies to natural-language research. There are several aspects to be considered: the choice of a suitable beginning point for a line of research or a chain of reasoning; the entities that are considered; the manner in which a system is viewed; the matter of equivalence, or *isomorphism,* of systems; and the general question of the bases of accepted reasoning.

In mathematics, as a general rule, any beginning point or approach to a given research problem is admissible; the only criterion is that it lead to something worthwhile. The discipline of mathematics is rich in concepts and methods, and many connections interlace its various parts. A research problem does not stand in isolation; the mathematical context of its statement typically suggests, directly or indirectly, alternative points of departure. A mathematical problem is often transformable into various equivalent forms, and each form may provoke the use of a different body of mathematical theory for attacking the problem.

In an empirical discipline, on the other hand, the determination of a suitable beginning point for the study of a problem is a more crucial and circumscribed question. In linguistics, this is closely tied to the matter of linguistic levels. This in turn can be reduced to a question of linguistic units, since linguistic levels are definable in terms of the nature and composition of the units that constitute them (*cf.* Garvin, "The Definitional Model of Language," earlier in this volume.) Linguists often indicate their search for a beginning point by asking, *On what lingiustic level is this problem to be treated?* An example of this is the problem of intonation patterns, which traditionally has been treated as a problem in phonetics, and which some recent investigators have attempted to treat as a problem in morphemics by proposing intonation morphemes,[1] or as a level of a generative grammar.[2]

[1]*Cf.* George L. Trager and Henry Lee Smith, Jr., "Outline of English Structure," *Studies in Linguistics,* Occasional Papers No. 3, p. 56, Norman, Oklahoma, 1951.

[2]*Cf.* Robert P. Stockwell, "The Place of Intonation in a Generative Grammar of English," *Language,* vol. 36, pp. 360–367, 1960. For a general discussion of the generative approach, see Stockwell, "The Transformational Model of Generative or Predictive Grammar," earlier in this volume.

In mathematics, entities are established by basic assumption: axioms or postulates set forth the properties that are assignable to primitive, or undefined, entities; definitions do the same for entities built on the undefined or previously defined ones. What the entities are is immaterial; what is important are the relations between them. In a formula $x \times y = y \times x$ our concern is not the meaning of x and y but the fact that the operation $\times$ is commutative and the inferences that can arise from this and other properties. Mathematical objects serve as blanks for expressing relational structure; their meaning is extensional, not intensional. It is true that their origins are connotational and intuitive, but these origins are left behind in the process of abstraction to mathematical form (at least in terms of strict mathematical theory). In practice, it is helpful and important to select terminology that keeps connotational origins alive and thereby facilitates thought and application; it is also dangerous. The "information" of information theory and the "strategy" of game theory are ideas of great originality, but confusing their formal mathematical content with common-sense meanings can lead to fruitless pursuit.

In linguistics, while there may be some general definition of types of units (such as phonemes or morphemes)—and there are few such types—the particular units relevant to a specific problem are either set forth as observationally given or have to be discovered by some empirical method.

The important problem here is to differentiate between the two: What units can be taken for granted, and what units have to be discovered? This is illustrated in language-data processing by the different treatment required for individual words and multiword units. Individual words are observationally given—spaces between words can be sensed by the input mechanism. For multiword units such as phrases or idioms, a recognition routine based on empirical criteria is required (it may be a relatively simple idiom routine or an elaborate syntax-recognition routine).

In pure mathematics, a mathematical system can be regarded as a collection of formal relationships which exist solely by virtue of the statement of these relationships. The statements may be intended to embody a correspondence with external reality, but their admissibility is not dictated by this; mathematics does not study the "truth" of its axioms, although it does raise the question of their mutual consistency. Research within a mathematical system is the search and discovery of connections which assert that fact or theory A implies fact or theory B. The search is directed in a broad way by a more or less general question of interest to the investigator. At any one of various levels of specificity he may be attempting to (1) establish or reject a conjecture; (2) characterize a given class of entities by properties expressed in particular terms; (3) generalize a known relation to a larger class; (4) extend a method of proof to a novel situation; (5) relate apparently distinct subsystems; etc.

The question in mathematics is *Does A imply B?*, not *What are A and B?*

In linguistics, on the other hand, the basic question is: *How shall the system be described?* Most theoretical disputes in linguistics center on the nature of the system of a language. This is best illutrated by the well-known linguistic debate about "levels." The discussions in Part 1 of this volume illustrate different conceptions of linguistic levels.

Isomorphism is used in mathematics to express the notion of sameness of structure of mathematical systems. Isomorphic systems represent formally identical sets of relations by alternative notations or conceptual constructs; this is in accordance with the purpose of mathematical entities to serve only as means of conveying relational form. One example is the theory of ordered sets, in which the *line* as a set of points is isomorphic to the set of *real numbers;* another is the ordinary system of decimal numbers, which is algebraically isomorphic to the ordinary system of binary numbers. Isomorphism must be understood as being relative to some general structural type; for example, the set of all natural numbers 1, 2, 3, . . . and the set of all proper positive fractions ½, ⅓, ⅔, ¼, ¾, . . . are the "same" with regard to their cardinality (they can be matched exactly, one-to-one), but they are nonisomorphic as algebraic systems.

Two systems may be revealed as isomorphic by matching the entities of one with those of the other in such a way that the basic relations in either system are copies of those in the other. Mathematical deduction discovers that which is common to isomorphic representations of a theory, not that which distinguishes them; distinctions not inherent in the basic premises must be sought by other means. Having determined the common elements, mathematics tends to generalize, rather than specialize, to more detailed levels of distinction. The discovery and proof of the isomorphism of two apparently distinct systems can be difficult, and its achievement may be a significant mathematical accomplishment; such identification and unification is often a major goal of mathematical research.

In linguistics, it is possible, as Hjelmslev has done,[3] to envision certain structures as isomorphs of each other, but these are not true isomorphs in the mathematical sense, since there are subtle changes in functional emphasis as one goes from one presumed linguistic isomorph to another. The most outstanding example of this lack of complete isomorphism is

[3]"Thus, various phonetic usages and various written usages can be ordered to the expression system of one and the same linguistic schema. A language can suffer a change of a purely phonetic nature without having the expression system of the linguistic schema affected, and similarly it can suffer a change of a purely semantic nature without having the content system affected." Louis Hjelmslev, *Prolegomena to a Theory of Language* (Francis J. Whitfield, tr.), Univ. of Wisconsin Press, Madison, Wis., 1961, p. 67.

the functional difference between the spoken and the written versions of a language; even when the writing system permits a very high degree of similarity (such as for instance in the case of Finnish), the two differ considerably in their social and cultural functioning. Thus the physical substance in which a linguistic system is manifested has definite functional significance. The Czech linguist Vachek has recently stated the functional difference between speech and writing as follows:[4]

> The spoken norm of a language is a system of phonically manifestable language elements whose function is to react to a given stimulus (which, as a rule, is an urgent one) in a dynamic way, i.e., in a ready and immediate manner, duly expressing not only the purely communicative but also the emotional aspect of the approach of the reacting language user.
>
> The written norm of language is a system of graphically manifestable language elements whose function is to react to a given stimulus (which, as a rule, is not an urgent one) in a static way, i.e., in a preservable and easily surveyable manner, concentrating particularly on the purely communicative aspect of the approach of the reacting language user.

Finally, we turn to the nature of reasoning. In mathematics, an acceptable conclusion is one that can be argued by a chain of deductive inferences. Regardless of the private processes of discovery, the validity of a mathematical proposition ultimately rests on the overt deductive proof which supports it. Since the entities of mathematics are undefined and the assumed relations are not required to conform to external reality, mathematical reasoning has been described as an activity in which we do not know what we are talking about or whether what we are saying is true. One can present a cogent case for the position that, in essence, mathematics is a complex tautology—which, of course, does not deny its usefulness or profundity. Nothing can be discovered in a mathematical theory that is not inherent in its basic assumptions, concealed though these implications may be.

By contrast, the basic method of reasoning of a subject-matter approach to linguistics is one of nontautological inference. The conclusions derived by the application of reasoning to a set of empirical data or previous knowledge are susceptible to later empirical verification. In a recent paper, this method has been described as follows:[5]

> Linguistic analysis is essentially an inductive process, in the sense that it attempts to derive a listing of elements and a set of statements from

[4]Josef Vachek, "Two Chapters on Written English," *Brno Studies in English*, vol. I, p. 12, Prague, 1959.

[5]Paul L. Garvin, "A Study of Inductive Method in Syntax," *Word*, vol. 18, pp. 107–120, 1962.

either an examination of the responses of informants or the study of texts. It is based on the assumption that in both of these sources of data it is possible to discern regularly recurrent elements of different types and orders of complexity. The classification of these elements and the statement of their conditions of distribution (= patterns of cooccurrence) resulting from the analysis is then considered to constitute an inductive description of the language.

AIMS AND EVALUATION CRITERIA

The aim of the researcher in pure mathematics is the resolution of mathematical questions which are significant as mathematics and challenge his ingenuity; surface problems or those that yield directly to known methods in an expected way are "trivial." That his results be correct—that is, established by sound logical reasoning—is his primary test of acceptability, but beyond this obvious requirement, the researcher uses "elegance" as a measure of accomplishment. Attainment of this elusive quality, more easily recognized than described, is what he strives for in his theorems and proofs. An elegant discovery is compounded of simplicity and depth; it exposes the essential clearly and naturally. Elegance is important mathematically as well as esthetically; it instructs and influences, it opens new doors and provides new means, it advances the starting point of research by making obvious what was once puzzling. For elegance, or other reasons, mathematicians may continue searching for alternative proofs of a central theorem even after one or more correct proofs are known. An outstanding example is Selberg's elementary proof of the famous theorem on the number of primes in an arithmetic progression published 112 years after Dirichlet's original difficult proof of 1837. (This theorem states that among the integers in the unending sequence $a + b, a + 2b, a + 3b, \ldots$, there are infinitely many prime integers, a and b being any positive integers with only 1 as a common factor.)

To illustrate the quality of elegance in an elementary way, we may consider the following simple problem in arithmetic. Suppose a tennis tournament (singles) is to be held involving a certain number of players in which the matches are set up as follows. In the first round, the original set of players is arranged in pairs by some process, say, by drawing lots, one player drawing a pass whenever there is an odd number of entrants. The winners in round one (and the pass-drawer, when there is one) are admitted to the second round, and these players are paired off similiary for the matches in round two. This procedure is continued until a single winner emerges. Question: *What is the total number of matches played in the tournament if* 1,027 *is the original number of entrants?* The direct method of solution would be to figure out the number of matches in each round and add these up; for example, there would be 513 matches in round one with one player drawing a pass (since 1027 ÷ 2 is 513 with remainder 1), 257 matches in round two with no pass (since 514 ÷ 2 = 257), etc. An elegant solution, on the other hand, would be to note that for each match played, there is exactly one person, the loser, who drops out of the tournament; since everyone except the final winner loses exactly once, there must be a total of 1,026 matches, one less than the number of entrants. Notice some of the implications of this solution. For one, it shows that $N - 1$ is the number of matches regardless of what the number of entrants N might be. For another, it suggests a general technique of determining the cardinality of a given set A: Search for a set B which is in one-to-one correspondence with A and whose cardinality is easier to determine.

Aims similar to those of the mathematician have been set forth in linguistics by Hjelmslev and Chomsky, under what we believe is the influence of modern logic. Hjelmslev has stipulated the well-known three requirements of the empirical principle—consistency, exhaustiveness, and simplicity. "The description shall be free of contradiction (self-consistent), exhaustive, and as simple as possible. The requirement of freedom from contradiction takes precedence over the requirement of exhaustive description. The requirement of exhaustive description takes precedence over the requirement of simplicity."[6] Significantly, the simplicity criterion is third in rank. Chomsky, on the other hand, though he does require a grammar "to meet certain *external conditions of adequacy*" (more or less corresponding to Hjelmslev's consistency and exhaustiveness), places the major emphasis on a simplicity criterion which he considers "a systematic measure." Note how close his "simplicity of the whole system" comes to the mathematician's elegance. Chomsky uses this notion of simplicity to rate his own "transformation" approach to grammar highest in applying what he calls "an evaluation procedure for grammars."[7]

Chomsky's stress on simplicity reflects his logic-oriented approach to linguistics. He is not primarily interested in the procedure for obtaining linguistic descriptions or the problem of their empirical verification. Many linguists disagree with him on the grounds that the nature of linguistic data does not allow such a neat formalization as he presents, and that his is a misplaced emphasis. In a subject-matter-oriented approach to linguistics, the important aim is general scientific discovery and empirical verifiability, and it outranks considerations of logical neatness.

The computer has made the empirical verification of linguistic information both possible and necessary. The basic requirement that any data-processing system places upon the information used by it is *reli-*

[6]Hjelmslev, *op. cit.,* fn. 4.

[7]N. Chomsky, *Syntactic Structures,* Mouton & Co., 's-Gravenhage, 1957, pp. 49–56.

ability, which is the engineering consequence of empirical verifiability (see Garvin, "A Linguist's View of Language-data Processing," earlier in this volume). Thus, at least for purposes of language-data processing, linguistics has to be a subject-matter-oriented discipline and meet corresponding requirements.

APPROACHES TO RESEARCH PROBLEMS

In this section we shall compare a mathematical approach to research problems with an empirically oriented linguistic approach. We shall consider three basic features of the process: the selection of a problem, its formulation, and its solution.

The Problem In pure mathematics esthetic appeal is a dominating factor in the selection of a research problem; the influence of this factor is expressed in the wide freedom exercised, which is more a characteristic of the arts than of empirical science. As a well- and broadly developed discipline, mathematics is replete with explicit unsolved problems whose resolution, partial or complete, would represent a significant contribution; the mathematician is free to sink his stake anywhere in this broad expanse and build his structure by whatever means he chooses. Well-defined problems and possible directions of attack exist at all levels of difficulty and significance. Famous examples such as the Riemann hypothesis, Fermat's last theorem, the continuum hypothesis, and Hilbert's list of problems for the twentieth century serve as challenges for the very ambitious and the great; most research mathematicians locate themselves at more modest points (which, however, can often be traced back to these or other outstanding questions).

The emergence (and submergence) of problems and means of approaching them is a dynamic process that accompanies the progression and expansion of mathematics. It is true that the new grows out of the old, but a research problem is not always well delineated. The creation of a major new theory may require the development of a new way of mathematical thinking, as illustrated by the calculus of Newton and Leibniz and the theory of infinite sets of Cantor. Here, too, the mathematician exercises freedom of choice, subject to such implicit factors as historical circumstance.

It is an oversimplification to suggest esthetic value as the exclusive reason for selecting a given problem. The mathematical researcher works in some more or less general area which he is seeking to illuminate. He chooses an aspect of this area that he believes will lead to interesting possibilities as he progresses. He turns to problems that are likely to yield to his special talents and training, and he is influenced by the present fashion in mathematics. However, he is not directly bound, as are the empirical scientists, to the requirements of explaining external phenomena (nor is he free to appeal to these for validation).

In linguistics, there is comparatively little freedom in the choice of a problem. Instead, the linguist chooses a field of interest—one of the subfields of linguistics, a particular language or set of languages, or one of the levels of language (since these levels admit of separate treatment). The chosen field of study will then present its own inherent problems which the linguist will detect as he observes his data. In a well-known field, new observations will allow him to contribute new approaches and new formulations to traditional problems[8] In a new field, such as the study of a hitherto undescribed language,[9] new problems will be revealed. Each problem will involve describing a detail of the system of the language which cannot simply be deduced from the linguist's theoretical assumptions but which emerges from his initial observations. Thus, a language may turn out to have a very unusual vowel pattern, or a very complex set of forms corresponding to an expected set of grammatical meanings such as a grammatical person system.

In language-data processing, on the other hand, it is possible to consider each task—such as machine translation or automatic abstracting—a problem in the engineer's sense. There, the choice of field constitutes a choice of problem.

Formulation In mathematics, a selected problem often comes already prepared in a precise enough form for research. Again, however, the mathematician has the freedom and means to transform the given statement into equivalent versions with which to work. Also, he may formulate a related problem with which he feels he can make progress, and, if the modification proves to be mathematically fruitful, can perhaps continue with this or branch out from it to the exclusion of the original problem. In any case, the formulation of a problem is regarded as adequate only when it is expressed in precise terminology and the concepts used suggest a possible means of attacking the problem.

Where the professed mathematical aim is initially less tangible, as in searching for a possible generalization or in founding a new theory, then the crystallization of the problem may take a variety of forms. Starting

[8] *Cf.* Roman Jakobson's structural formulation of the semantic description of the Russian inflectional system in "Zur Struktur des russischen Verbums," *Charisteria Guilelmo Mathesio . . . oblata,* Cercle Linguistique de Prague, Prague, 1932, pp. 74–84; and "Beitrag zur allgemeinen Kasuslehre," *Travaux du Cercle Linguistique de Prague,* vol. 6, pp. 240–288, Prague, 1936.

[9] *Cf.* the many descriptions of American Indian languages in the *International Journal of American Linguistics,* or *University of California Publications in Linguistics.*

from a common question, different directions of abstraction can diverge to distinct but equally significant mathematical theories. The attempts to discover non-Euclidean geometries in the nineteenth century illustrate this: Bolyai and Lobachevsky in the first half of the century created hyperbolic geometry (through a point P not on a line l there passes more than one line parallel to l), while Riemann in the middle of that century created elliptic geometry (through P there passes no line parallel to l). It should be pointed out that Riemann's profound general theory of spaces put both of these as well as Euclidean (parabolic) geometry in one conceptual framework that has greatly influenced modern mathematics.

In all natural-language research, the formulation of the problem is governed by the observed nature of the empirical data as much as is the initial discovery of a problem in linguistics.

This can be exemplified fairly convincingly from the field of machine translation. In the beginning of machine-translation research, many investigators simply took the position that the course of the research should follow the flow of processing from dictionary lookup to syntax to translation. A great deal of early effort was devoted to the construction of machine dictionaries. As the field developed, it became apparent that machine dictionaries are not very useful unless they are provided with the appropriate grammar codes, and the necessary grammar codes cannot be developed without at least a clear concept of the problems of syntax (for a discussion of this problem, see Garvin, "Syntax in Machine Translation," earlier in this volume). Thus, the problem could not be properly formulated until after some empirical experience was gained. At present, when the more sophisticated groups begin research on a new language pair they place considerably more emphasis on syntax than was the case in the early stages of the field.

Solution A mathematical result which is put forth is incontrovertible when it is supported by a sound mathematical proof; an assertion that from the hypothesis H follows the conclusion C may be superficial or profound, awkwardly or elegantly proved, but unless a flaw in the reasoning is detected, it stands as a mathematical truth. Whether certain final results are to be viewed as a "solution" of an originally proposed problem is often a matter of judgment and taste. True, in some cases, as with the objective of proving (or disproving by counterexample) an explicit mathematical statement, it is clear whether or not the objective has been attained. More typically, however, the objective is less explicit and shifts with the course of research; conclusions that provide partial answers or illuminate certain aspects of a problem may be considered highly successful results. For example, suppose that the original problem is to discover conditions under which a certain conclusion C holds; one may discover interesting conditions H which imply C, but which might be regarded as incomplete because even though H is sufficient for C, it is not necessary; again, there may be alternative sets of conditions H, each providing a different "solution" of the problem; or a significant result may be one which states conditions for a modified version of C to hold. These matters reflect the freedom in mathematical research mentioned before.

In an empirical discipline, everyone knows that there is no proof—there is only empirical verification. Verification is not as conclusive as mathematical proof; it is at best a close approximation. Where clear-cut experiments are not possible, the question of verification can become quite subjective.

In linguistics, until recently success in language-teaching applications was considered the only means of verification: A particular problem of linguistic description was considered solved if the proposed solution was pedagogically useful. Unfortunately, there seldom is general agreement as to "pedagogical usefulness."

Instead of searching for more objective means of verification, many linguists turned to other criteria for deciding the success of their analytic effort. These theoretical criteria have been discussed further above; without some definite means of relating them to external reality, they appear to be even more open to dispute than the pedagogical arguments.

The computer has provided natural-language research with an experimental laboratory. The output of a computer constitutes the first objective means of verification available to natural-language researchers. For those aspects of language in which the problem can be adequately formulated, the output will show whether it has been solved, since it will be apparent whether or not the intended operation has been performed. This is, for instance, the case with syntax in machine translation. One of the most complex operational problems is that of word rearrangement, which can be precisely formulated in terms of syntax. The printout will show whether or not a word sequence of the source language has been rearranged so as to result in the correct word order in the target language. The correct result then constitutes a verification of the syntactic analysis built into the machine-translation program.[10]

Speech recognition may in the near future present a comparable means of verification for phonemic analysis.

The problem area of linguistic meaning has not yet been formulated clearly enough to allow us to envision what the solution will be like in anything but the vaguest outline. It is nonetheless possible to foresee that, once a precise solution can be proposed, it will be possible to verify

[10]This question is discussed in more detail in Paul L. Garvin, "The Impact of Language Data Processing on Linguistic Analysis," *Proceedings of the Ninth International Congress of Linguists,* Cambridge, Mass., August, 1962.

this solution by including it in an automatic-indexing or -abstracting system.

MATHEMATICS IN EMPIRICAL FIELDS

The way in which mathematical methods can be integrated meaningfully into an empirical field can be illustrated by the experience of engineering, where a major advantage of mathematics lies in the help it gives in the taking of measurements. Often, it is possible to formulate an empirically derived relation precisely enough to specify the quantities which have to be measured. The physical nature of the quantities, however, may hinder easy measurement. This is a situation in which mathematics can be useful: If the relations can be expressed mathematically, the resulting expression can be operated on mathematically until quantities are derived which are in a form physically convenient for measurement.

A recent example of this use of mathematics can be found in the field of electronics. It concerns the operating parameters of transistors. Original specifications for transistors were in terms of the so-called "T" parameters, which represent intuitively significant properties but which are difficult to measure; these were later changed to "h" parameters, which are less direct but far simpler to measure. The "T" parameters may be derived from the "h" parameters by virtue of the mathematical relationship existing between them.[11]

In the physical sciences, mathematical technique can serve in a similar way. There again, it can often provide a means of representing and manipulating empirical relations to put them into a form more convenient for measurement, and to permit the observation of the unobservable by inference. These mathematically induced measurements and observations are the basis for the verification of a theory that has been given mathematical expression.

Two aspects of the application of mathematics to empirical problems are stressed here: (1) they presuppose an initial formulation arrived at by extramathematical means; (2) they allow convenient measurements and inferential observations to insure engineering applications or verification. Note that in both cases the purpose of mathematics is not to serve as a prototype of scientific method but as a support, where it is applicable, to empirical methods of explaining the external physical realities.

In natural-language research, the measurements and observations for which mathematics could be of assistance are far from obvious. This is illustrated by the difficulties encountered in the field of speech recogni-

[11]This well-known example was supplied by Jack Fromkin. Details can be found in any standard textbook of electronics.

tion (*cf.* Garvin, "A Linguist's View of Language-data Processing," earlier in this volume). The phonetic substance of language clearly lends itself physically to both reproduction and measurements, but very few of the parameters required for the recognition of the linguistic content of the acoustic signal have as yet been found.

What has become clear during the development of language-data processing is that before we can think of using mathematics for computation the boundaries and functions of linguistic units must be determined (*cf.* Garvin, "Syntax in Machine Translation," earlier in this volume). The specifications of these boundaries and functions are in our sense the *system constants* of a language, the values of which vary from case to case. They are thus the linguistic equivalent of the parameters in a physical engineering problem. The operational tests used to achieve this specification serve as the measuring instruments and experimental devices of linguistics (*cf.* Garvin, "The Definitional Model of Language," earlier in this volume). These tests are extramathematical; they are part of inductive method in linguistics.[12]

It appears that mathematics does not replace empirical methodology, although this is a role favored by some linguists. On the contrary, only after the units and relations of natural language have been ascertained by inductive method and appropriately verified (as, for instance, by computation), will the necessary conditions begin to be met for the application of interesting mathematics to natural language in a realistic way. Either the mathematician will then find that he is dealing with a new manifestation in nature of something already known to him, or it may suggest to him new modes of mathematical thinking.

The experience of engineering and physical-science applications suggests that the exploratory use of mathematics based on reliable linguistic foundations may be suggestive of new perspectives in linguistics; it may, for example, make us aware of hitherto unsuspected variables or point up new or statistically preferable measurements and observations.

[12]For a detailed discussion of inductive method in linguistics, see Garvin, *op. cit.*, fn. 5.

GLOSSARY

Algorithm A specific rule or set of rules for the solving of a certain type of problem (e.g., a machine-translation algorithm).

Automatic abstracting The process of mechanically producing a summary of the contents of a document.

Automatic indexing The process of automatically classifying documents and portions of documents in terms of their subject matter.

Binary A characteristic or property involving a selection, choice, or condition in which there are but two possible alternatives.

Command routine That portion of a natural-language computer program which deals with the generation of output sentences.

Computer A device for carrying out numerical computations. The term *computer* is most often used to refer to an electronic digital computer (*which see*).

Computer program A list of instructions, automatically applied (and often recursive), by which a computer (usually an electronic digital computer) solves a problem.

Dictionary lookup The process of mechanically matching words of a text against a stored dictionary.

Electronic digital computer A computer which operates with information represented by discrete units (as opposed to an analog machine). The operation of such a machine is directed by a computer program (*which see*).

Extract *See* Extract-abstract.

Extract-abstract An abstract created by selecting sentences from the original document.

Flowchart A diagram made prior to programming a problem, mapping out the steps of its solution in logical alternatives.

Generative grammar A formal deductive system whose terminal expressions are sentences in a given language.

Grammar A statement of the structure of a given language.

Grammar code A listing of grammatical properties of a word stored with the word in a machine glossary.

Grammaticalness The property of a particular linguistic construction of being deemed structurally permissible.

Grapheme A minimal contrastive unit of a writing system, such as a letter or character.

Heuristic programming A system of programming a computer so that the machine may be said to "learn" by a trial-and-error procedure.

Homograph One written form which represents two or more distinct parts of speech.

Idioglossary A limited dictionary composed of vocabulary peculiar to a particular field of discourse.

Informant A native speaker used as a source of information.

Information retrieval The process of retrieving stored documents, portions of documents, or other types of stored information relevant to a given request.

Input Data initially entered into the computer.

Juncture An interruption in the continuity of the stream of speech.

Kernel sentences In a transformational grammar, the terminal expressions of the phrase-structure portion.

Keypunching A means of preparing computer instructions or data in a machine-usable form. The process consists of punching small holes in cards (or other suitable material, such as paper tape) which can then be sensed by machine.

Key word A word which is indicative of the subject matter of the sentence or document in which it occurs.

Linguistics The science of language with language as its primary object of cognition.

Loop The repetition of a group of instructions in a routine.

Mathematical model A mathematical structure whose elements and expressions are isomorphic with some other structure.

Microglossary *See* Idioglossary.

Morpheme A minimum meaningful unit of language.

Morphemics Study of morphemes (*which see*).

Morphology Study of the internal structure of words.

MT Machine or mechanical translation.

Multiple meaning The problem that occurs when a source-language word has more than one possible equivalent in the target language.

Off-line Said of equipment not directly controlled by the computer.

On-line Said of equipment which operates under the direct control of the computer.

Phoneme A sign component of spoken language.

Phonemics Study of phonemes (*which see*).

Phrase-structure grammar A generative grammar (*which see*) consisting of a set of rewrite rules in the form of a logical tree.

Preediting Human editing of a text as a preliminary step before machine processing.

Postediting Human editing of a text translated or otherwise processed by machine.

Polysemy; polysemia *See* Multiple meaning.

Program *See* Computer program.

Recognition routine That portion of a computer program which deals with the recognition and explication of the structure of an input document.

Routine A set of coded instructions arranged in proper sequence to direct the computer to perform a desired operation or series of operations.

Semantics The study of meaning.

Source language The language from which a machine translation is made.

Syntax The study of the relations between words.

Target language The language into which a machine translation is made.

Thesaurus A list of words and expressions classified by similarity and dissimilarity of meaning.

Transformation rule One of a set of rules which operate on kernels to produce sentences.

Transformational grammar A generative grammar (*which see*) containing three components: a phrase-structure portion, a transformational portion, and a morphophonemic portion.

Transforms In a transformational grammar, the terminal expressions of the transformational portion.

Word-for-word translation Translation solely by dictionary lookup without the aid of syntax.

SELECTED REFERENCES

Alt, F. L., and I. Rhodes: "Recognition of Clauses and Phrases in Machine Translation of Languages," *Proceedings of the International Conference on Machine Translation of Languages and Applied Language Analysis,* Her Majesty's Stationery Office, London, 1962, vol. 1, pp. 125–142.

Describes a routine for the initial establishment of clause boundaries by a preliminary pass through the sentence.

Automatic Data Processing Glossary, Executive Office of the President, Bureau of the Budget, U.S. Government Printing Office, Washington, December, 1962.

"Automatic Translation of Languages," *Proceedings of the International Conference on Information Processing,* UNESCO, Paris, Munich, London, 1960, pp. 157–220.

State-of-the-art reports as of 1959.

Bar-Hillel Y.: "A Demonstration of the Nonfeasibility of Fully Automatic High Quality Translation," in Franz Alt (ed.), *Advances in Computers,* vol. 1, New York, 1960, pp. 158–163.

The basis for Bar-Hillel's assertion stems from certain examples of multiple meaning not solvable by means of any simple contextual search (i.e., without an encyclopedic knowledge of the nonlinguistic world).

________ : "Decision Procedures for Structure in Natural Languages," *Report on the State of Machine Translation in the United States and Great Britain,* Appendix III, pp. 1–9, Jerusalem, 1959.

Expresses doubt that syntax of natural languages is a decidable theory, i.e., that an algorithm exists for the recognition of the syntactic structure of an arbitrary sentence. A criticism of the "immediate-constituent" model of language.

________ : "A Logician's Reaction to Recent Theorizing on Information Search Systems," *American Documentation,* vol. 8, pp. 103–113, 1957.

A criticism of various approaches to the problems of information systems.

________ : "The Mechanization of Literature Searching," *Proceedings of a Symposium on Mechanization of Thought Processes,* Her Majesty's Stationery Office, London, 1959, pp. 789–800.

A critical appraisal of information retrieval.

________ : "Theoretical Aspects of the Mechanization of Literature Searching," in W. Hoffman (ed.), *Digital Information Processors,* Interscience Publishers, New York, 1962, pp. 406–443.

Current Research and Development in Scientific Documentation, National Science Foundation, Office of Science Information, Washington.

A semiannual report which describes nearly all the activities in scientific documentation both in the United States and abroad.

Delavenay, E., and K. Delavenay: *Bibliography of Mechanical Translation,* Mouton & Co., 's-Gravenhage, 1960.

Although somewhat out of date, includes most of the early work on machine translation as well as material on information theory, cybernetics, information retrieval, automatic abstracting, linguistics, and computers.

Documentation, Indexing, and Retrieval of Scientific Information, prepared by the Committee on Government Operations, U.S. Senate, Doc. No. 113, Washington, 1960.

Report of Senate hearings on information retrieval.

Edmundson, H. P. (ed.): *Proceedings of the National Symposium on Machine Translation,* held at the University of California, Los Angeles, February, 1960, Prentice-Hall International, Englewood Cliffs, N.J., 1961.

Probably the best general introduction to the subject of machine translation. The activities, projected activities, and philosophy of the various machine-translation groups in the United States are presented by members of the groups. The question periods following each of the sessions (current research, methodology, questions of grammar, syntax, dictionary organization, problems of information and linguistic analysis, the solution of problems of semantics, programming, and hardware) are especially interesting and bring out more clearly the differences of opinion among the various groups.

Edmundson, H. P., and D. G. Hays: *Studies in Machine Translation: Research Methodology,* The RAND Corporation, Santa Monica, Calif., 1957.

A brief description of the machine-translation process from Russian to English as carried out by The RAND Corporation.

Fairthorne, R. A.: *Toward Information Retrieval,* Butterworths, London, 1961.

A collection of articles on various aspects of information retrieval.

Garvin, P. L.: "Automatic Linguistic Analysis: A Heuristic Problem," *Proceedings of the International Conference on Machine Translation and Applied Language Analysis,* Her Majesty's Stationery Office, London, 1962, vol. 2, pp. 665–669.

Describes a program by which one might automatically perform a partial analysis of a language such as English based solely on distributional data derived from the processing of large amounts of text without the inputting of any morphological or syntactic information concerning the language in question.

________: "Machine Translation," *Proceedings of the Eighth International Congress of Linguists,* pp. 502–510, Oslo University Press, Oslo, 1958.

A state-of-the-art report as of 1958.

________: "Some Linguistic Problems in Machine Translation," *For Roman Jakobson,* Mouton & Co., 's-Gravenhage, 1956, pp. 180–196.

An early discussion from a linguistic standpoint.

_______ : "Syntactic Retrieval," *Proceedings of the National Symposium on Machine Translation,* Prentice-Hall International, Englewood Cliffs, N.J., 1961, pp. 286–292.

Describes the "fulcrum" technique for syntactic analysis (used by Thompson Ramo Wooldridge Inc. and Wayne State University, which is based on a search for the "fulcra" of a sentence—i.e., those words which give the most information about the other words in the sentence. (In Russian the fulcrum of the sentence is the predicate since it gives information about possible subjects and objects.)

"Grammar Coding," *Research in Machine Translation,* second annual report, Wayne State University, Detroit, Mich., 1960, pp. 1–87.

Contains one of the most comprehensive grammar-coding schemes to date, as well as a list of homograph types and words governing various cases and prepositions.

Hays, D. G.: *Basic Principles and Technical Variations in Sentence Structure Determination,* The RAND Corporation, Mathematics Division, Santa Monica, Calif., 1960, p. 1984.

Describes the system used at RAND for syntactic recognition based on dependency theory.

Information Retrieval Systems Conference, IBM September Conference, Poughkeepsie, 1960, IBM, White Plains, N.Y.

Kessler M. M.: "Technical Information Flow Patterns," *Proceedings of the Western Joint Computer Conference,* May, 1961.

A study of citation lists in technical articles is used to note patterns of information flow.

Kuhns, J. L.: "An Application of Logical Probability to Problems in Automatic Abstracting and Information Retrieval," presented at the First Congress on the Information System Sciences, Session 13, November, 1962.

A probabilistic schema is presented as a method of selecting sentences for document extracts. The same schema is shown to apply to predicting the relevance of a document to a given information-retrieval question. Some experimental results are presented.

Lamb, S. M., and W. H. Jacobson, Jr.: "A High Speed Large-capacity Dictionary System," *Mechanical Translation,* vol. 6, pp. 76–106, 1961.

A dictionary system is described by which an IBM 704 with 32,000 computer words of core storage can contain 20,000 dictionary entries at one time. These segmented entries can then generate several hundred thousand distinct word forms.

Luhn, L. P.: *Keyword-in-context Index for Technical Literature (KWIC Index),* RC 127, IBM Advanced Systems Development Div., Yorktown Heights, N.Y., 1959.

The use of key-word listings with context is discussed as a method of indexing and as a tool for bibliography compilation and dissemination. Simple formats are given, and machine problems are discussed.

Machine Indexing: Progress and Problems, papers presented at the Third Institute on Information Storage and Retrieval, Center for Technology and Administration, School of Government and Public Administration, The American University, Washington, February, 1961.

A collection of papers representative of the state of the art.

Machine Translation Techniques for Semantic Research, Thompson Ramo Wooldridge Inc., Canoga Park, Calif., 1961, 91 pp., AF 30 (602)-2036; C 72-147.

The report presents what is probably the best description of an operating machine-translation program in terms understandable to a layman. A sample translation is also included.

Maron, M. E.: "Automatic Indexing: An Experimental Inquiry," *Journal of the Association for Computing Machinery,* vol. 8, no. 3, July, 1961.

Presents a technique for automatically assigning subject classifications to documents. The basis of the technique is the use of statistical data relating key words to subject classifications. A statistical inference is then used as the frame for assigning the classification. Experimental results are given.

Maron, M. E., and J. L. Kuhns: "On Relevance, Probabilistic Indexing and Information Retrieval," *Journal of the Association for Computing Machinery,* vol. 7, no. 3, July, 1960.

Describes a technique for indexing and retrieval based on the theory of statistical inference. A description of search strategies which incorporate this technique as well as of numerical measures of "closeness" between index terms and documents is given. Results of actual tests are discussed.

Mathematical Linguistics and Automatic Translation, vols. 1–7, The Computation Laboratory of Harvard University, Cambridge, Mass., 1959-1961.

Periodic reports by the members of the Harvard Group.

Micklesen, L. R.: "Source-language Specification with Table Lookup and High Capacity Dictionary," *Proceedings of the International Conference on Machine Translation of Languages and Applied Language Analysis,* Her Majesty's Stationery Office, London, 1962, pp. 317–340.

A good discussion of the morphological problems and the solutions thereof in setting up a stem dictionary for Russian.

Montgomery, Christine, and Don R. Swanson: "Machine-like Indexing by People," *American Documentation,* vol. 12, no. 4, October, 1962.

A study of Index Medicus entries is presented. The results indicate that automatic procedures could be designed to give subject-heading assignments of comparable quality. An analysis of the adequacy of document titles as a source of retrieval clues is given.

Mooers, C. N.: "The Next Twenty Years in Information Retrieval: Some Goals and Predictions," *Proceedings of the Western Joint Computer Conference,* The Institute of Radio Engineers, New York, 1959.

Newman, S. M.: *Linguistic Problems in Mechanization of Patent Searching,* Patent Office Research and Development Report No. 4, U.S. Patent Office, Washington, 1957.

Discusses early ideas of "Ruly English."

Newman, S. M., and D. D. Andrews: *Storage and Retrieval of Contents of Technical Literature,* U.S. Patent Office, Washington, 1956.
Reports on some early Patent Office work in information retrieval.

Oettinger, A. G.: *Automatic Language Translation,* Harvard University Press, Cambridge, Mass., 1960.
Some general discussion of computers and the problems of machine translation, along with a fairly detailed description of the "Harvard automatic dictionary."

Oettinger, A. G., and M. E. Sherry: "Current Research on Automatic Translation at Harvard University and Predictive Syntactic Analysis," *Proceedings of the National Symposium on Machine Translation,* Prentice-Hall International, Englewood Cliffs, N.J., 1961, pp. 173–182.
Gives some data on the Harvard automatic dictionary as well as a description of predictive analysis for syntactic analysis as employed at Harvard at that time.

Perry, J. W. et al.: *Machine Literature Searching,* Interscience Publishers, New York, 1956.
An early survey of the state of the art.

________: *Tools for Machine Literature Searching,* Interscience Publishers, New York, 1958.
An early compendium of information-retrieval techniques and uses.

Proceedings of the International Conference on Machine Translation of Languages and Applied Language Analysis, National Physical Laboratory, Symposium No. 13, Her Majesty's Stationery Office, London, 1962, 2 vols.
Contains many interesting papers on all aspects of machine translation.

Proceedings of the International Conference on Scientific Information, vol. 1, area 4, pp. 665–812; vol. II, areas 5, 6, pp. 817–1409, National Research Council, National Academy of Sciences, Washington, 1959.
Sums up state of the art in information retrieval as of 1959.

Research on Mechanical Translation, hearings before the Special Investigating Subcommittee of the Committee on Science and Astronautics, U.S. House of Representatives, Eighty-sixth Congress, 2d session, no. 9, Washington, May, 1960.
A short history of MT followed by a description of the situation in MT in the United States as of May, 1960. Reports on their activities were given by several individual MT groups.

Research on Mechanical Translation, Report of the Committee on Science and Astronautics, U.S. House of Representatives, Eighty-sixth Congress, 2d session, serial d, June, 1960, U.S. Government Printing Office, Washington, 1960.
Report of House hearings on information retrieval.

Rhodes, I.: *A New Approach to the Mechanical Syntactic Analysis of Russian,* National Bureau of Standards Report No. 6295, 10 pp., Washington, 1959.
Presents the basic principles of the predictive analysis technique used by the National Bureau of Standards and, in modified form, by Harvard University for syntactic analysis.

Swanson, Don R.: "Information Retrieval: State of the Art," *Proceedings of the Western Joint Computer Conference,* May, 1961, pp. 239–246.
Basic problem areas in information retrieval are discussed.

_______ : "Interrogating a Computer in Natural Language," *Proceedings of the Congress of the International Federation of Information Processing Societies,* Munich, August, 1962.
Describes the experimental results of a fully automatic procedure of request formulation, search, and retrieval wherein the computer takes a natural-language "retrieval question" as input and produces a list of documents responsive to the question. The procedure utilizes a thesaurus to produce the match between question and document. Implications for automatic indexing are presented.

_______ : "Research Procedures for Automatic Indexing," *Machine Indexing: Progress and Problems,* papers presented at the Third Institute on Information Storage and Retrieval, Center for Technology and Administration, School of Government and Public Administration, The American University, Washington, February, 1961.
The problem of designing retrieval experiments is discussed. Actual experiments are described as an exemplification.

_______ : "Searching Natural Language Text by Computer," *Science,* vol. 132, no. 3434, pp. 1099–1104, October, 1960.
Basic information-retrieval experiments on a model information system are described. Results of text-searching by machine are given as well as results using subject-heading indexing. The problem of automatic indexing is discussed.

Vickery, B. C.: *On Retrieval System Theory,* Butterworths, London, 1961.
A general discussion of the problem of information storage and retrieval.

Yngve, V. H.: "Random Generation of English Sentences," *Proceedings of the International Conference on Machine Translation and Applied Language Analysis,* Her Majesty's Stationery Office, London, 1962, vol. 1, pp. 65–80.
Description of a program written to randomly generate English sentences based on ten original sentences selected from a children's book.

NAME INDEX

SUBJECT INDEX